AGARD

Bibliography I

Enlarged Edition

MAGNETO-FLUID-DYNAMICS
CURRENT PAPERS AND ABSTRACTS

AGARD

BIBLIOGRAPHY I

Enlarged Edition

MAGNETO-FLUID-DYNAMICS

Current Papers and Abstracts

Edited by

L. G. NAPOLITANO and G. CONTURSI

Istituto di Aeronautica
Università degli Studi di Napoli

Published for and on behalf of

ADVISORY GROUP FOR
AERONAUTICAL RESEARCH AND DEVELOPMENT
NORTH ATLANTIC TREATY ORGANIZATION

by

PERGAMON PRESS

New York · Oxford · London · Paris
1962

PERGAMON PRESS INC.
122 East 55th Street, New York 22, N.Y.
1404 New York Avenue N.W.,
Washington 5, D.C.

PERGAMON PRESS LTD.
Headington Hill Hall, Oxford
4 & 5 Fitzroy Square, London W.1

PERGAMON PRESS S.A.R.L.
24 Rue des Écoles, Paris V⁰

PERGAMON PRESS G.m.b.H.
Kaiserstrasse 75, Frankfurt am Main

Library of Congress Card No. 61–11542

Set in Baskerville 9 on 10 pt. and printed in Great Britain at
PITMAN PRESS, BATH

CONTENTS

FOREWORD

Magneto-fluid-dynamics is the science which studies the inter-action between flow fields of conducting fluids and electromagnetic fields from both the macroscopic and the microscopic (or particle) point of view. This new chapter of physics has attained an ever increasing importance in a large variety of fields of basic problems and hints at very promising future technological implications and developments. Especially all branches of Astronautics and Space Research will be directly or indirectly influenced by the progress that will be made in this science which I have proposed to call magneto-fluid-dynamics.

The last decade has exhibited a suddenly enhanced interest in magneto-fluid-dynamics and has already produced a very large and varied harvest of papers. A large amount of research has been devoted to the physical properties of both fully and partially ionized gases at low densities. Nevertheless much remains to be done in order to understand in detail the basic phenomena governing the dynamics of ionized gases in the processes of strong interaction with external electro-magnetic fields. This field of research will require great ingenuity and a large amount of experimental and theoretical work before reaching a conclusion about the possible technical application of the magneto-fluid-dynamics.

Such intense and prolific production must necessarily be coupled with a dispersion, in time and space, of the works appearing in the world literature. Hence, I believe that a thorough bibliography on magneto-fluid-dynamics which lists contributions made throughout the scientific world, in such fields as astrophysics, geophysics, thermo-nuclear physics, astronautics and so on, is a very timely initiative.

The early stage of the art does not permit a strictly rational and universally agreed upon subject classification, nor does it yield the right perspectives for critical surveys.

The material included in this Bibliography suggests a first tentative subject classification and provides the information necessary to accelerate the processes of diffusion and osmosis which must necessarily be a pre-lude to coordinate progress in magneto-fluid-dynamics and to the consequential critical surveys.

THEODORE VON KÁRMÁN

INTRODUCTION

Less than a quarter of a century after the first experiments of Hartmann and Lazarus and less than twenty years after the first theoretical treatment by Alfvén the interest in magneto-fluid-dynamics waves has spread, with different degrees of depth, into a variety of fields of physics. Early applications to cosmical, astrophysical and geophysical problems were to be joined, in more recent times, by applications to nuclear and high temperature physics, fluid-dynamics and astronautics.

Multiplication of interests means an increased number of contributions, multiplicity of points of view and different, when not contrasting, degrees of simplification. At the quarter century mark, it might prove useful for all workers in the field and vital for the rapid pursuance of further advances in sciences, to start a process of osmosis between the contributions made by scientists of different and, up to now, seemingly divergent fields.

This necessity was first felt by Dr. Vannucci of AGARD who put forth an extensive and inclusive Bibliography on Magneto-Fluid-Dynamics which has received wide diffusion and has met with the approving interest of all workers in the field.

This first edition of the Bibliography had *a fortiori* a preliminary character which, together with the success it met, pointed to the necessity of pursuing the work and making as many improvements as possible.

This is the task we undertook, being confident in the help we would receive from the users of the first edition of the Bibliography.

It is difficult, in such a new and broad field, to make clear-cut distinctions between what is pertinent and what is not, between what should be included in a Bibliography on magneto-fluid-dynamics and what should not.

As a general policy we have tried to include all the contributions dealing with the macroscopic and particle approach to the motion of ionized fluids and with their possible applications to several branches of physics and technology.

We have also tried a preliminary classification by subjects which duplicates that used in the first edition. Although far from being conclusive and definitive, this classification met with the almost general agreement of the leading scientists in the field.

The classification is based on seven main groups. The first two deal with the macroscopic aspects of the problems: Magneto-Hydro-Dynamics, for the first one, as related to incompressible fluids and

Magneto-Gas-Dynamics for the second one, as related to compressible fluids; the fourth one deals with m.f.d. waves, the fifth one with the particle approach (Plasma Physics) and the last two with the applications (Laboratory, Aero-Astronautical, Astrophysical and Geophysical, Thermonuclear Applications, etc.) and the properties of conducting fluids.

A work such as this cannot be free from involuntary faults and omissions. We are sure that, in spite of our prolonged researches, some very worthy contributions may have been omitted. For these and other imperfections we apologize in advance, just as we thank in advance those who will be kind enough to go to the trouble of pointing them out to us.

A particular tribute must once again be paid to Dr. von Kármán who was, as usual, the first to see things in the right perspective and to realize the usefulness of this Bibliography.

Thanks are also due to all whose contribution is acknowledged at the end of the Bibliography, and to Dr. Siestrunck for his valuable criticism.

It is finally our pleasure and our duty to acknowledge the valuable and efficient co-operation of Dr. Vannucci of AGARD.

LUIGI G. NAPOLITANO and GIORGIO CONTURSI

LIST OF ABBREVIATIONS

ABBREVIATION	TITLE	COUNTRY
Acad. Rep. Pop. Rom.	*Académie de la République Populaire Roumaine*	R
Acad. Sci. Pol.	*Académie Polonaise des Sciences*	Pol.
Accad. Lincei, Roma	*Accademia Nazionale dei Lincei, Roma*	I
Accad. Sci. Torino	*Accademia Scientifica, Torino*	I
Acid. Sci. U.S.A.	*National Science Academy*	U.S.A.
Acta Physica Austriaca		A
Acta Physica Hungarica		H
Addison-Wesley	Addison-Wesley Publishing Corp.	U.S.A.
Advanc. Phys.	*Advances in Physics*	U.K.
AEC	Atomic Energy Commission, Washington	U.S.A.
AERE	Atomic Energy Research Establishment, Harwell	U.K.
Aeronaut. Engin. Rev.	*Aeronautical Engineering Review*	U.S.A.
Aerotecnica	*L'Aerotecnica, Roma*	I
AFCRC	AF Cambridge Research Center	U.S.A.
AFOSR	U.S. Air Force Office of Scientific Research	U.S.A.
AGARD	Advisory Group for Aeronautical Research and Development, Paris	NATO
Amer. Astronaut.	American Astronautical Society	U.S.A.
Amer. Math. Monthly	*American Mathematical Monthly*	U.S.A.
Amer. J. Phys.	*American Journal of Physics*	U.S.A.
Amer. Phys. Soc.	American Physical Society, N.Y.	U.S.A.
Ann. Astronaut.	*Annales d'Astronautique*	F
Ann. Astrophys.	*Annals of Astrophysics*	U.S.A.
Ann. Mat. Pura Appl.	*Annali di Matematica Pura e Applicata*	I
Ann. Phys.	*Annals of Physics, N.Y.*	U.S.A.
Ann. Telecom.	*Annals of Telecommunications*	U.S.A.
Ann. Univ. "C. I. Parhon"	*Annals University "C. I. Parhon" Bucarest*	R
Appl. Mech. Rev.	*Applied Mechanics Review*	U.S.A.
Appl. Sci. Res.	*Applied Science Research*	Ne
Arch. Mech. Anal.	*Archiv for Rational Mechanics and Analysis*	Ge
Ark. Fys.	*Arkiv for Fysik, Stockholm*	S
Ark. Mat. Astr. Fys.	*Archiv för Matematik, Astronomi och Fysik*	S

ABBREVIATION	TITLE	COUNTRY
Ark. Nat. Fys.	*Arkiv. Natural Fysic*	Ge
ARC	Aeronautical Research Council	U.K.
ARDC	Air Research and Development Command	U.S.A.
ARS	American Rocket Society, N.Y.	U.S.A.
ASTIA	Armed Services Technical Information Agency	U.S.A.
Astronautics	*Astronautics*	U.S.A.
Astron. Zh.	*Astronautik Zhurnal*	Ge
Astrophys. J.	*Astrophysical Journal, Chicago*	U.S.A.
Astrophys. Norwege	*Astrophysics Norwege*	N
Astr. Soc. Ne.	Astronomical Society, Netherlands	Ne
Atom. En.	Atomic Energy	G.B.
Aust. J. Phys.	*Australian Journal of Physics*	Australia
AVCO Res. Lab. Rep.	AVCO Research Laboratory Report	U.S.A.
Av. Weekly	*Aviation Weekly*	U.S.A.
Bell Syst. Tech. J.	*Bell System Technical Journal*	U.S.A.
Bull. Amer. Phys. Soc.	*Bulletin American Physical Society*	U.S.A.
Bull. Astr. Soc.	*Bulletin of Astronautical Society*	S
Boll. Un. Mat. Ital.	*Bollettino Unione Matematica Italiana*	I
CADO, Dayton	Central Air Documents Office, Dayton	U.S.A.
Cah. Phys.	*Cahiers de Physique, Paris*	F
Calcutta Math. Soc.	Calcutta Mathematical Society	India
Cambridge Res. Centre	Cambridge Research Centre	U.S.A.
Canad. J. Phys.	*Canadian Journal of Physics*	Canada
Coll. Aero.	College of Aeronautics, Cranfield	U.K.
Conf. Dyn. Ion.	Conference on the Dynamics of Ionized Media	U.S.A.
Conf. Fluid Mech.	Conference on Fluid Mechanics, Ann Arbor	U.S.A.
Conf. Mat. Sem.	Conferences of Mathematics Seminary, Bari	I
Congress Appl. Mech.	9th International Congress of Applied Mechanics	U.S.A.
Congress Astronaut.	Astronautics Congress, 1958 Amsterdam	NL
Cont. Phys.	*Contemporary Physics*	U.S.A.
Cornell U. Aero. Lab.	Cornell University, Aeronautical Laboratory	U.S.A.
C. R. Acad. Sci., Paris	*Académie de Sciences, Paris (Comptes rendus)*	F
Dokl. Akad. Nauk., SSSR	*Proceedings of the Academy of Sciences of the U.S.S.R.*	U.S.S.R.
Douglas Res.	Douglas Research, Santa Monica, California	U.S.A.

ABBREVIATION	TITLE	COUNTRY
DRTE, RPL	Defence Research Telecommunications, Radio Physics Laboratory	Canada
DVL	Deutsche Versuchsanstalt für Luftfahrt E.V.	Ge
Electronics	*Electronics*	U.S.A.
Endeavour	*Endeavour*	F
Fluid Mech. Inst.	Heat Transfer and Fluid Mechanics Institute	U.S.A.
Fortschr. Phys.	*Fortschritt der Physik*	Ge
2nd Geneva Conf.	II Geneva Conference on peaceful use atomic energy U.N. 1958	CH
Geofys. Publ.	*Geofysik Publications, Dublin*	U.K.
Helv. Phys. Acta	*Helvetica Physica Acta*	CH
IAS	Institute of Aeronautical Sciences	U.S.A.
Indian J. Meteorol. Geophys.	*Indian Journal of Meteorology and Geophysics, New Delhi*	India
Indian J. Phys.	*Indian Journal of Physics*	India
Ind. Eng. Chem.	Industrial Engineering Chemistry	U.S.A.
Ingenieria Aeronautica y Astronautica		E
Ital. Phys. Society	Italian Physics Society, Milano	I
Izv. Akad. Nauk. Lat. SSR	*Bulletin of the Latviiskoy Academy of Sciences*	U.S.S.R.
Izv. Akad. Nauk., SSSR	*Bulletin of the Academy of Sciences*	U.S.S.R.
Izv. Vys. Uch. Zav.	*Bulletin of Higher Educational Institutions, Radiophysics Section*	U.S.S.R.
K. Danske Vidensk. Selske, Mat. Fis. Medd.	*Kongelige Danske Vindenskabernes Selskab, Mathematisk Fysiske Meddelesler, Copenhagen*	D
K. Tek. Higskol., Handl.	Kungliga Tekniska Hogskolans Sweded Handligar (Royal Institute of Technology, Sweden)	S
J. Acoust. Soc. Amer.	*Journal of Acoustical Society of America*	U.S.A.
J. Aero. Sci.	*Journal of the Aeronautical Sciences*	U.S.A.
J. Aero/Space Sci.	*Journal of the Aero/Space Sciences, N.Y.*	U.S.A.
J. Atmos. Terr. Phys.	*Journal of Atmospherical and Terrestrial Physics*	U.S.A.
J. Electronics and Control	*Journal Electronics and Control*	U.S.A.
J. Exp. Theor. Phys.	*Journal of Experimental and Theoretical Physics (Translation)*	U.S.S.R.
J. Fluid Mech.	*Journal of Fluid Mechanics, London*	U.K.
J. Franklin Inst.	*Journal of Franklin Institute*	U.S.A.
J. Geophys. Res.	*Journal of Geophysical Research*	U.S.A.
J. Math. Mech.	*Journal of Mathematics and Mechanics*	U.K.

ABBREVIATION	TITLE	COUNTRY
J. Math. Phys.	*Journal of Mathematics and Physics*	U.S.A.
J. Nucl. Energy	*Journal of Nuclear Energy*	U.K.
J. Opt. Soc. Amer.	*Journal Optical Society*	U.S.A.
J. Phys. Chem.	*Journal of Physical Chemistry*	U.S.A.
J. Phys. Czech.	*Czech Journal of Physics*	CS
J. Phys. Earth	*Journal of Physics of the Earth*	Japan
J. Phys. Rad.	*Journal of Physics of Radiations*	U.S.A.
J. Phys. Soc. Japan	*Journal of the Physical Society of Japan*	Japan
J. Rat. Mech. Anal.	*Journal of Rational Mechanics and Analysis*	U.S.A.
J. Roy. Aero. Soc.	*Journal of the Royal Aeronautical Society*	U.K.
J. Sci. Inst.	*Journal of Scientific Instruments, London*	U.K.
J. Soc. Automot. Engrs.	*Journal of the Society of Automotive Engineers, N.Y.*	U.S.A.
Jet Propulsion	*Jet Propulsion, New York*	U.S.A.
Lvtv. Pr. S. Zinat Akad. Vestis	*Proceedings of the Popular Republic Lutuana Academy*	Lithuania
Mathematika	*Mathematica, London*	U.K.
MIT	Massachusetts Institute of Technology	U.S.A.
Mon. Not. Roy. Astr. Soc.	Monthly Notices of Royal Astronomical Society	U.K.
NACA	National Advisory Committee for Aeronautics	U.S.A.
NASA	National Aeronautical Space Administration	U.S.A.
Nature, Lond.	*Nature, London*	U.K.
Naturwissenschaften		Ge
Nederl. Tijdschz.	Nederlander Tijdenschz Naturnik	N.L.
Nippon Elec. Comm. Eng.	*Nippon Electronics Committee Engineering*	Japan
NRL	Naval Research Laboratory, U.S. Navy	U.S.A.
Nuclear Instruments	*Nuclear Instruments*	U.S.A.
Nucleonics Power	Nucleonics Power	U.S.A.
Nuovo Cimento Suppl.	*Nuovo Cimento Supplemento*	I
Odin Ass.	Odin Association	U.S.A.
ONERA	Office National d'Etudes et de Recherches Aéronautiques, Paris	F
Phil. Mag.	*Philosophical Magazine*	U.K.
Phil. Trans.	*Philosophical Transactions*	U.S.A.
Phil. Trans. Roy. Soc.	*Philosophical Transactions Royal Society*	G.B.
Phys. Fluids	*Physics of Fluids*	U.S.A.

ABBREVIATION	TITLE	COUNTRY
Phys. Ionosph.	*Physics of the Ionosphere,* Cambridge	G.B.
Phys. Rev.	*Physical Review*	U.S.A.
Physics To-day		
Phys. Z. Sow.	*Physik Zeitschrift Sowjetumum*	U.S.S.R.
Plasmadyne	Giannini Plasmadyne Corp. Cal.	U.S.A.
Prikl. Mat. Mekh.	Prikldnaya Matematika i Mekhanika (Applied Mathematics and Mechanics)	U.S.S.R.
Proc. Camb. Phil. Soc.	*Proceedings Cambridge Philosophical Society*	U.K.
Proc. IRE	*Proceedings International Radio Engineering*	U.S.A.
Proc. Math. Sem.	*Proceedings of Mathematics Seminary —University Torino*	I
Proc. Nat. Acad. Sci.	*Proceedings National Academy Science*	U.S.A.
Proc. Nat. Inst. Sci.	*Proceedings National Institute Science, India*	India
Proc. Phys. Soc.	*Proceedings Physical Society*	U.K.
Proc. Roy. Astr. Soc.	*Proceedings of the Royal Astronomical Society, London*	U.K.
Proc. Roy. Irish Acad.	*Proceedings of Royal Irish Academy*	U.K.
Proc. Roy. Soc.	*Proceedings of the Royal Society*	U.K.
Proc. Soc. Exp. Biol. Med.	*Proceedings of Society of Experimental Biology and Medicine*	U.S.A.
Proc. Venice Conf.	*Proceedings Venice Conference*	I
Progr. Sci. Phys.	*Progrès des Sciences Physiques*	F
Progr. Theor. Phys. Jap.	*Progress of Theoretical Physics*	Japan
Quart. Appl. Math.	*Quarterly of Applied Mathematics*	U.S.A.
Quart. J. Mech. Appl. Math.	*Quarterly Journal of Mechanics and Applied Mathematics, London*	U.K.
Ramo-Wooldridge	The Ramo-Wooldridge Corp., Los Angeles	U.S.A.
R.C.A. Review	*R.C.A. Review*	U.K.
R. C. Sci. Fis. Mat. Nat.	*Rendiconti Scienze Fisiche Matematiche e Naturali*	I
Rech. Aeron.	*La recherche aéronautique*	F
Republic Av. Rep.	Republic Aviation Corp. Report, Farmingdale	U.S.A.
Rend. Phys. School "E. Fermi"	*Rendiconti della Scuola Internazionale di Fisica "E. Fermi"—Varenna*	I
Rev. Gén. Elect.	*Revue générale d'électricité*	F
Rev. Mod. Phys.	*Reviews of Modern Physics, N.Y.*	U.S.A.
Rev. Physique	*Revue de Physique—Bucarest*	B.G
Rev. Sci. Instr.	*Review of Scientific Instruments*	U.S.A.
Riv. Aeronaut.	*Rivista Aeronautica, Roma*	I
Rozprawy Electrotech.	*Electrotechnical Catalogue*	U.S.S.R.

ABBREVIATION	TITLE	COUNTRY
Sandia Corp.	Sandia Corp. Albuquerque, New Mexico	U.S.A.
S.B. Deutsch. Akad. Wiss. Berlin	*Sitzungsberichte der Deutschen Akademie der Wissenschaften*	Ge
Sci. Amer.	*Scientific American, N.Y.*	U.S.A.
Science and Culture	*Science and Culture*	G.B.
Smithsonian Inst.	Smithsonian Institution, Astrophysical Observatory	U.S.A.
Sov. J. Atom. Energ.	*Soviet Journal of Atomic Energy*	U.S.S.R.
Sov. Phys. Dokladi	*Soviet Physics Dokladi (Translation)*	U.S.S.R.
Sov. Phys. Tech. Phys.	*Soviet Physics, Technical Physics*	U.S.S.R.
Space/Aero	*Space-Aeronautics*	U.S.A.
Space Res. Lab.	Physical Research Laboratory, Space Research Laboratory	U.S.A.
Symp. gaseous masses	Symposium on the Motion of Gaseous Masses, Paris	F
Technology	*Technology* (Review)	U.S.A.
Tellus	*Tellus, Stockholm*	S
TIL/MOS	Technical Information and Library Services, Ministry of Supply, London	U.K.
T.N.	Technical Note	
Tohoku Univ. Sci. Rept.	*Tohoku University Scientific Report*	Japan
T.R.	Technical Report	
T.M.	Technical Memorandum	
USTIA	Toronto University Institute of Aerophysics	Canada
Usp. Fiz. Nauk.	Uspechi Fisiceschi Nauk	U.S.S.R.
Volta Conf.	Volta Conference, Roma	I
WADC	U.S. AF Wright Air Development Center, Dayton	U.S.A.
Z. Angew. Math. Mech.	*Zeitschrift für angewandte Mathematik und Mechanik*	Ge
Z. Angew. Math. Phys.	*Zeitschrift für angewandte Mathematik und Physik*	Ge
Z. Astrophys.	*Zeitschrift für Astrophysik* (Journal of Astrophysics)	Ge
Z. Naturforsch.	*Zeitschrift für Naturforschung*	Ge
Z. Phys.	*Zeitschrift für Physik*	Ge
Zh. Eksp. Teoret. Fiz.	*Zhurnal Eksperimentalnoi i teoreticheskoi Fiziki* (Journal de Physique Expérimentale et Théorique)	U.S.S.R.
Zh. Tekh. Fiz.	*Zhurnal Tekhnicheskoi Fiziki* (*Journal Technique de l'Académie des Sciences de l'URRS*)	U.S.S.R.
Zinat Akad. Vestis	*Zinat Akademie Vestis*	U.S.S.R.

LIST OF CONTRIBUTORS

Aeronautical Research Institute of Sweden
  S. BERND, *Director*, Stockholm, Sweden

Air Force Office of Scientific Research and Development Command
  E. HAYES, *Deputy Director Aero Sciences*, Washington, D.C.

Air Research and Development Command
  MRS. MARGARET P. PAPESCH, *Librarian*, European Office, Shell Building, 47, Rue Canterstein, Bruxelles, Belgium

Air Research and Development Command
  EDWARD H. SCHWARTZ, *Chief Operations Office Aircraft Laboratory*, H.Q. Wright Air Development Center, Wright-Patterson AF Base, Ohio, U.S.A.

Applied Mechanics Review
  STEPHEN JUHSZ, Southwest Research Institute, 8500 Culebra Road, San Antonio 6, Texas, U.S.A.

Associazione Italiana di Aerotecnica
  PROF. A. EULA, Piazza San Bernardo 101, Roma, Italy

ASTIA
  Headquarters, Arlington Hall Station, Arlington 12, Virginia, U.S.A.

AVCO-Everett Research Laboratory
  MISS BARBARA A. SPENCE, *Technical Librarian*, 2385 Revere Beach Parkway, Everett 49, Massachusetts, U.S.A.

AVCO Research and Advanced Development
  SAMUEL GLOBE, *Assistant for Research to the Vice-President*, 201 Lowell Street, Wilmington, Massachusetts, U.S.A.

Brookhaven National Laboratory
  DR. JOHN P. BINNINGTON, *Head of Research Library*, Upton, L.I., New York, U.S.A.

California Institute of Technology
  Jet Propulsion Laboratory, Pasadena, California, U.S.A.

Cambridge University Press
  DR. J. A. SHERCLIFF, Engineering Laboratory, Cambridge, England

Cavendish Laboratory
G. K. BATCHELOR, Cambridge University, Cambridge, England

Centre National de la Recherche Scientifique
16, Rue Pierre Curie, Paris, France

Convair
C. H. CRITCHFIELD, *Director of Scientific Research*, 3165 Pacific Highway, San Diego 12, California, U.S.A.

Cornell Aeronautical Laboratory, Inc.
JOSEPH P. DESMOND, *Librarian*, 4455 Genesee Street, Buffalo 21, New York, U.S.A.

Cornell University Press
DR. SEARS, *Vice-President for Research*, Ithaca, New York, U.S.A.

Deutsches Raketen und Raumfahrt Museum E.V.
ALFRED FRITZ, *Museumsleiter*, Reinburgstrasse 54, Stuttgart, Germany

Deutsche Versuchsanstalt für Luftfahrt E.V.
MARS VERVATING, Institut für Theoretische Gasdynamik, Theaterstrasse 13, Aachen, Germany

Deutsche Versuchsanstalt für Luftfahrt E.V.
PROF. DR. A. NEUMANN, Technische Hochschule, Institut für Angewandte Gasdynamik, Aachen, Germany

École Polytechnique Fédérale
DR. J. P. SYDLER, *Asst. Director Library*, Leonhardstrasse 33, Zurich, Switzerland

General Electric Company
Flight Propulsion Laboratory, Cincinnati 15, Ohio, U.S.A.

General Motors Corporation
E. B. JACKSON, *Librarian*, Research Laboratories, Box 188, North End Station, Detroit 2, Michigan, U.S.A.

Giannini Plasmadyne Corporation
GABRIEL GIANNINI, 3839 S. Main Street, Santa Ana, California, U.S.A.

Harvard University
PROF. H. W. EMMONS, Division of Engineering and Applied Physics, Pierce Hall, Cambridge 38, Massachusetts, U.S.A.

Imperial College of Science and Technology
DR. L. E. FRAENKEL, Dept. of Aeronautics, University of London, South Kensington, London S.W.7, England

Institut de Mécanique
    PROF. J. DUCARME, Université de Liège, 75 Rue du Val-Benoît, Liège, Belgique

Institute of the Aeronautical Sciences
    ROBERT R. DEXTER and JOHN GLENNON, 2 East 64th Street, New York 21, N.Y., U.S.A.

Institute for Fluid Dynamics and Applied Mechanics
    DR. S. S. LUDFORD, Maryland University, College Park, Maryland, U.S.A.

Institute for Fluid Dynamics and Applied Mechanics
    DR. J. M. BURGERS, *Research Professor*, Maryland University, College Park, Maryland, U.S.A.

Institute of Mathematical Sciences
    MISS SUSAN A. SCHULTZ, New York University, 25 Warverly Place, New York 3, N.Y., U.S.A.

Istituto di Aeronautica
    PROF. L. G. NAPOLITANO, Università di Napoli, via Mezzocannone, 16, Napoli, Italy

    PROF. G. CONTURSI

James Walt Engineering Laboratory
    PROF. W. J. DUNCAN, Dept. of Aeronautics and Fluids Mechanics, The University, Glasgow, W.2.

Lockheed Aircraft Corporation
    DR. A. E. HINDMARSH, Missiles and Space Division, Technical Information Center, Sunnyvale, California, U.S.A.

Maryland University
    DR. W. M. McDONALD, *Asst. Prof. of Physics*, Department of Physics, College Park, Maryland, U.S.A.

Massachusetts Institute of Technology
    Naval Supersonic Laboratory, Cambridge, Massachusetts, U.S.A.

Ministero Difesa
    COLONEL P. FORMENTINI, Conte S.R.I., Stato Maggiore Aeronautica, Ufficio Studi, Roma, Italy

Ministry of Aviation
    HAYLOR, L. J. H., Technical Information Library Services (TIL) U.K.

Ministry of Aviation
    A. BRAY, *Deputy Librarian*, Royal Aircraft Establishment Library, Farnborough, Hants, England

Missili

Prof. C. Cremona, Rivista dell'Associazione Italiana Razzi, Piazza San Bernardo 101, Roma, Italy

National Aeronautics and Space Administration, (N.A.S.A.)
B. A. Mulcahy, *Director*, Technical Information Division, 1520 H Street, N.W., Washington 25, D.C.

National Aeronautics and Space Administration, (N.A.S.A.)
Ira H. Abbot, *Deputy Director*, Aeronautical and Space Research Division, 1520 H Street, N.W., Washington 25, D.C.

National Bureau of Standards
Department of Commerce, Washington 25, D.C.

National Physical Laboratory
W. P. Jones, *Superintendent*, Department of Scientific and Industrial Research, Aerodynamics Division, Teddington, Middlesex, England

National Research Council
Miss O. M. Leach, *Librarian*, National Aeronautical Establishment, Ottawa, Ontario, Canada

Netherlands Delegation to AGARD
A. H. Geudeker, *Secretary*, Kanaalstraat 10, Delft, Netherlands

North American Aviation, Inc.
E. R. van Driest, *Director*, Missile Division, Aero-Space Laboratories, 12214 Lakewood Boulevard, Downey, California, U.S.A.

Norwegian Astronautical Society
Ing. Karl H. Höie, *Secretary*, Storgaten 37, Oslo, Norway

Office National d'Etudes et de Recherches Aéronautiques, (O.N.E.R.A.)
G. de Faget, *Chef du Service des Relations Exterieures et de Documentation*, 25, avenue de la Division Leclerc, Châtillon-sous-Bagneux (Seine), France

Oxford University Press
John Brown, *Publisher*, Amen House, Warwick Square, London E.C.4, England

Physics of Fluids
Dr. F. N. Frenkiel, *Editor*, Applied Physics Laboratory, The Johns Hopkins University, Silver Spring, Maryland, U.S.A.

RCA Victor Co.
Research Laboratories, Montreal, Canada

Republic Aviation Corporation
Raphael Coleman, *Manager*, Missile Systems Division, Advanced Projects Department, 223 Jericho Turnpike, Minsola, Long Island, N.Y., U.S.A.

Rocketdyne, A Division of North American Aviation, INC.
 ROBERT H. BODEN, 6633 Canoga Ave, Canoga Park, California, U.S.A.

School of Aeronautical Engineering
 PROF. P. S. LYKOUDIS, Pardue University, Lafayette, Indiana, U.S.A.

School of Mechanical Engineering
 P. E. LILEY, *Asst. Professor of Mechanical Engineering*, Pardue University, Lafayette, Indiana, U.S.A.

Service de Documentation et d'information Technique, (S.D.I.T.)
 G. H. FRENOT, *Chef du Group Exploitation Documentaire*, 4, Avenue de la Porte d'Issy, Paris 15ème, France

Space Technology Laboratories
 M. U. CLAUSER, *Vice-President and Director*, P.O. Box 95002, Los Angeles, California, U.S.A.

Stanford University Press
 JAMES W. TORRENCE, JR., Sales Department, Stanford, California, U.S.A.

Sud-Aviation
 S. MELVILLE, Service de Documentation, 40, Rue de l'Industrie, Courbevoie (Seine), France

The Technological Institute
 PROF. ALI BULENT CAMBEL, *Chairman Mechanical Engineering*, Northwestern University, Evanston, Illinois, U.S.A.

Università di Pisa
 PROF. E. PISTOLESI, Istituto di Meccanica Applicata ed Aeronautica, Pisa, Italy

Université Libre de Bruxelles
 50, avenue Franklin Roosevelt, Bruxelles, Belgique

Université de Paris
 PROF. RAYMOND SIESTRUNCK, Faculté des Sciences, Paris, France

BIBLIOGRAPHY

1. ACKERET, J. "A system of plasma propulsion using reactors and gas turbines". IX Intern. Astronautical Meeting, Amsterdam, 25–30 Aug. 1958.

2. ACTON, O. "Piccole pompe elettromagnetiche per metalli liquidi" *L'ingegnere*, No. 2, pp. 3–12, 1957.

3. ADAMS, E. N. "Auxiliary conditions in the Bohm-Pines theory of the electron gas" *Phys. Rev.* Vol. 98, p. 1130, May 1955.

4. ADAMS, M. C. and CAMAC, M. "The arc heated plasma thrust chamber". ARS Controllable Satellites Conference, M.I.T., 30 April–1 May 1959.

5. ADLAM, J. and ALLEN, J. "Hydromagnetic disturbances of large amplitude" *Proc. 2nd Geneva Conf.*, Vol. 31, pp. 221–4 (P/I UK), 1958.

*6. ADLAM, J. H. and ALLEN, J. E. "The structure of strong collision-free hydromagnetic waves" *Phil. Mag.* No. 29, pp. 448–55 (2 figs.), May 1958.

7. ADLAM, J. H. and PYLE, I. C. "Collision free compression of a plasma" *Ionization Phenomena in Gases*, Vol. II, p. 1077. Amsterdam, North-Holland, 1960.

*8. ADLAM, J. D. and TAYLER, R. J. "The Diffusion of magnetic fields in a cylindrical conductor". AERE/M–160, U.K.

*9. AGOSTINELLI, C. "Figure di equilibrio ellissiodali per una massa fluida elettricamente conduttrice uniformemente rotante, con campi magnetici variabili col tempo" *Accad. Lincei, Roma*, serie VIII, 23, fasc. b., dic. 1957.

10. AGOSTINELLI, C. "Magnetoidrodinamica cosmica" *Proc. Math. Sem. Univ. Bari*, No. 8, p. 16, 1955.

*11. AGOSTINELLI, C. "Magneto-hydrodynamic oscillations in a liquid cosmic mass, uniformly rotating within an axial and an equatorial magnetic field" *Accad. Sci. Torino*, I, Vol. 89, pp. 68–92, 1954–55.

*12. AGOSTINELLI, C. "Magneto-hydrodynamic oscillations in a rotating ellipsoidal liquid mass of cosmic dimensions" *Accad. Sci. Torino*, I, Vol. 89, pp. 41–58, 1954–55.

*13. AGOSTINELLI, C. "Moti magnetoidrodinamici simmetrici rispetto ad un asse. Caso delle piccole oscillazioni in una massa fluida sferoidale" *Accad. Sci. Torino*, I, Vol. 91, pp. 263–98, 1956–57.

14. AGOSTINELLI, C. "Onde elettromagnetiche guidate entro un tubo cilindrico percorso da un fluido dielettrico in moto traslatorio uniforme" *Proc. Math. Sem. Univ. Torino*, No. 14, pp. 257–68, 1954–55.

*15. AGOSTINELLI, C. "Ondes magnétohydrodynamiques dans une masse incompressible cylindrique circulaire". Congress Appl. Mech. U.S.A., 1957.

16. AGOSTINELLI, C. "On the magneto-dynamic and adiabatic equilibrium of a gaseous mass with a uniform rotational and gravitational motion". Int. Symp. on M.F.D., Washington, Jan. 1960.

17. AGOSTINELLI, C. "Sull'equilibrio adiabatico magnetodinamico di una massa fluida gravitante, in rotazione uniforme" *Accad. Lincei, Roma*, Vol. XXVIII, fasc. 3, pp. 278–83, marzo 1960.

*18. AGOSTINELLI, C. "Su alcuni moti magnetoidrodinamici ai quali è applicabile la teoria di Helmoltz sui vortici" *Proc. Math. Sem. Univ. Torino*, I, Vol. 16a, 1956–57.

*19. AGOSTINELLI, C. "Sui vortici sferici in magnetoidrodinamica" *Accad. Lincei, Roma*, serie VIII, 24, fasc. 1, pp. 35–42, Jan. 1958.

Note: A * which appears before some of entries, indicates that abstracts are available towards the end of this book.

20. AGOSTINELLI, C. "Sulla compatibilità di una forma ellisoidale a tre assi per una massa fluida cosmica rotante, elettricamente conduttrice, immersa in un campo magnetico uniforme" *Boll. Un. Mat. Ital.*, Vol. 10, pp. 17–23, 1955.

*21. AGOSTINELLI, C. "Sull'equilibrio relativo magnetoidrodi-namico di masse elettricamente conduttrici uniformemente rotanti e gravitanti" *Boll. Un. Mat. Ital.*, Vol. 14a, pp. 95–101,

*22. AGOSTINELLI, C. "Sulle equazioni dell'equilibrio adiabatico magnetodinamico di una massa fluida gassosa uniformemente rotante e gravitante" *Accad. Lincei, Roma*, Vol. 26. No. 5, pp. 665–70, May 1959.

*23. AGOSTINELLI, C. "Sur quelques mouvements magnétohydrodynamiques dans une masse fluide cylindrique en rotation qui interessent la cosmogonie". Congress Appl. Mech. U.S.A., 1957.

*24. AGOSTINELLI, C. "Stationary solutions of the magnetohydrodynamical equations of interest in cosmogony" *Accad. Lincei, Roma*, Vol. 17, pp. 216–21, 1954.

25. AGOSTINELLI, C. "Turbolenza in magnetoidrodinamica" *Corso sulla teoria della turbolenza*, Lib. Ed. Univ. Levrotto e Bella, Vol. II, pp. 289–335, Torino, 1958.

*26. AGRANOVICH, V. M. and RUKHADZE, A. A. "On the propagation of electromagnetic waves in a medium with appreciate spatial dispersion" *J. Exp. Theor. Phys.*, No. 4, p. 685, April 1959.

*27. AGRANOVICH, V. M., PAFONOF, V. E. and RUKHADZE, A. A. "Cerenkov radiation of an electron moving in a medium with spatial dispersion" *J. Exp. Theor. Phys.*, No. 1, p. 160, July 1959.

28. AITKEN, K. L., BURCHAM, J. N. and REYNOLDS, P. "Experiments with linear pinch and inverse pinch systems" *Ionization Phenomena in Gases*, Vol. 2, p. 896. Amsterdam, North-Holland, 1959.

29. AKASOFU, S. "The Helicoidal structures in the cosmical electrodynamics" *Tellus*, Vol. 10, pp. 409–14, 1958.

30. AKHIEZER, A. I. "On the interaction of electromagnetic waves with charged particles and the oscillations of the electronic plasma" *Nuovo Cimento Suppl.*, Vol. 3, serie X, No. 4, pp. 591–613, 1956.

31. AKHIEZER, A. I. and POLQVIN, R. "Oscillations of the plasma in crossed electric and magnetic fields" *Zh. Tekh. Fiz.*, Vol. 22, pp. 1794–802, 1952 (in Russian).

32. AKHIEZER, A. I. and FAINBERG, Y. B. "High-frequency oscillations of an electron plasma" *Zh. Eksp. Teoret. Fiz.*, Vol. 21, pp. 1262, 1951.

33. AKHIEZER, A. I. and POLOVIN, R. V. "Theory of wave motion of an electron plasma" *J. Exp. Theor. Phys.*, No. 3, pp. 696–705, 1956.

34. AKHIEZER, A. I., FAINBERG, I., SITENKO, A., STEPANOV, K., KULILKO, V., GORBATENKO, M. and KIROCHKIN, U. "High-frequency plasma oscillations" *Proc. 2nd Geneva Conf.*, Vol. 31, pp. 99–111 (P/2300 U.S.S.R.), 1958.

35. AKHIEZER, A. I., LYBARSKII, G. and POLOVIN, R. "Simple waves and shock waves in magneto-hydrodynamics" *Proc. 2nd Geneva Conf.*, Vol. 31, pp. 225–9 (P/2500 Ukrainian U.S.S.R.), 1958.

36. AKHIEZER, A. I. and LYBARSKII, Y. G. "On the non-linear theory of electron plasma oscillation" *Dokl. Akad. Nauk, SSSR*, Vol. 80, p. 193, 1951.

37. AKHIEZER, A. I. and PARGAMANIK, L. "Free oscillations of an electron plasma in a magnetic field". AEC report tr-3492 (Translated from *Uch. Zap. Kharkov*, Vol. 25, pp. 75–104, 1958).

38. AKHIEZER, A. I. and LYBARSKII, G. and FAINBERG, I. "Contribution to non-linear theory of oscillations in plasma" *Uch. Zap. Kharkov*, Vol. 64, pp. 73–80, 1958 (in Russian).

*39. AKHIEZER, A. I., POLOVIN, R. V. and TSINTSADZE, N. L. "Simple waves in the Chevv-Goldberger-Low approximation" *Zh. Eksp. Teoret. Fiz.*, Vol. 37, No. 3 (9), pp. 756–9, 1959; *J. Exp. Theor. Phys.*, Vol. 37 (10), No. 3, pp. 539–41, 1960.

*40. AKHIEZER, A. I. and POLOVIN, R. V. "Motion of a conducting piston in a magnetohydrodynamical medium" *Zh. Eksp. Teoret. Fiz.*, Vol. 38, No. 2, pp. 529–33, 1960.

*41. AKHIEZER, A. I., LYBARSKII, G. Y. and POLOVIN, R. V. "On the stability of shock waves in magneto-hydrodynamics" *Zh. Eksp. Teoret. Fiz.*, Vol. 35, No. 3, pp. 731–737 (Fig. 6), 1958; *Sov. Phys. JETP* No. 3, pp. 307–311, March 1959.

42. AKHIEZER, A. I. and SITENKO, A. G. "Electron plasma oscillations in an external electric field" *J. Exp. Theor. Phys.*, Vol. 3, pp. 140–41, 1956.

43. AKHIEZER, A. I. and POLOVIN, R. V. "Plasma oscillations in crossed electric and magnetic fields" *J. Exp. Theor. Phys.*, Vol. 22, pp. 1794–820, 1952.

44. AKHIEZER, A. I. and POLOVIN, R. V. "Relativistic plasma oscillations" *Dokl. Akad. Nauk. SSSR*, Vol. 102, pp. 919–20, 1955.

*45. AKHIEZER, A. I. and POLOVIN, R. V. "Sur la thèorie des ondes magnetohydrodynamiques relativistes" *Zh. Eksp. Teoret. Fiz.*, Vol. 36, No. 6, pp. 1845–52, 1959.

*46. AKHIEZER, A. I., PROKHODA, I. G. and SITENKO, A. G. "On the scattering of electromagnetic waves in a plasma" *Zh. Eksp. Teoret. Fiz.*, Vol. 33, p. 750, 1957.

*47. AKHIEZER, A. I., LYBARSKII, G. Y. and POLOVIN, R. V. "Simple waves in magnetohydrodynamics" *Ukr. fiz. Zh.*, Vol. 3, pp. 433–8, 1958; *Zh. Tekh. Fiz.*, Vol. 29, No. 8, pp. 933–8, 1959 (in Russian).

*48. AKHIEZER, A. I. and SITENKO, A. G. "Théorie de l'excitation des ondes hydromagnétiques" *Zh. Eksp. Teoret. Fiz.*, Vol. 35, No. 1, July 1958, pp. 116–20; *J. Exp. Theor. Phys.*, No. 1, p. 82, Jan. 1959.

49. ALCOCK, E. D. "The effect of an electric field on the viscosity of liquids" *Physica*, Vol. 7, p. 126, 1936.

50. ALFVÉN, H. "Collision between a non-ionized gas and a magnetized plasma". Symp. M.F.D., Washington, January 1960.

51. ALFVÉN, H. and COHN–PETERS, H. "Eine neue Art von Hochfrequenz-Entladung im Vakuum und Deren Verwendung als Ionequelle" *Ark. Mat. Astr. Fys.*, Vol. 31A, No. 18, p. 17, 1945.

*52. ALFVÉN, H. *Cosmical Electrodynamics*. Oxford, Clarendon Press, 1950.

53. ALFVÉN, H. "Tentative theory of solar prominences" *Ark. Mat. Astr. Fys.*, Vol. 27A, No. 20, p. 10, 1940.

54. ALFVÉN, H. *Cosmical Hydrodynamics*. Oxford, Clarendon Press, 1950.

55. ALFVÉN, H. "On the motion of a charged particle in a magnetic field" *Ark. Mat. Astr. Fys.*, Vol. 27A, No. 22, p. 20, 1940.

56. ALFVÉN, H. "Discussion of the origin of the terrestrial and solar magnetic fields" *Tellus*, Vol. 2, p. 74, 1950.

57. ALFVÉN, H. "On the electric field theory of magnetic storms and aurorae" *Tellus*, Vol. 7, pp. 50–64, 1955.

58. ALFVÉN, H. "Existence of electromagnetic-hydrodynamic waves" *Nature, Lond.*, Vol. 150, pp. 405–6, 1942; *Ark. Mat. Astr. Fys.*, Vol. 29B, No. 2, p. 7, 1943.

59. ALFVÉN, H. "Magnetohydrodynamics and the thermonuclear problem" *Proc. 2nd Geneva Conf.*, Vol. 31, pp. 3–5 (P/145 Sweden), 1958.

60. ALFVÉN, H. "Granulation magneto-hydrodynamic waves and the heating of the solar corona" *Mon. Not. Roy. Astr. Soc.*, Vol. 107, pp. 211–19, 1947.

61. ALFVÉN, H. "Line currents in cosmic physics" *Proc. Roy. Soc. A*, Vol. 233, p. 296, 1955.

62. ALFVÉN, H. "Magneto-hydrodynamic waves and solar prominences" *Indian J. Meteorol. Geophys.*, Vol. 5, pp. 133–6, 1954.

63. ALFVÉN, H. "Magneto-hydrodynamic waves and sunspots" *Mon. Not. Roy. Astr. Soc.*, Vol. 105, pp. 3–16, 1945.

64. ALFVÉN, H. "Magneto-hydrodynamic waves and sunspots III" *Ark. Nat. Fys.*, Vol. 34A, No. 23, 1947.

*65. ALFVÉN, H. "Magneto-hydrodynamic waves in the atomic nucleus" *Phys. Rev.* Vol. 107, p. 632, 1957.

*66. ALFVÉN, H. "Magneto-hydrodynamic waves in the sun AF". Cambridge Res. Centre, Geophysical Res. Papers No. 30, pp. 515–25, AF CRC-TR 54–203, July 1954.

67. ALFVÉN, H. "On the effect of a vertical magnetic field in a conducting atmosphere" *Ark. Mat. Astr. Fys.*, Vol. 29A, No. 11, 1943.

68. ALFVÉN, H. "Remarks on the rotation of a magnetized sphere with application to solar rotation" *Ark. Mat. Astr. Fys.*, Vol. 28A, No. 6, 1941.

69. ALFVÉN, H. "Plasma Physics" *Rend. Phys. School "E. Fermi"* corso XIII, pp. 1–9, Varenna, 1959.

70. ALFVÉN, H. "Sunspots and magneto-hydrodynamics II" *Mon. Not. Roy. Astr. Soc.*, Vol. 105, pp. 382–94, 1945.

71. ALFVÉN, H. "The impossibility of determining the sun's general magnetic field by Zeeman effect measurements" *Nature, Lond.*, Vol. 168, p. 1036, 1951.

72. ALFVÉN, H. and LEHNERT, B. "The sun's general magnetic field" *Nature, Lond.*, Vol. 178, p. 1339, 1956.

73. ALLAN, D. and BULLARD, E. "Distortion of a toroidal field by convection" *Rev. Mod. Phys.*, Vol. 30, p. 1087, 1958.

74. ALLEN, J. E. "Fast circuits" *Rend. Phys. School "E. Fermi"* corso XIII, pp. 69–76, Varenna, 1959.

75. ALLEN, J. E. "An elementary theory of the transient pinched discharge" *Proc. Phys. Soc.*, Vol. 708, pp. 24–30, 1957.

76. ALLEN, J. and HINDMARSH, W. "The Bremsstrahlung radiation from ionized hydrogen". AERE CP/R 1761, p. 9, 1955.

77. ALLEN, J. E., BOYD, R. L. F. and REYNOLDS, P. "The collection of positive ions by a probe inserted in a plasma" *Proc. Phys. Soc.*, Vol. 70B, p. 297, 1957.

78. ALLEN, J. E. "Radiation belts around the earth" *Sci. Amer.*, Vol. 200, pp. 39–47, 1959.

79. ALLEN, J. E. "Magnetic confinement and different machines" *Rend. Phys. School "E. Fermi"* corso XIII, pp. 61–9, Varenna, 1959.

80. ALLEN, J. E. "Langmuir probes and boundary phenomena" *Rend. Phys. School "E. Fermi"* corso XIII, pp. 51–61, Varenna, 1959.

81. ALLEN, J. E. "Collision-free hydromagnetic waves" *Rend. Phys. School "E. Fermi"* corso XIII, pp. 38–51, Varenna, 1959.

82. ALLEN, J. E. and MAGISTRELLI, F. "The plasma-sheath transition in the presence of a magnetic field" *Ionization Phenomena in Gases*, Vol. II, p. 599. Amsterdam, North-Holland, 1959.

83. ALLEN, J. E. "Thermonuclear power and the pinch effect" *Endeavour*, Vol. 17, pp. 117–26, 1958.

84. ALLEN, T. K. "Experiments on generation of plasma Alfvén waves" *Phys. Rev. Letters*, Vol. 2, pp. 383–4, 1958.

*85. ALLEN, J. E. and SEGRÉ, S. E. "Experiments on the orthogonal pinch effect" *Ionization Phenomena in Gases*, Vol. 2, p. 1073, Amsterdam, North-Holland, 1959.

86. ALLEN, K., BODIN, H. CURRAN, S. and FITCH, R. "Observation on transient pinched discharges" *Proc. Int. Conf. on Ionization Phenomena in Gases, Venice, 1957*, pp. 26–32.

87. ALLEN, W. A., MORRISON, H. L., RAY, D. B. and ROGERS, J. W. "Fluid mechanics of copper" *Phys. Fluids*, Vol. 2, p. 329, 1959.

88. ALLIBONE, T. E. *et al.* "Review of controlled thermonuclear research at A.E.I. research laboratory" *Proc. 2nd Geneva Conf.*, Vol. 31, pp. 169–80, 1958.

89. ALLIS, W. P. "Electric fields and currents in a highly ionized gas". Preprint, third biennial gas dynamic symposium ARS, Northwestern Univ., 24–26 Aug. 1959.

90. ALLIS, W. P. "Motions of ions and electrons". Research Laboratory of Electronics, Cambridge, Mass. Report No. 299, June 1956; *Handbuch der Physik*, Vol. XXI, pp. 176–250, Berlin, Springer-Verlag, 1956.

91. ALLIS, W. P. *et al.* "Series of lectures on physics of ionized gases". Los Alamos Report LA-2055 March 1955, June 1956.

*92. ALLIS, W. P. and BUCHSBAUM, S. J. "The conductivity of an ionized gas in a magnetic field". Presented at the ARS Northern Gas Dynamics Symposium at Northwestern University Evanston, Illinois, 24–26 Aug. 1959.

93. ALLIS, W. "Gas discharges". AEC Report LA-1432, p. 32, 1951.

94. ALPHER, R. A. "Optical properties of dissociated and ionized gases VA 2". Spring Meeting, Amer. Phys. Soc. Washington, D.C., 30 May 1959.

95. ALPHER, R. A. and RUBIN, R. "Magnetic dispersion and attenuation of sound in conducting fluids and solids" *J. Acoust. Soc. Amer.*, Vol. 26, pp. 452–3, 1954.

96. ALPHER, R. A. and WHITE, D. R. "Optical refractivity of high-temperature gases. II. Effects resulting from ionization of monatomic gases" *Phys. Fluids*, Vol. 2, p. 162, 1959.

97. ALPHER, R. A., HURWITZ, H. Jr., JOHNSON, R. H. and WHITE, D. R. "Free surface mercury magnetohydrodynamics". Int. Symposium on M.F.D., Washington, Jan. 1960.

98. ALPHER, R. A. and WHITE, D. R. "Interferometric measurement of electron concentrations in plasmas" *Phys. Fluids*, Vol. I, pp. 452–3, Sept. Oct. 1958.

99. ALSMILLER, R. "The effect of partially ionized impurities on a DCX device". AEC Report ORNL-2581, p. 21, 1958.

100. AMER, S. "Non-linear theory of plasma oscillations and waves" *J. Electronics and Control*, Vol. 5, pp. 105–13, 1958.

101. ANADI SHANKAR GUPTA "Flow on an electrically conducting fluid past a porous flat plate in the presence of a transverse magnetic field" *Z. Angew. Math. Phys.*, No. 1, pp. 43–50, 1960.

102. ANDERSON, N. W. "Longitudinal magneto-hydrodynamic waves" *J. Acoust. Soc. Amer.*, Vol. 25, pp. 528–32, 1953.

*103. ANDERSON, O. A., BAKER, W. R., BZATENAHL, A., FURTH, H. P. and KUNKEL, W. B. "Hydromagnetic capacitor" *J. Appl. Phys.*, Vol. 30, No. 2, pp. 188–96, 1959.

*104. ANDERSON, O. A., FURTH, H. P., STONE, J. M. and WRIGHT, R. E. "The inverse pinch effect" *Phys. Fluids*, Vol. 1, pp. 489–94, 1958.

105. ANDERSON, O. A. *et al.* "Study and use of a rotating plasma" *Proc. 2nd Geneva Conf.*, Vol. 32, pp. 155–60, 1958.

106. ANDERSON, O. A., BAKER, W. R., ISE, J. Jr., KUNKEL, W. B., PYLE, R. V. and STONE, J. M. "Sheet pinch devices" *Proc. 2nd Geneva Conf.*, Vol. 32, pp. 150–5, 1958.

107. ANDERSON, O. A. and BAKER, W. R. "Linear pinch-work in Berkeley" AEC Report UCRL-3468, 13 pages, 1958.

108. ANDERSON, J. M. and GOLDSTEIN, L. "Interaction of Electromagnetic waves of radio frequency in isothermal plasmas: Collision cross-section of helium atoms" *Phys. Rev.*, Vol. 100, p. 1037, 1955.

109. ANDRADE, E. N., DA, C. and DODD, D. "The effect of an electric field on the viscosity of liquids" *Proc. Roy. Soc. A*, Vol. 204, pp. 449–64, 1951; *ibid.*, Vol. 187, p. 296, 1946.

110. ANDRUCKINA, E. D., GREBENSHINKOV, S. E., RABINOVITCH, M. S., REISER, M. D., SAFRANOV, A. J. and SHPIGEL, I. S. "Some peculiarities of induction gas discharges" *Ionization Phenomena in Gases*, Vol. 2, p. 1050. Amsterdam, North-Holland, 1959.

111. ANISIMOV, A. I., GOLANT, V. E., KONSTANTINOV, B. P. and VINOGRODOV, N. I. "A method for studying the space distribution of electrons in a plasma" *Ionization Phenomena in Gases*, Vol. 2, p. 729. Amsterdam, North-Holland, 1959.

*112. ARKHIPOV, V. N. "Influence du champ magnétique sur la stabilité de la couche limite" *Dokl. Akad. Nauk. SSSR*, Vol. 129, No. 4, pp. 751, 753 (2 fig.), 1959.

113. ARTSIMOVICH, L. A., ANDRIANOV, A. M., BAZELENSKAYA, O. A., PROKHOROV, YU. G. and FILIPPOV, N. V. "An investigation of high-current pulsed discharges" *J. Nucl. Energy*, Vol. 4, p. 203, 1957.

114. ARTSIMOVICH, L. A., ANDRIANOV, A. M., DOBROKHOLOV, E. I., LUKYUNOW, S. Y., PODGORVAI, I. M., SINITSYN, V. I. and FILIPPOV, N. V. "High-energy radiation from pulsed discharges" *J. Nucl. Energy*, Vol. 4, p. 213, 1957.

115. ARTSIMOVICH, L. A. "Research on controlled thermonuclear reactions in the URSS" *Sov. Phys. Uspekhy*, Vol. 66 (1), No. 2, pp. 191–207, 1958.

116. ARTSIMOVICH, L. A. "On the passage of high current through a plasma in the presence of a longitudinal magnetic field" *Plasma Physics and the Problem of Controlled Thermonuclear Reactions"*. Oxford, Pergamon Press, 1959.

*117. ARTSIMOVICH, L. A., LUK'YANOV, S. Y., POOGORNYI, I. M. and CHUVATIN, S. A. "Electrodynamical acceleration of plasma bunches" *Zh. Eksp. Teoret. Fiz.*, Vol. 33, p. 3, 1957; *J. Exp. Theor. Phys.*, No. 1, Jan. 1958.

118. ASAMI, Y. and SAITO, M. "Resonance phenomena in ionised gases and their effect on the propagation characteristics of electromagnetic waves" *Nippon Elect. Comm. Eng.*, No. 15, p. 564, 1939.

119. ASCOLI-BARTOLI, U. and RASETTI, F. "Measurements of the refractive index of a plasma in the optical region" *Ionization Phenomena in Gases*, Vol. II, p. 839. Amsterdam, North-Holland, 1959.

120. ASH, E. A. and GABOR, D. "Experimental investigations on electron interaction" *Proc. Roy. Soc.* A, Vol. 228, p. 447, 1955.

121. ASKARIAN, G. A. "Coherent scattering and radiation of electromagnetic waves by a plasma in a non-uniform magnetic field" *Zh. Eksp. Teoret. Fiz.*, Vol. 33, p. 1576, 1957.

122. ASTRÖM, E. "Magneto-hydrodynamic waves in a plasma" *Nature, Lond.*, Vol. 165, pp. 1019–20, 1950.

123. ASTRÖM, E. "On waves in an ionized gas" *Ark. Fys.*, Vol. 2, pp. 443–57, 1950.

*124. ATKINSON, W. R., FOWLER, R. G. and HOLDEN, W. "Magneto-hydrodynamic flows in hydrogen and helium" *Phys. Rev.*, Vol. 95, p. 634, 1954.

125. ATKINSON, W. R. and HOLDEN, W. R. "Ionized gas flow in electrically energized shock tubes". Univ. Oklahoma. Tech. Rep. Project NR/061/087 Contract N. 982 (02), 1954.

*126. ATKINSON, W. R., HOLDEN, W. R. and FOWLER, R. G. "Shock waves reflected by magnetic fields" *J. Appl. Phys.*, Vol. 30, No. 6, pp. 801–2, 1959.

*127. AUER, P. L., HURWITZ, H. Jr. and MILLER, R. D. "Collective oscillations in a cold plasma" *Phys. Fluids*, Vol. 1, No. 6, pp. 501–15, 1958.

128. AXFORD, W. I. "The oscillating plate problem in magnetohydrodynamics" *J. Fluid Mech.*, P.I, Vol. 8, pp. 97–102, 1960.

129. BABAKIAN, J. "An investigation of electron and ion beams under outer space conditions". ARDC, Conference on Ion and Plasma Research, University of Maryland, 30 Sept.–2 Oct. 1958.

130. BABCOCK, H. W. "Stellar magnetic fields" *Nature, Lond.*, Vol. 166, p. 249, 1950.

131. BABCOCK, H. W. and BABCOCK, H. D. "The sun's magnetic field" *Astrophys. J.*, Vol. 121, pp. 349–66, 1955.

*132. BABSUKOV, K. A. and KOLOMENSKII, A. R. "Doppler effect in an electron plasma in a magnetic field" *Sov. Phys. Tech. Phys.* (New York), Vol. 4, No. 8, pp. 868–70, 1960; *Zh. Eksp. Teoret. Fiz.*, Vol. 29, No. 8, pp. 954–7, 1959.

133. BACKUS, G. "A class of self-sustaining dissipative spherical dynamics" *Ann. Phys.* (N.Y.), Vol. 4, p. 372, 1958.

134. BACKUS, G. "Linearized plasma oscillations in arbitrary electron velocity distribution" *J. Math. Phys.*, Vol. I, No. 3, pp. 178–91, 1960.

135. BACKUS, G. "The axisymmetric self-excited fluid dynamo" *Astrophys. J.*, Vol. 125, p. 500, 1957.

136. BACKUS, G. "The external field of a rotating magnet" *Astrophys. J.*, Vol. 123, pp. 508–12, 1956.

137. BACKUS, G. E. and CHANDRASEKHAR, S. "On Cowling's theorem on the impossibility of self-maintained axisymmetric homogeneous dynamos" *Proc. Nat. Acad. Sci.*, Vol. 42, pp. 105–109, 1956.

*138. BADE, W. L. "Hydromagnetic effects of upwelling near a boundary". Univ. of Utah, Dept. of Physics, Tech. Rep. 10. 1955.

*139. BADER, M. and CARLSON, W. C. A. "Measurement of the effect of an axial magnetic field on the Reynolds number of transition in mercury flowing through a glass tube". NACA TN 4274, May 1958.

140. BAGLIN, H., BRIN, A., DELCROIX, J. L., OZIAS, Y. and SALMON, J. "Action d'un champ électrique alternatif sur un plasma totalement ionisé" *Ionization Phenomena in Gases*, Vol. II, p. 640. Amsterdam, North-Holland, 1959.

141. BAILEY, V. A. "Electromagneto-ionic theory" *Phys. Rev.*, Vol. 75, p. 1104, 1949; *ibid.*, Vol. 77, p. 418, 1950; *ibid.*, Vol. 78, p. 428, 1950; *ibid.*, Vol. 83, pp. 439–54, 1951.

142. BAILEY, V. A. "Plane waves in an ionized gas with static electric and magnetic fields present" *Austr. J. Sci. Res.* A, Vol. 1, pp. 351–9, 1948.

143. BAILEY, V. A. and LARSDECKER, K. "Electro-magnetic-ionic waves" *Nature, Lond.*, Vol. 166, p. 259, 1950.

144. BAKER, W. R., BRATENAHL, A., DE SILVA, W. A. and KUNKEL, W. B. "Viscous effects in highly ionized rotating plasmas" *Ionization Phenomena in Gases*, Vol. 2, p. 1171. Amsterdam, North-Holland, 1959.

145. BALESCU, R. "Transport equation of a plasma". Int. Symposium on M.F.D. Washington, Jan. 1960.

*146. BALESCU, R. "Irreversible processes in ionized gases" *Phys. Fluids*, Vol. 3, No. 1, pp. 52–64, 1960.

*147. BANISTER, J. R. "Separation of magnetic driving and ohmic heating" *Phys. Fluids*, Vol. 3, No. 4, pp. 648–55, 1960.

148. BANNERJEE, S. S. and SINGH, B. N. "Effect of a transverse magnetic field on refractive index and conductivity of ionized air" *Science and Culture*, Vol. 4, p. 597, 1959.

149. BAÑOS, A. "Fundamental wave functions in an unbounded magneto-hydrodynamic field. 1: General theory" *Phys. Rev.*, Vol. 97, pp. 1435–43, 1955.

150. BAÑOS, A. "Magneto-hydrodynamic waves in incompressible and compressible fluids" *Proc. Roy. Soc.* A, Vol. 233, pp. 350–66, 1955; U.S.A. AFOSR, TN 320, 1956.

*151. BAÑOS, A. "Theoretical study of magnetodynamic, magneto-acoustic, and magneto-elastic phenomena". California Un. Final Technical Report, 15 May 1957, 31 p.; Rept. No. AFOSR, TR-57-35.

152. BAÑOS, A. Jr. and VERNON, R. "Large amplitude waves in a collision free plasma. I: Single pulse with isotropic pressure" *Nuovo Cimento*, Vol. XV, No. 2, pp. 269–88, 1960.

*153. BARABANENKOV, U. N. "Solution de l'equation cinétique du plasma dans un champ magnétique variable" *Zh. Eksp. Teoret. Fiz.*, Vol. 37, No. 2 (8), pp. 427–9, 1959; *J. Exp. Theor. Phys.*, Vol. 37 (10), No. 2, pp. 305–6, 1960.

154. BARABANENKOV, U. N. "Hydrodynamic analysis of the compression of a rarefied plasma in an axially-symmetric magnetic field" *J. Exp. Theor. Phys.*, No. 5, p. 893, 1959.

155. BARLY, J. and DOW, W. "Supersonic wind at low pressures produced by an arc in magnetic field" *Physics*, Vol. 79, p. 186, 1950.

*156. BARNES, A. H. "Direct current electromagnetic pump" *Nucleonics*, Vol. 11, p. 16, 1953.

*157. BARROS, D. Jr. "Fundamental wave functions in an unbounded magneto-hydronamic field. V: General theory" *Phys. Rev.*, Vol. 97, p. 1435, 1955.

158. BARTELS, H. "A new method of temperature measurement in high temperature arc discharges" *Z. Phys.*, Vol. 127, p. 243, 1950.

159. BARTELS, H. and BEUCHELT, R. "On typical states in the spectra of dense plasmas I" *Z. Phys.*, Vol. 149, p. 594, 1957.

160. BARTELS, H. and BEUCHELT, R. "On typical states in the spectra of dense plasmas II" *Z. Phys.*, Vol. 149, p. 608, 1957.

161. BARTELS, H. D., GANSAUGE, P. und BARTFELDT, J. "Über pinchähnliche Erscheinungen an explodierenden Drähten" *Ionization Phenomena in Gases*, Vol. 2, p. 1196. Amsterdam, North-Holland, 1959.

162. BARTHEL, J. R. and LYKOUDIS, P. S. "The slow motion of a permanently magnetized sphere in an electrically conducting medium". School of Aeronautical Engineering, Report, N.A.-5911, Purdue University, 1959.

*163. BARTHEL, J. R. and LYKOUDIS, P. S. "The slow motion of a magnetized sphere in a conducting medium" *J. Fluid Mech.*, Vol. 8, Pt. 2, pp. 307–14, 1960.

164. BATCHELOR, G. K. "On the spontaneous magnetic field in a conducting liquid in turbulent motion" *Proc. Roy. Soc.* A, Vol. 201, pp. 405–16, 1950.

165. BATTEN, H. W., SMITH, H. L. and EARLY, H. C. "Plasma fluctuations in crossed electric and magnetic fields" *J. Franklin Inst.*, Vol. 262, pp. 17–30, 1956.

166. BAUER, A. "Zur Temperaturmessung an plasmaschichten mittlerer Absorption" *Ionization Phenomena in Gases*, Vol. 2, p. 817. Amsterdam, North-Holland, 1959.

167. BAULKNIGHT, C. W. "Transport property equations for partially ionized gases" *Ionization Phenomena in Gases*, Vol. 2, p. 584. Amsterdam, North-Holland, 1959.

*168. BAY, W. "Theoretical treatment in magneto-hydrodynamics". CRC, TR-57-242, 1956.

169. BAYET, M. "EM properties of plasmas in a magnetic field" *J. Phys. Rad.*, Vol. 15, p. 258, 1954.

170. BAYET, M. "Properties electromagnétiques des plasmas" *J. Phys. Rad.*, Vol. 13, p. 579, 1952.

171. BAYET, M. *et al.* "Sur le tenseur de conductivité des plasmas électriques en presence d'un champ magnétique constant" *C. R. Acad. Sci., Paris*, Vol. 237, p. 1503, 1953.

172. BAYET, M., DELCROIX, J. L. and DENISSE, J. F. "Distribution function of electrons in a discharge" *Appl. Sci. Res.* B, Vol. 5, p. 331, 1955.

173. BAYET, M., DELCROIX, J. L. and DENISSE, J. F. "On the solutions of Boltzmann's equation for a Loretzian gas: application to weakly ionised gases" *C. R. Acad. Sci., Paris*, Vol. 238, p. 2146, 1954.

174. BAYET, M., DELCROIX, J. L. and DENISSE, J. F. "Théorie cinetique des plasmas homogenes faiblement ionisés I" *J. Phys. Rad.*, Vol. 15, p. 795, 1954.

175. BAYET, M., DELCROIX, J. L. and DENISSE, J. F. "Théorie cinetique des plasmas homogenes faiblement ionises III: l'operateur de collision dans le cas du gaz de Lorenz imparfait" *J. Phys. Rad.*, Vol. 17, p. 923, 1956.

176. BAYET, M., DELCROIX, J. L. and DENISSE, J. F. "Théorie cinetique des plasmas homogenes faiblement ionisés IV: étude de l'evolution de la parte isotropique de la function de distribution" *J. Phys. Rad.*, Vol. 17, p. 1005, 1956.

177. BAZER, J. "Non-linear hydromagnetic wave motion". ARDC Conference on Ion and Plasma Research, University of Maryland, 30 Sept.–2 Oct. 1958.

*178. BAZER, J. and ERICSON, W. B. "Hydromagnetic shocks" *Astrophys. J.*, Vol. 129, pp. 758–85, 1959.

*179. BAZER, J. and FLEISCHMAN, O. "Propagation of weak hydromagnetic discontinuities" *Phys. Fluids*, Vol. 2, No. 4, pp. 366–78, 1959; AFCRC TN-59-255.

*180. BEARD, D. B. "Cyclotron radiation from magnetically confined plasmas" *Phys. Fluids*, Vol. 2, p. 379, 1959.

181. BEARD, D. B. "Relativistic calculation for cyclotron radiation from hot plasmas" *Phys. Fluids*, Vol. 3, No. 2, p. 324, 1960.

*182. BEARD, D. B. "Incoherent microwave radiation from an ionized gas confined by a magnetic field". Lockheed Missiles and Space Div. Rept. LMSD-48394, p. 47, 27 Feb. 1959.

183. BEDENOV, A. A. "Thermodynamic properties of a degenerate plasma" *J. Exp. Theor. Phys.*, No. 2, p. 446, August 1959.

184. BEDNARCYZK, H. "Acceleration of conducting particles by magnetic fields". IX Int. Astronautical Meeting, Amsterdam, August 25–30, 1958.

*185. BEGIASHVILI, G. A. and GEDALIN E. V. "Motion of a charged particle in an Anistropic medium" *J. Exp. Theor. Phys.*, No. 6, p. 1059, June 1959.

186. BEISER, A. "On an interplanetary magnetic field" *J. Geophys. Res.*, Vol. 60, p. 155–59, 1955.

187. BEKEFI, G. "The study of plasmas through their interaction with high frequency electromagnetic waves." ARDC, Conference on Ion and Plasma Research, University of Maryland, 30 Sept.–2 Oct. 1958.

*188. BELOKON, V. A. "The permanent structure of shock wave with joule dissipation" *J. Exp. Theor. Phys.*, No. 4, p. 932, Oct. 1959.

189. BENNETT, F. D. "Cylindrical shock waves from exploited wires of hydrogen-charged palladium" *Phys. Fluids*, Vol. 2, p. 470, 1959.

190. BERG, F. "On the theory of plasma waves" *Proc. Phys. Soc.*, Vol. 69B, p. 939, 1956.

191. BERGER, J. M., BERNSTEIN, I. B., FRIEMAN, E. A. and KULSURUD, R. M. "On the ionization and ohmic heating of a plasma" *Phys. Fluids*, Vol. 1, p. 297, 1958.

*192. BERGER, J. M., NEWCOMB, W. A., DAWSON, J. M., FRIEMAN, E. A., KULSRUD, R. M. and LENARD, A. "Heating of a confined plasma by oscillating electromagnetic fields" *Phys. Fluids*, Vol. 1, p. 301, 1958.

193. BERGLUND, S. *et al.* "Fusion experiments in deuterium plasma" *Nuclear Instruments*, Vol. 1, pp. 233–41, 1957.

194. BERNSTEIN, I. B. "Plasma oscillations perpendicular to a constant magnetic field" *Phys. Fluids*, Vol. 3, No. 3, pp. 489–90, 1960.

*195. BERNSTEIN, I. B. "Waves in plasma in a magnetic field" *Phys. Rev.*, Vol. 109, pp. 10–21, 1958.

*196. BERNSTEIN, I. B. *et al.* "An energy principle for hydromagnetic stability problems" *Proc. Roy. Soc.* A, Vol. 224, pp. 17–40, 1958.

197. BERNSTEIN, I. B. and RABINOWITZ, I. N. "The velocity distribution of plasma electrons in an external electric field" *Ionization Phenomena in Gases*, Vol. 2, p. 634. Amsterdam, North-Holland, 1959.

*198. BERNSTEIN, I. B. and RABINOWITZ, I. N. "Theory of electrostatic probes in a low-density plasma" *Phys. Fluids*, Vol. 2, p. 112, 1959.

199. BERNSTEIN, I. B., GREENE, J. M. and KRUSKAL, M. D. "Exact nonlinear plasma oscillations" *Phys. Rev.*, Vol. 108, pp. 546–50, 1957.

200. BERNSTEIN, I. B., FRIEMAN, E. A., KRUSKAL, M. D. and KULSRUD, R. M. "An energy principle for hydromagnetic stability problems" *Proc. Roy. Soc.* A, pp. 17–40 (20 refs.), 25 Feb. 1958.

*201. BERNSTEIN, I. B., FRIEMAN, E. A., KULSRUD, R. M. and ROSENBULTH, M. M. "Ion wave instabilities" *Phys. Fluids*, Vol. 3, No. 1, pp. 136–7, 1960.

*202. BERNSTEIN, W. and KRANZ, A. Z. "Ohmic heating in the B-1 Stellarator" *Phys. Fluids*, Vol. 2, p. 57, 1959.

203. BERNSTEIN, W., KRANZ, A. Z. and TENNEY, F. "Oscillations in the B-1 Stellarator" *Phys. Fluids*, Vol. 2, p. 713, 1959.

*204. BERNSTEIN, W., CHEN, F. F., HEALD, M. A. and KRANZ, A. Z. "Runaway electrons and cooperative phenomena in B-1 stellarator discharges" *Phys. Fluids*, Vol. 1, No. 5, pp. 430–7, 1958.

*205. BERSHADER, D. *Magneto-dynamics of Conducting Fluids* (A symposium on magneto-hydrodynamics), Stanford, California (about 150 pp. illus. diags. biblio.). Stanford, Univ. Press, 1959.

206. BERSHADER, D. "Some results of electric-discharge shock tube diagnostics". Int. Symposium on M.F.D. Washington, Jan. 1960.

*207. BERSHADER, D. and LANDSHOFF, R. "Magneto-hydrodynamics—A symposium report." *Phys. To-day*, No. 4, pp. 26–8, Apr. 1958.

*208. BERTOTTI, B. "Uniform electromagnetic field in the theory of general relativity" *Phys. Rev.*, Vol. 116, No. 5, pp. 1331–3, 1959.

*209. BEZBATCHENKO, A. L. and GOLOVIN, I. N. "The influence of a longitudinal magnetic field on the impulsive gas discharge of high current intensity" *Dokl. Akad. Nauk. SSSR*, Vol. 111, pp. 319–21, 1956; DSIR CTS 363.

*210. BEZBATCHENKO, A. L., GOLOVIN, I. N., IVANOV, D. P., KIRILLOV, V. D. and YAVLINSKY, N. A. "An investigation of a high-current gas discharge in a longitudinal magnetic field" *J. Nucl. Energy*, Vol. 5, No. 1, pp. 71–85, 1957 (English translation of article in: *Atomnaya Energya*, Vol. I, No. 5, p. 26, 1956).

211. BEZBATCHENKO, A. L., GABRVIN, I. N., IVANOV, D. P., KIRILLOV, V. D. and YAVLNSKII, N. A. "The effect of a longitudinal magnetic field on a heavy-current pulsed gas discharge" *Dokl. Akad. Nauk. SSSR*, Vol. 3, p. 319, 1956.

*212. BHATNAGAR, P. L. "The equilibrium of a self-gravitating incompressible fluid sphere with magnetic field" *Sci. Roy. Aero.*, Section A and B, Vol. 40, No. 2, pp. 50–73, 1958.

213. BICKERTON, R. J. "The amplification of a magnetic field by a high current discharge" *Proc. Phys. Soc.*, Vol. 72, pp. 618–24, 1958.

214. BICKERTON, R. J. "Experiments with waves in a plasma" *Rend. Phys. School "E. Fermi"* corso XIII, pp. 119–26, Varenna, 1959.

215. BICKERTON, R. J. "Coulomb collision and plasma conductivity" *Rend. Phys. School "E. Fermi"* corso XIII, pp. 107–19, Varenna, 1959.

216. BICKERTON, R. J. "Pinch effect" *Rend. Phys. School "E. Fermi"* corso XIII, pp. 126–45, Varenna, 1959.

217. BICKERTON, R. J. "Stability experiments" *Rend. Phys. School "E. Fermi"* corso XIII, pp. 145–51, Varenna, 1959.

218. BICKERTON, R. J. and JUKES, J. D. "The direct conversion of thermonuclear energy to electrical power in the stabilized pinch" *J. Nucl. Energy*, Vol. 8, pp. 206–14, 1959.

*219. BIERMANN, L. "Stellar atmospheres as a plasma" *Nuovo Cimento Suppl.*, Vol. 13, No. 1, pp. 189–200, 1959.

220. BIERMANN, L. *et al.* "Axisymmetric configurations in magneto-hydrodynamic equilibrium" *Proc. Venice Conf.*, pp. 110–11, 1947.

221. BIERMANN, L. *et al.* "Axialsymmetric Lösungen der magneto-hydrostatischen Gleichung mit Oberflächenenströmen" *Z. Naturforsch.*, pp. 826–32, 1957.

222. BIERMANN, L. and PFIRSCH, D. "Microinstabilities in inhomogeneous plasmas and their effect on particle diffusion across a magnetic field". Int. Symposium on M.F.D. Washington, Jan. 1960.

*223. BIERMANN, L. and PFIRSCH, D. "Kooperative Phänomene und Diffusion eines Plasmas quer zu einem Magnetfeld (I)" *Z. Naturforsch.*, pp. 10–12, Jan. 1960.

224. BIERMANN, L. and SCHLÜTER, A. "Cosmic radiation and cosmic magnetic fields, II: Origin of cosmic magnetic fields" *Phys. Rev.*, Vol. 82, p. 863, 1951.

*225. BIRZVALK, Y. and VEZE, A. "Velocity distribution in electromagnetic pump channels, with a rectangular cross-section" *Latv. Pr. S. Zinat. Akad. Vestis*, No. 10 (147), pp. 85–9, 1959.

*226. BISHOP, A. *Project Shewood*. Addison-Wesley U.S.A., 1958.

227. BITTER, F. and WAYMOUTH, J. F. "Radiation temperature of a plasma" *J. Opt. Soc. Amer.*, Vol. 46, p. 882, 1956.

228. BITTNER, G. "On wave propagation in a 'plasma cable' with external magnetic field" *Z. Angew Math. Phys.*, Vol. 10, pp. 117–22, 1958.

229. BJORNSTAHL, Y. "The influence of an electric field on the viscosity of aeolotropic liquids" *Physica*, Vol. 6, p. 257, 1935.

230. BLACKMAN, V. H. "Acceleration and channelling of plasma jets by magnetic fields". ARDC, Conference on Ion and Plasma Research, University of Maryland, 30 Sept.–2 Oct. 1958.

231. BLACKMAN, V. H. "Continuous high temperature gas flow facility for magneto-hydrodynamic studies". TN-59-681, AD 225–412, Plasmadyne, June 1959.

232. BLACKMAN, V. H. and NIBLETT, B. "Experiments using a hydromagnetic shock tube" *The Plasma in a Magnetic Field*, 130 pp., fig. (Ce. 1536). Stanford University Press, 1958.

233. BLACKMAN, V. H., NIBLETT, G. B. F. and SCHRANK, G. "Hydromagnetic shock tube" *Bull. Amer. Phys. Soc.*, Vol. 2, p. 216, 1957.

*234 BLANK, A. A. and GRAD, H. "Notes on magnetohydrodynamics. Fluid magnetic equations—General properties". New York University, July 1958.

235. BLANK, A. A. and GRAD, H. "Notes on magnetohydrodynamics. Fluid dynamical analogies". New York University, July 1958.

*236. BLANK, A. A., FRIEDRICHS, K. O. and GRAD, H. "Notes on magnetohydro-dynamics theory of Maxwell's equations without displacement current". New York University, Nov. 1957.

237. BLANKFIELD, J. and McVITTIE, A. A. "A method of solution of the equations of magnetohydrodynamics" *Arch. Mech. Anal.*, Vol. 2, No. 5, pp. 411–22, 1959.

*238. VAN BLERKOM, R. "Magnetohydrodynamic flow of a viscous fluid past a sphere" *J. Fluid Mech.*, Vol. 8, Pt. 3, pp. 432–51, 1960.

*239. BLEVISS, Z. O. "Magneto gas dynamics of hypersonic Couette flow". Douglas Aircraft Co. Rep. SM-23098, Feb. 1958; *J. Aero/Space Sci.*, No. 10, pp. 601–15, 1958.

*240. BLEVISS, Z. O. "The effects of combined electric and magnetic fields on hyper-sonic Couette flow". Douglas Aircraft Co. Rep. SM-23314, Oct. 1958.

*241. BLEVISS, Z. O. "A study of the structure of a steady magnetohydrodynamic switch-on-wave". Meeting of the Heat Transfer and fluid Mechanics Institute, 1959.

*242. BLEVISS, Z. O. "Transmission of electromagnetic waves through ionized air surrounding hypersonic aircraft". Douglas Research Rep. SM-22965, Oct. 1957.

*243. BLOKHINTSEV, D. I. "On a possible limit on the applicability of quantum electrodynamics" *J. Exp. Theor. Phys.*, No. 1, p. 174, 1959.

244. BLOXSOM, D. E. "Production of high temperature moderate pressure gases by means of electrical spark discharge". AEDC ARO, 1956.

245. BOA-TEH-CHU "Thermodynamics of electrically conducting fluid and its application to magnetohydrodynamics". WADC TN-57-350 ASTIA Doc. No. AD 142039; *Phys. Fluids*, Vol. 2, p. 473, 1959.

246. BODEN, R. H. "Ion rocket studies". ARDC Conference on Ion and Plasma Research, University of Maryland, 30 Sept.–2 Oct. 1958.

247. BODEN, R. H. "Recent developments in ion propulsion system for space travel". ASME AV. Conference Los Angeles, Calif., Mar. 1959, pap. 59-AV-45, 32 pp.

248. BODEN, R. H. "Research chamber for experimental studies on ion propulsion". ARDC Conference on Ion and Plasma Research, University of Maryland, 30 Sept.–2 Oct. 1958.

*249. BODIN, H. A. B., GREEN, T. S., NIBLETT, C. B. F. and PEACOCK, N. J. "An

11

experimental investigation of the rapid compression of a plasma using azimuthal currents". Amsterdam, North-Holland, 1959.

*250. BOGDANKEVICH, L. S. "Radiation from a current carrying ring moving uniformly in a plasma situated in a magnetic field" *J. Exp. Theor. Phys.*, No. 3, p. 589, Sept. 1959.

251. BOHM, D. and GROSS, E. P. "Effect of plasma boundaries on plasma oscillations" *Phys. Rev.*, Vol. 79, p. 992, 1950.

252. BOHM, D. and GROSS, E. P. "Theory of plasma oscillations; A: Origins of medium-like behavior" *Phys. Rev.*, Vol. 75, p. 1851, 1949.

253. BOHM, D. and GROSS, E. P. "Theory of plasma oscillations; B: Excitation and damping of oscillations" *Phys. Rev.*, Vol. 75, p. 1864, 1949.

254. BOHM, D. and VIGIER, J. P. "Relativistic hydrodynamics of rotating fluid masses" *Phys. Rev.*, Vol. 72, No. 109, p. 1881, 1958.

255. BOHM, D. and PINES, D. "A collective description of electron interaction; I: Magnetic interaction" *Phys. Rev.*, Vol. 82, p. 624, 1951.

256. BOHM, D. and PINES, D. "A collective description of electron interaction; III: Coulomb in a degenerate electron gas" *Phys. Rev.*, Vol. 92, p. 609, 1953.

*257. BOLOTOVSKII, B. M. and RUKHADZE, A. A. "Field of a charged particle in a moving medium" *Zh. Eksp. Teoret. Fiz.*, Vol. 37, No. 5 (11), pp. 1346–51, 1959.

258. BOMELBURG, H. J. "Heat loss from very thin heated wires in rarefied gases" *Phys. Fluids*, Vol. 2, p. 717, 1959.

*259. BOND, J. W. "Plasma physics and hypersonic flight" *J. Exp. Theor. Phys.*, Vol. 28, pp. 228–35, 1958.

260. BONDI, H. and SALPTERER, E. E. "Thermonuclear reactions and astrophysics" *Nature, Lond.*, Vol. 169, p. 304, 1952.

261. BONIN, Y. "Hydromagnetic wall shielding". ARDC Conference on Ion and Plasma Research, University of Maryland, 30 Sept.–2 Oct. 1958.

262. BONNAL, F., BRIFFOD, G. and MANUS, C. "Oscillations et diffusion dans les plasmas faiblement ionisés" *C. R. Acad. Sci., Paris.*, Vol. 250, 17, pp. 2859–61, 1960.

263. BONNET, M., MATRICOM, M. and ROULINE, E. "A study at 10000 Mc/s of the Faraday effect in a plasma" *Ann. Telecom.*, Vol. 10, p. 150, 1958.

*264. BONNEVIER, B. and LEHNERT, B. "The motion of charged particles in a rotating plasma" *Ark. Fys.*, Vol. 16, Paper 22, pp. 231–6, 1959.

265. BONWITT, W. and ROE, G. "Change of thermal conductivity of gases in electrostatic fields" *Z. Phys.*, Vol. 72, p. 600, 1931.

*266. BOON, M. H. and LAING, E. W. *et al.* "Hydromagnetic instabilities of a cylindrical gas discharge. Part 6: Energy principle calculations for axisymmetric perturbation". AERE TR-2503, Atom. En. Res. Est. U.K.

267. BOOT, H. A. H., SELF, S. A. and SHERSBY-HARVIE, R. B. R. "Containment of fully-ionised plasma by radio-frequency fields "*J. Electronics and Control*, Vol. 4, p. 434, 1958.

*268. BOPP, F. "Remarks on the conformal invariance of electrodynamics and the basic equations of dynamics" *Ann. Phys.*, Vol. 4, No. 15, pp. 96–102, 1959.

269. BORG, S. F. "A phenomenon in unsteady magnetohydrodynamic flow theory" *J. Aero/Space Sci.*, Vol. 27, No. 6, p. 472, 1960.

270. BORMAN, G. "Magnetohydrodynamics". General Electric Co. Cincinnati, Ohio (U.S.A.) DF 58-AGT539.

271. BORMAN, G. and PODOLSKY, B. "One dimensional analysis of plasma accelerators". General Electric Co. Cincinnati, Ohio (U.S.A.) R59 AGT36.

272. BORMAN, G. and SHERMAN, A. "MHD bibliography". General Electric Co. Cincinnati, Ohio (U.S.A.), Flight Propulsion lab. Plasma Propulsion Unit, May 1959.

*273. BORRUNOV, M. A., ORLINSKII, D. V. and OSOVETS, S. M. "Investigation of high current plasma discharge in conical chambers" *J. Exp. Theor. Phys.*, No. 3, p. 502, Sept. 1959.

274. Bostick, W. H. "Experimental study of ionized matter projected across a magnetic field" *Phys. Rev.*, Vol. 104, p. 292–9, 1956.

275. Bostick, W. H. "Experimental study of plasmoids" *Phys. Rev.*, Vol. 106, pp. 404–12, 1957.

*__276.__ Bostick, W. H. and Levine, M. A. "Experiments on the behaviour of an ionized gas in a magnetic field" *Phys. Rev.*, Vol. 97, pp. 13–21, 1955.

*__277.__ Bostick, W. H. and Levine, M. A. "Relationship involved in the H_z-$E\phi$ pinch effect". Res. Lab. of Physical Electronics, Tufts Coll. Medford, Mass., Rept., 8 pp. (incl. illus.), 1 Sept. 1953.

278. Bostick, H. and Levine, M. A. "Experimental demonstration in the laboratory of the existence of magneto-hydrodynamic waves in ionized He" *Phys. Rev.*, Vol. 87, p. 671, 1952.

*__279.__ Bostick, W. H., Levine, M. A. and Morton, A. "Magneto-hydrodynamic waves generated in an ionized gas in a toroidal tube having an annular D-C magnetic field". Res. Lab, of Physical Electronics, Tufts Coll. Meldford Mass., Rept., 12 pp. (incl. illus.), 15 Oct. 1952.

280. Bostick, W. H., Finkelstein, D., Koslov, S., Nankivell, J. and Rogers, K. "A review of the plasma research program in the physic department". ARDC, Conference on Ion and Plasma Research, University of Maryland, 30 Sept.–2 Oct. 1958.

*__281.__ Bostick, W. H., Weintraub, H. and Levine, M. A. "Diffusion of a plasma across an inhomogeneous magnetic field". Res. Lab. of Physical Electronics, Tufts Coll. Meldford Mass., Rept., 13 pp. (incl. illus.), 15 Sept. 1953.

*__282.__ Boullod, A. "The effect of temperature on pre-breakdown currents in compressed gases" *C. R. Acad. Sci., Paris*, Vol. 249, No. 14, pp. 1202–4, 1959.

*__283.__ Bourdeau, R. E., Whipple, E. C. Jr., Clark, J. F. "Analytic and experimental electrical conductivity between the stratosphere and ionosphere" *J. Geophys. Res.*, Vol. 64, No. 10, pp. 1363–70, 1959.

284. Boyd, R. L. F. "A mass-spectrometer probe method for the study of gas discharge" *Nature, Lond.*, Vol. 165, p. 142, 1950.

285. Boyd, G. D. "Excitation of plasma oscillations and growing plasma waves" *Phys. Rev.*, Vol. 109, p. 1993, 1958.

286. Boyd, R. L. F. and Morris, D. "A radio-frequency probe for the mass-spectrometric analysis of ion concentrations" *Proc. Phys. Soc.*, A, Vol. 68, p. 1, 1955.

*__287.__ Boyd, R. L. F. and Twiddy, N. D. "Electron energy distribution in plasmas, I" *Proc. Roy. Soc.*, A, Vol. 250, pp. 53–69, 1959.

288. Boyd, R. L. F. and Twiddy, N. D. "Electron energy distribution in the striated hydrogen discharge" *Nature, Lond.*, Vol. 173, p. 633, 1954.

*__289.__ Braginskii, S. I. "The behaviour of a completely ionized plasma in a strong magnetic field" *J. Exp. Theor. Phys.*, No. 3, pp. 494–501, March 1958; *Zh. Eksp. Teoret. Fiz.*, Vol. 33, pp. 645–54, 1958.

290. Braginskii, S. I. "Transport phenomena in a completely ionized low-temperature plasma" *Zh. Eksp. Teoret. Fiz.*, Vol. 33, p. 459, 1957.

*__291.__ Braginskii, S. I. "Magnetohydrodynamics of weakly conducting liquids" *Zh. Eksp. Teoret. Fiz.*, Vol. 37, No. 5 (11), pp. 1417–30, 1959.

292. Braginskii, S. I. "Types of plasma oscillations in a magnetic field" *Dokl. Akad. Nauk., SSSR*, Vol. 115, pp. 470–8, 1957.

293. Braun, W. C. "Plasma generation and control". ARDC, Conference on Ion and Plasma Research, University of Maryland, 30 Sept.–2 Oct. 1958.

*__294.__ Brin, A., Delcroix, J. and Ozias, Y. "Action d'un champ électrique continu sur un plasma: établissment de l'équation donnant la fonction de distribution" *C. R. Acad. Sci., Paris*, Vol. 249, pp. 1093–5, 1959.

295. BRINKMAN, H. C. "Theoretical aspects of the behaviour of a plasma in electric and magnetic fields" *Meder. Tijdschz*, Vol. 25, pp. 133–41 (Ge), 1959.

*296. BRINKMAN, H. C. "The vortex equations of magneto-hydrodynamics" (Les equations du tourbillon en Aéromagnétodynamique) *Physica*, No. 11, pp. 1063–6, 1959.

297. BRITTIN, W. E. "Statistical mechanical theory of transport phenomena in a fully ionized gas" *Phys. Rev.*, Vol. 106, pp. 843–7, 1957.

298. BRODE, H. L. "Blast wave from a spherical charge" *Phys. Fluids*, Vol. 2, p. 217, 1958.

299. BROER, L. J. F. "Mechanical analogy of the Hall effect". Int. Symposium on M.F.D., Washington, Jan. 1960.

300. BROER, L. J. F. "Motion of a charged particle in a slowly varying magnetic field". Int. Symposium on M.F.D., Washington, Jan. 1960.

*301. BROGAN, T. R. "The conduction of electric current to cold electrodes in shock tubes". Cornell. U. Grad. School of Aero. Eng. (Thesis) June 1956.

302. BROUGHT, R. "Correlation energy of high-density gas: plasma coordinates" *Phys. Rev.*, Vol. 108, pp. 515–17, 1957.

303. BROWN, S. C. "High-frequency waves in ionized gases" *Ionization Phenomena in Gases*, Vol. 2, p. 687. Amsterdam, North-Holland, 1959.

304. BROWN, S. C. and ALLIS, W. P. "Basic data of electrical discharges". MIT Research Laboratory of electronics T.R. 283, 3rd Edition, 1956.

305. BROYLES, A. A. "Calculation of fields on plasma ions by collective coordinates" *Z. Phys.*, Vol. 151, p. 187, 1958.

306. BRUECKNER, K. A. and WATSON, K. M. "Use of the Boltzmann equation for the study of ionized gases of low density II" *Phys. Rev.*, Vol. 102, pp. 19–27, 1956.

307. BRUNELLI, B. "Ricerche sul plasma presso il laboratorio di gas ionizzati del C.N.R.N." *Nuovo Cimento Suppl.*, No. 1, pp. 76–81, 2° Trimestre, 1960.

*308. BUCHSBAUM, S. J. "Resonance in a plasma with two ion species" *Phys. Fluids*, Vol. 9, No. 3, pp. 418–21, 1960.

309. BUHLER, R. D. "Preliminary engineering evaluation of advanced propulsion systems and power sources". ARDC, Conference on Ion and Plasma Research, University of Maryland, 30 Sept.–2 Oct. 1958.

310. BUHLER, R. D. "Basic study of energy exchange progress between an electric arc and a gas flow". ARDC, Conference on Ion and Plasma Research, University of Maryland, 30 Sept.–2 Oct. 1958.

311. BULLARD, E. C. "The magnetic field within the earth" *Proc. Roy. Soc. A*, Vol. 197, pp. 433–53, 1949.

312. BULLARD, E. C. "Electromagnetic induction in a rotating sphere" *Proc. Roy. Soc. A*, Vol. 199, pp. 413–43, 1949.

*313. BULLARD, E. C. "A discussion on magneto-hydrodynamics: Introduction" *Proc. Roy. Soc. A*, Vol. 223, pp. 289–96, 1955.

314. BULLARD, E. C. "The stability of a homopolar dynamo" *Proc. Camb. Phil. Soc.*, Vol. 51, pp. 744–60, 1955.

315. BULLARD, E. C. and GELLMAN, H. "Homogeneous dynamos and terrestrial magnetism" *Phil. Trans. Roy. Soc.*, Vol. 247, pp. 213–78, 1954.

316. BULLARD, E. C. and GELLMAN, H. "MHD stability" *Phil. Trans.*, Vol. 247, pp. 213–78, 1954.

*317. BUNEMAN, O. "Instability, turbulence and conductivity in current carrying plasma" *Phys. Rev. Letters*, Vol. 1, No. 1, pp. 8–9, 1958.

*318. BUNEMAN, O. "Transverse plasma waves and plasma vortices" *Phys. Rev.*, Vol. 112, pp. 1504–12, 1958.

*319. BURGERS, J. M. "Penetration of a shock wave into a magnetic field". Symposium on MHD, Stanford U.P. Oxford, 1957; TN BN-102 Landshoff, R.K.M. University of Maryland. AFOSR TN-57-527, AD 136511.

320. BURGERS, J. M. "The bridge between particle mechanics and continuum mechanics" *Symposium on Plasma Dynamics, Woods Hole 1958*. Addison-Wesley, 1959.

*321. BURGERS, J. M. "The application of transfer equations to the calculation of diffusion, heat conduction, viscosity and electric conductivity". Inst. Fluid. Dyn. and Appl. Math., Univ. Maryland. AFOSR TN-58-427 and 427a, May 1958.

322. BURGERS, J. M. "Motion of a fully ionized gas across a magnetic field in the absence of collision". Int. Symposium on M.F.D. Washington, Jan. 1960.

323. BURGERS, J. M. "Selected topics from the theory of gas flow at high temperatures. Some aspect of particle interaction in gases". Univ. of Maryland, TN pp. 22–34 BN-176, June 1959.

324. BURGERS, J. M. "Phenomena surrounding high speed flight". ARDC, Conference on Ion and Plasma Research, University of Maryland, 30 Sept.–2 Oct. 1958.

325. BURKHARDT, L. C., DUNAWAY, R. E., MATHER, J. M., PHILLIPS, J. A., SAWYER, G. A., STRATTON, T. F., STOVALL, E. J. and TUCK, J. L. "Pinch effect" *J. Appl. Phys.*, Vol. 28, pp. 519–21, 1957.

326. BURKHARDT, L. C., LOVEBERG, R. H., SAWYER, G. A. and STRATTON, T. F. "Stabilities studies with longitudinal magnetic field on a straight pinched discharge" *J. Appl. Phys.*, Vol. 29, pp. 964–8, 1958.

*327. BURNETT, C. R., GROVE, D. J., PALLADINO, R. W., STIX, T. H. and WAKEFIELD, K. E. "The divertor, a device for reducing the impurity level in a stellarator" *Phys. Fluids*, Vol. 1, No. 5, pp. 438–45, 1958.

328. BUSEMAN, A. "Problems of flow existence and stability in magnetohydrodynamics of conducting fluids." In *The Magnetodynamics of Conducting Fluids* (edited by D. Berstrider). Stanford, U.P., 1959.

*329. BUSH, W. B. "Magneto-hydrodynamic-hypersonic flow past a blunt body" *J. Aero/Space Sci.*, Vol. 25, No. 11, pp. 685–90, 728, 1958.

*330. BUSH, W. B. "Compressible flat-plate boundary-layer-flow with an applied magnetic field". Space Res. Lab. GM-TR-0165-00466; *J. Aero/Space Sci.*, pp. 49–58, Jan. 1960.

*331. BUSH, W. B. "On one dimensional channel flow in the presence of a magnetic field". Space Tech. Lab. Pri., TR-59-0000-00660, 1959.

332. BUSH, W. B. "A note on magneto-hydrodynamic hypersonic flow past a blunt body". Phys. Res. Lab. Space Technology Laboratories Inc. Los Angeles, Calif., 11 March, 1959; Readers' Forum, *J. Aero/Space Sci.*, p. 536, Aug. 1959.

333. BUTLER, J. W. "Stability of electromagnetic plasma confinement in spherical geometry" *Ionization Phenomena in Gases*, Vol. 2, p. 620. Amsterdam, North-Holland, 1959.

*334. BUTZ, J. S. Jr. "Basic factors complicate plasma work" *Av. Week*, No. 22, pp. 36–9 (5 figs.), June 1958.

*335. BUTZ, J. S. Jr. "Magneto-hydrodynamics; I: Hope for space" *Av. Week*, No. 19, pp. 48–50, May 1958.

*336. BUTZ, J. S. Jr. "Magneto-hydrodynamics; II: Controlled fusion studies open space engine field" *Av. Week*, No. 19, pp. 50–7, May 1958.

337. CABANNES, H. "Attached stationary shock waves in ionized gases". Int. Symposium on M.F.D. Washington, Jan. 1960.

*338. CABANNES, H. "Calcule de la conductivité thermique d'un courant ionique" *C. R. Acad. Sci., Paris*, Vol. 249, pp. 47–9, 1959.

*339. CABANNES, H. "Dynamique des gaz ionisés: determination des chocs stationnaires attachés à la pointe d'un dièdre" *Rech. Aéron.*, July-Aug. 1959.

340. CABANNES, H. "On the motion of an electrically conducting compressible fluid" *C. R. Acad. Sci., Paris*, Vol. 245, pp. 1379–82, 1957.

*341. CABANNES, H. "Sur l'attachement des ondes de choc dans les écoulements à deux dimensions" *C. R. Acad. Sci., Paris*, Vol. 250, No. 11, pp. 1968–70 (4 figs.), 1960.

*342. CABANNES, H. "Sur la propagation des discontinuités du premier ordre dans un fluide compressible doué de conductivité électrique". Memo Technique No. 10 ONERA, 1958.

343. CAIRO, L. "Méthode de perturbation pour la propagation des ondes électromagnétiques dans un plasma remplissant partiellement un guide d'ondes circulaires" *C. R. Acad. Sci., Paris*, Vol. 250, No. 25, pp. 4129–31, 1960.

344. CALCOTE, H. F. "Generation of supersonic dissociated and ionized non-equilibrium streams". AFSOR TN 58-1080 (10/58), 33 pp. (13 figs.). Aero Chem. Research Laboratories, Princeton, TM 10.

345. CALCOTE, H. F. and ROSNER, D. E. "Development of a low temperature plasma jet". ARDC, Conference on Ion and Plasma Research, University of Maryland, 30 Sept.–2 Oct. 1958.

346. CALKER, J. and BRAUMISCH, H. "Temperature of condensed spark discharges" *Z. Naturforsch.*, Vol. 11a, p. 612, 1956.

347. CAMAC, M. "Plasma propulsion". *Astronautics*, October 1959.

*348. CAMAC, M. and JAMES, G. S. "Applied magneto-hydrodynamics at AVCO-Everett Research Laboratory". Preprint Third Biennal Gas Dynamic Symposium ARS, Northwestern Univ., 24–26 Aug. 1959.

349. CAMAC, M., KANTROVITZ, A. and PETSCHEK, H. "Plasma propulsion devices for space flight". ASTIA AD 213885, Feb. 1959; IRE Trans. on Military Electronics, April 1959.

350. CANN, G. L. "Shock tube driver with a plasma jet supply". Divisional meeting of the division of fluid dynamics, American Physical Society, San Diego, Cal., 24–26 Nov. 1958.

351. CANOBBIO, E. and KIPPENHAHN, R. "Sulla interazione tra un fascio di ioni modulato e un plasma in campo magnetico". Proc. XLV Congress Italian Physics Soc., Pavia 1–7 ottobre 1959.

352. CARINI, G. "On the equations of magnetohydrodynamics" *Accad. Lincei, Roma*, Vol. 21, p. 436, 1956.

353. CARINI, G. "Observations on cylindrical waves in magnetohydrodynamics" *Accad. Lincei, Roma*, Vol. 22, pp. 482–8, 1957.

354. CARINI, G. "On stationary solutions of the hydromagnetic equations" *Accad. Lincei, Roma*, Vol. 22, pp. 38–43, 1957.

*355. CARINI, G. "Energy considerations in magnetohydrodynamics" *Accad. Lincei, Roma*, Vol. 27, No. 1–2, pp. 48–53, 1959.

356. CARINI, G. "Magneto-fluid-dynamics of viscous compressible flow" *Accad. Lincei, Roma*; *R. C. Sci. Fis. Mat. Nat.* (8), Vol. 25, No. 6, pp. 470–3, 1958.

*357. CARRIER, G. F. and GREENSPAN, H. P. "The time-dependent magnetohydrodynamic flow past a flat plate" *J. Fluid. Mech.*, Vol. 7, Pt. I, pp. 22–3, 1960.

358. CARRUTHERS, R. and DAVENPORT, P. A. "Observation of the instabilities of constricted gas discharges" *Proc. Phys. Soc.*, Vol. 70B, pp. 49–58, 1957.

*359. CARSTOIU, J. "Sur le mouvement lent d'un fluide visqueux conducteur entre deux plans parallèles" *C. R. Acad. Sci., Paris*, Vol. 246, No. 14, pp. 1192–3, 1959.

*360. CARSTOIU, J. "Hydromagnetic waves in a compressible fluid conductor" *Acad. Sci., U.S.A.*, Vol. 46, No. 1, pp. 131–6, 1960.

361. CARSTOIV, J. "Analogies et differences dans les turbillons et champ magnétique" *C. R. Acad. Sci., Paris*, Vol. 251, No. 4, pp. 509–11, 1960.

362. CAVAILLES, P., JANCEL, R., KAHAN, T. "Magnétohydrodynamique d'un plasma ternaire et types d'ondes associées" *C. R. Acad. Sci., Paris*, Vol. 250, No. 23, pp. 3789–91, 1960.

*363. CESS, R. D. "Magnetohydrodynamics effects upon heat tran..fer for laminar flow across a flat plate". American Society of Mechanical Engineers, New York, Paper No. 59-HT-14 (8/59) 7 pp., (3 figs.), 1959.

364. CHACE, W. G. "Observation in high density plasmas produced by exploding wires" *Ionization Phenomena in Gases*, Vol. 2, p. 1191, Amsterdam, North-Holland, 1959.

365. CHACE, W. G. "Liquid behaviour of exploding wires" *Phys. Fluids*, Vol. 2, p. 230, 1959.

*366. CHAKRABORTY, B. B. and RAMAMORTY, P. "On the pulsations of an infinite cylinder with a force-free magnetic field" *Z. Astrophys.*, Vol. 43, No. 3, pp. 186–91, 1960.

367. CHAMPION, K. S. W. and ZIMMERMAN, S. P. "Transport phenomena in a fully ionized gas including wave-particle interactions" *Ionization Phenomena in Gases*, Vol. 2, p. 589, Amsterdam, North-Holland, 1959.

368. CHANDRASEKHAR, S. "Adiabatic invariants in the motion of charged particles" *The Plasma in a Magnetic Field*: 130 pp., Stanford U.P., 1958.

369. CHANDRASEKHAR, S. "Axisymmetric magnetic fields and fluid motions" *Astrophys. J.*, Vol. 124, pp. 232–43, 1956.

370. CHANDRASEKHAR, S. "Effect of internal motions on the decay of a magnetic field in a fluid conductor" *Astrophys. J.*, Vol. 124, pp. 244–65, 1956.

371. CHANDRASEKHAR, S. "Hydromagnetic oscillations of a fluid sphere with internal motions" *Astrophys. J.*, Vol. 124, pp. 571–9, 1956.

372. CHANDRASEKHAR, S. "Hydromagnetic turbulence; 1: A deductive theory; 2: An elementary theory" *Proc. Roy. Soc.* A, Vol. 233, pp. 322–50, 1955.

*373. CHANDRASEKHAR, S. "The stability of non-dissipative Couette flow in hydromagnetics" *Acad. Sci. U.S.A.*, Vol. 46, No. 2, pp. 253–7, 1960.

374. CHANDRASEKHAR, S. "On characteristic value problems in high order differential equations which arise in studies on hydrodynamics and hydromagnetic stability" *Amer. Math. Monthly*, Vol. 61, pp. 32–45, 1954.

375. CHANDRASEKHAR, S. "On force-free magnetic fields" *Acad. Sci. U.S.A.*, Vol. 42, p. 1, 1956.

*376. CHANDRASEKHAR, S. "The stability of viscous flow between rotating cylinders in the presence of a magnetic field" *Proc. Roy. Soc.* A, Vol. 16, pp. 293–306, 1953.

377. CHANDRASEKHAR, S. "On the inhibition of convection by a magnetic field". Parts I and II: *Phil. Mag.*, Vol. 43, pp. 501–32, 1952; *ibid.*, Vol. 45, p. 1117, 1954.

*378. CHANDRASEKHAR, S. "The partition of energy in hydromagnetic turbulence" *Ann. Phys.*, Vol. 2, pp. 615–26, 1957.

379. CHANDRASEKHAR, S. "The instability of a layer of fluid heated below and subject to the simultaneous action of a magnetic field and rotation" *Proc. Roy. Soc.* A, Vol. 225, pp. 173–84, 1954.

380. CHANDRASEKHAR, S. "The invariant theory of isotropic turbulence in magneto-hydrodynamics". *Proc. Roy. Soc.* A, Vol. 204, pp. 435–49, 1950; *ibid.*, Vol. 207, pp. 301–6, 1951.

*381. CHANDRASEKHAR, S. "The gravitational instability of an infinite homogeneous medium when Coriolis force is acting and a magnetic field is present" *Astrophys. J.*, Vol. 119, pp. 7–9, 1954.

382. CHANDRASEKHAR, S. "On the stability of the simplest solution of the equations of hydromagnetics" *Acad. Sci. U.S.A.*, Vol. 42, pp. 273–6, 1956.

383. CHANDRASEKHAR, S. "Problems of stability in hydrodynamics and hydromagnetics" *Mon. Not. Roy. Astr. Soc.*, Vol. 113, pp. 667–78, 1953.

384. CHANDRASEKHAR, S. "Studies in magneto-hydrodynamics and hydrodynamic astrophysics" *Mon. Not. Roy. Astr. Soc.*, Vol. 113, No. 6, p. 667, 1953.

*385. CHANDRASEKHAR, S. *et al.* "Properties of an ionized gas of low density in a magnetic field" *Ann. Phys.*, Vol. 5, pp. 1–26, 1958.

386. CHANDRASEKHAR, S. and FERMI, E. "Problems of gravitational stability in the presence of a magnetic field" *Astrophys. J.*, Vol. 118, pp. 113–41, 1953.

*387. CHANDRASEKHAR, S. and LIMBER, D. N. "On the pulsation of a star in which there is a prevalent magnetic field" *Astrophys. J.*, Vol. 119, pp. 10–13, 1954.

388. CHANDRASEKHAR, S. and PRENDERGAST, K. H. "The equilibrium of magnetic stars" *Acad. Sci. U.S.A.*, Vol. 42, p. 5, 1956.

389. CHANDRASEKHAR, S., KAUFMAN, A. N. and WATSON, K. M. "Properties of an ionized gas of low density in a magnetic field". Part 3, *Ann. Phys.*, Vol. 2, pp. 435–70, 1957.

*390. CHANDRASEKHAR, S., KAUFMAN, A. N. and WATSON, K. M. "The stability of the pinch; Appendix; The propagation of plane hydromagnetic waves in an infinite medium" *Proc. Roy. Soc.* A, Vol. 245, pp. 435–55 (10 refs.), 8 July 1958.

*391. CHANG, C. C. and LUNDGREN, T. S. "The flow of an electrically conducting fluid through a duct with transverse magnetic field" *Proc. Meeting Heat Transfer and Fluid Mech.*, Stanford U.P., pp. 41–54, June 1959.

392. CHANG, C. C. and LUNDGREN, T. S. "Flow of an incompressible fluid in a hydromagnetic capacitor" *Phys. Fluids*, Vol. 2, p. 637, 1959.

393. CHANG, C. C. and YEN, J. T. "On unsteady incompressible flow of electrically conducting fluids through two-dimensional channels". Paper W-4, Amer. Phys. Soc. Spring Meeting, Washington, D.C., May 30, 1959.

394. CHANG, C. C. and YEN, J. T. "Exact solution of impulse motion of a flat plate in magnetohydrodynamics". Paper X-8 Symp. High Temperature Plasma, Amer. Phys. Soc., New York Meeting, Jan.–Feb. 1958.

*395. CHANG, C. C. and YEN, J. T. "On Rayleigh's problem in magneto-hydrodynamics" *Phys. Fluids*, Vol. 2, p. 393, 1959.

*396. CHAO-KAI-HUA "Surface oscillation of a charged column in a longitudinal magnetic field" *J. Exp. Theor. Phys.*, Vol. 35, 1959.

397. CHAPMAN, S. "Ionized gases in magnetic fields". Lecture Series No. 20, Univ. of Maryland, 1952.

398. CHAPMAN, S. "Thermal diffusion in ionized gases" *Proc. Phys. Soc.*, Vol. 72, pp. 353–62, 1958.

399. CHAPMAN, S. "Idealized problems of plasma dynamics relating to geomagnetic storms". Int. Symposium on M.F.D. Washington, Jan. 1960.

400. CHAPMAN, S. and COWLING, T. G. *The Mathematical Theory of Non-uniform Gases*. Cambridge University Press, 1953.

401. CHARATIS, G. and WILKERSON, T. D. "Excitation temperature of chromium in the shock tube" *Phys. Fluids*, Vol. 2, p. 578, 1959.

*402. CHARIKADZE, D. V. "Movements analogiques et explosion ponctuelle en magnétohydrodynamique dans le cas d'une conductibilité de gaz infinie" *Dokl. Akad. Nauk., SSSR*, Vol. 127, No. 6, pp. 1183–6, 1959.

403. CHATTERJEE, S. D. "Influence of magnetic field on the coefficient of viscosity of liquids" *Indian J. Phys.*, Vol. 10, p. 399, 1936.

*404. CHAU-CHIN WEI "Relativistic hydrodynamics for a charged non viscous fluid" *Phys. Fluids*, Vol. 3, No. 2, p. 323, 1960.

405. CHAU-CHIN WEI, "Errata: relativistic hydrodynamics for a charged non viscous fluid" *Phys. Fluids*, Vol. 3, No. 4, p. 666, 1960.

*406. CHESTER, W. "The effect of a magnetic field on Stokes flow in a conducting fluid" *J. Fluid Mech.*, Vol. 3, Pt. 3, pp. 304–8, Dec. 1957.

407. CHEW, G. F., GOLDBERGER, M. L. and Low, F. E. "The Boltzmann equation in the adiabatic approximation" (In Allis, W. *et al.*: Series of lectures on physics of ionized gases). Los Alamos Sci. Lab. Rep. 2055, 12 pp., 1955–1956.

408. CHEW, G. F., GOLDBERGER, M. L. and Low, F. E. "The Boltzmann equation and the one-fluid hydromagnetic equations in the absence of particle collision" *Proc. Roy. Soc.* A, Vol. 236, pp. 112–18, 1956.

*409. CHIA-SHUN YIH "Effects of gravitational electromagnetic fields on fluid motion" *Quart. Appl. Math.*, pp. 409–15, Jan. 1959.

*410. CHIA-SHUN YIH, "Inhibition of hydrodynamic instability by an electric current" *Phys. Fluids*, No. 2, pp. 125–30, March–April 1959.

*411. CHIA-SHUN YIH, "Ring vortices generated electromagnetically" *J. Fluid Mech.*, Pt. 3, pp. 436–45, April 1959.

412. CHICK, D. R. "Plasma research at A.E.I. research laboratory, Aldermaston Court" *Ionization Phenomena in Gases*, Vol. 2, p. 944. Amsterdam, North-Holland, 1959.

413. CHICK, D. R. "Plasma research" *Cont. Phys.*, Vol. 1, No. 3, pp. 169–90, 1960.

*414. (CHING-SHENG) WU "A class of exact solutions of the magnetohydrodynamic Navier-Stokes equations". Princeton U. Dept. Aero. Eng. Rep. 436, AFOSR TN-58-895 (AD 204134), 51 pp., Sept. 1958.

*415. (CHING-SHENG) WU. "Simple vorticity laws in magneto-hydrodynamics". Princeton U. Dept. Aero. Eng. Rep. 445, AFOSR TN-58-1044 (AD 206756), 16 pp., Nov. 1958.

*416. (CHING-SHENG) WU "Hypersonic viscous flow past a blunt body with an applied magnetic field". Princeton U. Dept. Aero. Eng. Rep. 443, AFOSR TN-58-11-5 (AD 207834), 26 pp., Nov. 1958.

*417. (CHING-SHENG) WU and HAYES, W. D. "Axisymmetric stagnant flow of a viscous and electrically conducting fluid near the blunt nose of a spinning body with presence of magnetic field. Part I: Exact solution of incompressible and constant-properties model. Part II: Consideration of realistic conditions. Compressible viscous layer and small magnetic Reynolds number". James Forrestal Research Center. Princeton N.J., p. 46, Rept. No. 431, AFOSR, TN-58-405 and 58-711, 1958.

*418. CHING-SHILIU "Magnetogasdynamic flow regimes" *ARS J.*, Vol. 29, p. 871, 1959.

*419. CHINITZ, W., EISEN, C. L. and GROSS, R. A. "Aerothermodynamic and electrical properties of some gas mixtures to Mach 20". Rep. AFOSR TN-58-869.

420. CHODOROW, M. and KINO, G. S. "Plasma research at Stanford University". ARDC Conference on Ion and Plasma Research, University of Maryland, 30 Sept.–2 Oct. 1958.

*421. CHOPRA, K. P. "Some problems in hydromagnetics". Rept. No. 56–205; AFOSR TN-59-265; 210 pp. incl. illus., Jan. 1959.

422. CHOPRA, K. P. "On the induction drag of a sphere moving in a conducting fluid in the presence of a magnetic field" *Indian J. Phys.*, Vol. 30, pp. 605–10, 1956.

*423. CHOPRA, K. P. "Induction drag" *Indian J. Phys.*, Vol. 31, No. 6, pp. 332–3, 1957.

*424. CHOPRA, K. P. "On the radial adiabatic pulsations of an infinite cylinder in the presence of magnetic field parallel to its axis" *Proc. Nat. Inst. Sci., India* A, Vol. 21, No. 5, pp. 314–20, 1955.

*425. CHOPRA, K. P. and TALWAR, S. P. "On the radial pulsation of an infinite cylinder with a magnetic field parallel to its axis" *Proc. Nat. Inst. Sci., India* A, Vol. 21, No. 5, pp. 302–13, 1955.

*426. CHOPRA, K. P. et SINGER, S. F. "La trainée s'éxerçant sur une sphère se déplaçant dan un fluide conducteur en présence d'un champ magnétique". Heat Transfer and Fluid Mechanics Institute, Preprints of Papers, pp. 166–75, FMc. 185, 1958.

*427. CHOPRA, K. P. and SINGER, S. F. "Drag of a sphere moving in a conducting fluid in presence of a magnetic field". University of Maryland, Physics Department, Technical Report, No. 97, 12 pp., Jan. 1958. Heat Transfer and Fluid Mechanics Institute, Preprints of Papers, pp. 166–75, 1958.

428. CHRISTIANSEN, J. "Veber die kompression einer plasmasaule in magnetichen vierpolfeld" $\mathcal{Z}$. *Naturforsch.*, Vol. 13a, pp. 951–61, 1958.

429. CHRISTOFILOS, N. C. "Astron thermonuclear reactor" *Proc. 2nd Geneva Conf.*, Vol. 32, pp. 279–90, 1958.

430. CHU, B. T. "Wave propagation and the method of characteristics in reacting gas mixtures with application to hypersonic flow". Brown Un.WADC,TN-57-213.

*431. CHU, B. T. "Thermodynamics of electrically conducting fluids" *Phys. Fluids*, No. 5, pp. 473–84, 1959.

*432. CHU, B. T. "Thermodynamics of electrically conducting fluids and its application to magneto-hydrodynamics". WADC-TN 57–350, ASTIA AD 142039, 31 pp., Dec. 1957.

*433. CHU, E. L. "The Lagrangian and the energy momentum tensors in the perturbation theory of classical electrodynamics". Microwave Lab. Stanford U. Californ. May 1959, p. 24 (M.L. Rep. n. 599; Scientific Rep. No. 12; 18 refs. AFCRC TN-59-199) Contract AF 19(604/1930).

434. CHUAN, R. L. "Addition of heat to a gas through electrical discharges" AEDC-TN-5951, 18 pages, 1959.

*435. CHUAN, R. L. "Plasma heating of supersonic gas flow". AFORS, TN 57-762 (Univ. So. Calif. Engng. Center Rep. 56–202, ASTIA AD 136 751), 19 pp. + 2 figs., Dec. 1957.

436. CHUAN, R. L. "Plasma heating of supersonic air flow" *Bull. Amer. Phys. Soc.* II, Vol. 3, p. 288, 1958.

*437. CHUAN, R. L. "Preliminary results of plasma heating of high speed air flow". USCEC Rep. 56–203 (AFOSR TN 58–650), 31 July 1958.

*438. CHUAN, R. L. and SMETANA, F. O. "Experiments on a Radio Frequency discharges plasma in supersonic flow". Heat Transfer and Fluid Mech. Inst., Univ. Calif., Los Angeles, Calif., pp. 236–43, June 1959; *Appl. Mech. Rev.*, Vol. 12, p. 878, 1959.

439. CIAMPOLINI, F. "Studio della pompa elettromagnetica a flusso elicoidale" *L'energia elettrica*, No. IX, pp. 915–27, 1957.

440. CIAMPOLINI, F. "Studio sulle pompe elettromagnetiche a conduzione" *L'energia elettrica*, No. II, pp. 1053–69, 1958.

*441. CLARKE, J. F. "The linearized flow of a dissociating gas" *J. Fluid Mech.*, Vol. VII, Pt. IV, pp. 577–95, 1960.

442. CLAUSER, F. H. "Magnetohydrodynamics". ARDC Conference on Ion and Plasma Research, University of Maryland, 30 Sept.–2 Oct. 1958.

*443. CLAUSER, M. U. "State of the art, 1959: magnetohydrodynamics" *Astronautics*, No. 11, pp. 134–6, Nov. 1959.

444. CLAUSER, M. U. "Equations for a fast pinch". Phys. Space Res. Lab. ARL, 57-1010.

445. CLAUSER, M. U. "Magnetohydrodynamics". Space Res. Lab. G.M. TR-0000–00411.

446. CLAUSER, M. U. and WEIBEL, E. S. "Radiation pressure confinement, the shock pinch and feasibility of fusion propulsion". Space Techn. Lab. Inc. Los Angeles, Calif., 1959.

447. CLEMMAN, P. C. and WILSON, A. V. "The dispersion equation in plasma oscillations" *Proc. Roy. Soc.* A, Vol. 237, p. 117, 1956.

*448. CLINTON, A. C. "Magnétohydrodynamique" *Aeronautics* No. 11, pp. 20–4, 16 figs., Dec. 1959.

449. COBINE, J. D. *Gaseous Conductors*. Dower Publications, 1958.

450. COENSGEN, F. H. and FORD, F. C. "Pyrotron plasma heating experiments" *Proc. 2nd Geneva Conf.*, Vol. 32, pp. 266–72, 1948.

*451. COENSGEN, F. H., CUMMINS, W. F. and SHERMAN, A. E. "Multiplage magnetic compression of highly ionized plasma" *Phys. Fluids*, Vol. 2, p. 350, 1959.

452. COHEN, R. S., SPITZER, L. and ROUTLY, P. McR. "Electrical conductivity of an ionized gas" *Phys. Rev.*, Vol. 80, p. 230, 1950.

*453. COLE, G. H. A. "Some aspects of magneto-hydrodynamics" *Advanc. Phys.*, Vol. 5, pp. 452–97, 1956.

454. COLE, G. H. A. "On the dynamics of a non-uniform electrically conducting fluid" *Nuovo Cimento*, Vol. 4, p. 779, 1956.

*455. COLE, J. D. "Magneto-hydrodynamic waves". Magnetodynamics of conducting fluids; a symposium on M.F.D., Stanford U.P., 1959.

456. COLE, J. D. and HUTH, J. H. "Some interior problems of hydromagnetics" *Phys. Fluids*, Vol. 2, p. 624, 1959.

457. COLGATE, S. A. "Liquid sodium hydromagnetic equilibrium measurements". Int. Symposium on M.F.D. Washington, Jan. 1960.

458. COLGATE, S. A. "Collisionless plasma shock" *Phys. Fluids*, Vol. 2, p. 485, 1959.

*459. COLGATE, S. A. "A description of a shock wave in free particle hydrodynamics with internal magnetic fields". Radiation Lab. U. Calif. (Berkley), p. 20, Feb. 1957.

460. COLGATE, S. A. "A summary of the Berkley and Livermore pinch programs" *Proc. 2nd Geneva Conf.*, Vol. 32, pp. 123–8, 1958.

461. COLGATE, S. A. *et al.* "A toroidal stabilized pinch" *Proc. 2nd Geneva Conf.*, Vol. 32, pp. 129–40, 1958.

462. COLGATE, S. A. *et al.* "A partly stabilized dynamic pinch" *Proc. 2nd Geneva Conf.*, Vol. 32, pp. 140–5, 1958.

463. COLGATE, S. A. and FURTH, H. "The stabilized pinch and its role the development of controlled fusion power" *Science*, Vol. 128, pp. 337–43, 1958.

464. COLGATE, S. A. and AAMODT, R. L. "Plasma reactor promises direct electric power" *Nucleonics*, Vol. 15, pp. 50–5, 1957.

465. COLGATE, S. A. and WRIGHT, R. E. "Collapse. The shock heating of a plasma" *Proc. 2nd Geneva Conf.*, Vol. 32, pp. 145–9, 1958.

466. COLGATE, S. A. and FURTH, H. "Large toroidal stabilized pinch proposal". AEC Report UCRL, 21 pages, 1958.

*467. COLOMBO, S. "Dynamo effect in hydromagnetic theory" *Rev. Gen. Elect.*, Vol. 66, pp. 325–32, 1957.

*468. COLOMBO, S. "La théorie hydromagnétique" *Cah. Phys.*, No. 92, pp. 129–53, 1958.

469. CONSOLI, T. and DAGAI, M. "Polarization rotatoire magnétique dans les plasmas. Application à la mesure de la densité électronique" *C. R. Acad. Sci., Paris*, Vol. 250, No. 6, pp. 1010–17, 1960.

470. CONTURSI, G. "Studio magneto fluidodinamico delle pompe elettromagnetiche". Università di Napoli. C.F.S. M19, 1960.

471. COOK, M. A. "Quasi-lattice model of plasma and universal gravitation". Utah Engineering Experiment Station, Bulletin No. 93, 21 pp, 1958.

472. COOK, M. A., KEYES, R. T. and UDY, L. L. "Propagation characteristics of detonation-generated plasmas" *J. Appl. Phys.*, Vol. 30, No. 12, pp. 1881–92, 1959.

473. COOK, M. A. and McEWAN, W. S. "Cohesion in plasma" *J. Appl. Phys.*, Vol. 29, p. 1612, 1958.

*474. COOR, T., CUNNINGHAM, S. P., ELLIS, R. A., HEALD, M. A. and KRANZ, A. Z. "Experiments on the ohmic heating and confinement of plasma in a stellarator" *Phys. Fluids*, Vol. 1, No. 5, pp. 411–20, 1958.

475. COUSINS, S. W. and WARE, A. A. "Pinch effect oscillation in a high current toroidal ring discharge" *Proc. Phys. Soc.* B, Vol. 64, p. 159, 1951.

*476. COVERT, E. E. "On some fundamentals in magneto-fluid-mechanics". M.I.T. Naval Supersonic Lab., *Tech. Report 247*, 299 pp., 1958.

*477. COVERT, E. E. "A microscopic analysis of magneto-gas-dynamics". Preprint

Third Biennial Gas Dynamics Symposium, ARS Northwestern Univ., 24–26 Aug. 1959.

478. COVERT, E. E. and KERNEY, K. "A review of the literature of plasma physics". WADC TR-373 (contract AF 33(616)5693).

479. COWLEY, M. D. "A magnetogasdynamic analogy" *ARS J.*, Vol. 30, No. 3, p. 271, 1960.

480. COWLING, T. G. "The dissipation of magnetic energy in an ionized gas" *Mon. Not. Roy. Astr. Soc.*, Vol. 116, p. 114, 1956.

481. COWLING, T. G. "Electrical conductivity of ionized gas in the presence of a magnetic field" *Mon. Not. Roy. Astr. Soc.*, Vol. 95, p. 90, 1932.

482. COWLING, T. G. "Magneto-hydrodynamic oscillation of a rotating fluid globe" *Proc. Roy. Soc.* A, Vol. 233, pp. 319–22, 1955.

*483. COWLING, T. G. *Magneto-Hydrodynamics.* 115 pp. (17 figs.). New York, Interscience, 1957.

484. COWLING, T. G. "Alfven's theory of sunspots" *Mon. Not. Roy. Astr. Soc.*, Vol. 106, p. 446, 1946.

485. COWLING, T. G. "Magnetic field of sunspots" *Mon. Not. Roy. Astr. Soc.*, Vol. 94, pp. 39–48, 1933.

486. COWLING, T. G. "On the sun's general magnetic field" *Mon. Not. Roy. Astr. Soc.*, Vol. 105, pp. 166–74, 1945.

487. COWLING, T. G. "The electrical conductivity of an ionized gas in a magnetic field with applications to the solar atmosphere and the ionosphere" *Proc. Roy. Soc.* A, Vol. 183, pp. 453–79, 1945.

488. COWLING, T. G. "The growth and decay of the sunspot magnetic field" *Mon. Not. Roy. Astr. Soc.*, Vol. 106, pp. 218–21, 1946.

489. COWLING, T. G. "The oscillation theory of magnetic variable stars" *Mon. Not. Roy. Astr. Soc.*, Vol. 112, pp. 527–39, 1952.

490. COWLING, T. G. "The dynamo maintenance of steady magnetic fields" *Quart. J. Mech. Appl. Math.*, Vol. 10, pp. 129–36, 1957.

491. COWLING, T. G. "What MHD is about" *Nature, Lond.*, Vol. 181, pp. 1361–2, 1958.

*492. COWLING, T. G. and HARE, A. "Two-dimensional problems of the decay of magnetic fields in magneto-hydrodynamics" *Quart. J. Mech. Appl. Math.*, Vol. 10, pp. 385–405, 1957.

493. CRAUSSE, E. and POIRIER, Y. "Turbulent flow in an electrically conducting liquid subjected to a transverse magnetic field" *C. R. Acad. Sci., Paris,* Vol. 244, pp. 2772–4, 1957.

494. CRAUSSE, E. and POIRIER, Y. "Sur l'écoulement d'un liquid conducteur à travers un diaphragme, en présence d'un champ magnétique" *C. R. Acad. Sci., Paris*, Vol. 250, No. 22, pp. 3573–5, 1960.

495. CRAUSSE, E. and POIRIER, Y. "Actions dynamiques, sur un obstacle, d'un liquide conducteur, en presence, d'un champ magnétique" *C. R. Acad. Sci., Paris,* Vol. 250, No. 14, pp. 2533–5, 1960.

*496. CRUPI, G. "Sulla velocità di gruppo nella magnetoidrodinamica" *Boll. Un. Mat. Ital.* (3), Vol. 13, pp. 539–42, 1958.

497. CSADA, I. K. "On the magnetic effects of turbulence in ionized gases" *Acta Phys. Hungarica*, Vol. I, p. 235, 1952.

498. CULLER, G. J. and FRIED, B. D. "The propagation of shock waves (I)". Space Res. Lab. ARL-6.20.

*499. CURLE, N. "On the stability in the presence of a coplanar magnetic field of a laminar mixing region in a viscous electrically conducting fluid". ARC 18720, Oct. 1956.

*500. CUSHING, V. and SODHA, M. S. "Confinement of plasma by standing electromagnetic waves" *Phys. Fluids*, Vol. 2, p. 494, 1959.

501. CUTHRIE, A. and WAKERLING, R. R. *The Characteristics of Electrical Discharges in Magnetic Fields*". N.Y., McGraw-Hill, 1949.

*__502.__ DAMBURG, R. Y. "Flow of a viscous conducting liquid round an infinite cylinder in the presence of a magnetic field" *Latv. Pr.S. Zinat. Akad. Vestis*, No. 5, Vol. 142, pp. 81–4, 1959 (in Russian).

*__503.__ DAMBURG, R. Y. and KRAVTCHENKO, V. Y. "Excitation of hydromagnetic wave in a plasma by a moving charge" *Latv. Pr.S. Zinat. Akad. Vestis*, No. 7, Vol. 144, pp. 87–92, 1959 (in Russian).

504. DAMM, C. C. and EBY, F. S. "Pyrotron high energy experiments" *Proc. 2nd Geneva Conf.*, Vol. 32, pp. 273–4, O.N.U., 1958.

505. DARROW, K. K. "High frequency phenomena in gases—Part I" *Bell. Syst. Tech. J.*, Vol. 11, p. 576, 1932.

506. DATTNER, A. "Acceleration of plasma" *Ionization Phenomena in Gases*, Vol. 2, p. 1151. Amsterdam, North-Holland, 1959.

507. DATTNER, A. *The Plasma Resonator*, Vol. 13, p. 309. Ericcson Technics, 1957, *Proc. Venice Conf. 1957*, pp. 215–17. Amsterdam, North-Holland, 1960.

*__508.__ DAVIES, T. V. "On steady axially symmetric solutions of the idealized hydromagnetic equations for a compressible gas in which there is no diffusion of vorticity, heat or current" *Quart. J. Mech. Appl. Math.*, Vol. XIII, Pt. 2, pp. 169–83, 1960.

509. DAVIS, L. "The strength of interstellar magnetic fields" *Phys. Rev.*, Vol. 81, p. 890, 1951.

*__510.__ DAVIS, L., LÜST, R. and SCHLÜTER, A. "The structure of hydromagnetic shock waves; Part I: Nonlinear hydromagnetic waves in a cold plasma" *Z. Naturforsch.*, Vol. 13a, No. 11, pp. 916–36, 1958; *Appl. Mech. Rev.*, Dec. 1959.

511. DAWSON, J. M. "Plasma oscillations of a large number of electron beams". Divisional Meeting of the Div. of Fluid-Dynamics, American Physical Society, San Diego, 24–26 Nov. 1958.

*__512.__ DAWSON, J. M. "Plasma oscillations of a large number of electron beams" *Phys. Rev.*, Vol. 118, No. 2, 15 April 1960.

513. DAWSON, J. M. "Non-linear electron oscillations in a cold plasma" *Phys. Rev.*, Vol. 113, pp. 383–7, 1959.

*__514.__ DAWSON, J. M. and OBERMAN, C. "Oscillations of a finite cold plasma in a strong magnetic field" *Phys. Fluids*, Vol. 2, pp. 103–11, 1959.

*__515.__ DAWSON, J. M., FRIEMAN, E. A., KULSRUD, R. M., LENARD, A., BERGER, J. and BERNSTEIN, I. "Heating of a confined plasma by oscillating electromagnetic fields" *Phys. Fluids*, Vol. 1, pp. 301–7, 1958.

516. DE HOFFMAN, F. and TELLER, E. "Magnetohydrodynamic shocks" *Phys. Rev.*, Vol. 80, p. 692, 1950.

517. DELCROIX, J. L. *Introduction à la théorie des gas ionisés*. Paris, Dunod, 1959.

518. DELLIS, A. N. "The measurement of electron temperature by microwave measurements". AERE (Harwell), report Gp/R 2265, 1957.

519. DEMETRIADES, A. "A possible fully developed hydromagnetic pipe flow". Readers' Forum, *J. Aero/Space Sci.*, Vol. 27, No. 5, pp. 388–9, 1960.

*__520.__ DEMETRIADES, S. T. "Magnetogasdynamic acceleration of flowing gases and applications"—Northrop (Aircraft, Inc. Hawthorne, Calif.), 23 March 1959.

521. DEMIRKHANOV, R. A., GEVORKOV, A. K. and POPOV, A. F. "The interaction of a beam of charged particles with a plasma" *Ionization Phenomena in Gases*, Vol. 2, p. 665. Amsterdam, North-Holland, 1959.

*__522.__ DEMKOV, Y. N. and ERMOLAEV, A. M. "Fock expansion for the wave functions of a system of charged particles" *J. Exp. Theor. Phys.*, Vol. 36, No. 3, pp. 633–5, 1959.

523. DENISOV, N. G. "On a singularity of the field of an electromagnetic wave propagation in an inhomogeneous plasma" *Zh. Eksp. Teoret. Fiz.*, Vol. 31, p. 609, 1956.

23

*524. DENISOV, N. G. "Resonance absorption of electromagnetic waves by an inhomogeneous plasma" *J. Exp. Theor. Phys.*, Vol. 34, No. 2, p. 364, 1958.

525. DESLOGES, E. A. *et al.* "Conductivity of plasmas to microwaves" *Phys. Rev.*, Vol. 112, pp. 1441–4, 1958.

526. DE SOCIO, M. L. "Sul fronte di un'onda elettromagnetica in un gas ionizzato soggetto ad un campo magnetico" *Accad. Lincei, Roma*, Serie VIII, Vol. XXVII, pp. 368–73, 1959.

527. DE SOCIO, M. L. "Ancora sul fronte di un'onda elettromagnetica in un gas ionizzato soggetto ad un campo magnetico" *Accad. Lincei, Roma*, Serie VIII, Vol. XXVIII, pp. 622–6, 1959.

528. DE SOGIS, M. "On the propagation of non-sinusoidal waves in an ionized gas subjected to a magnetic field" *Accad. Sci., Torino*, Vol. 92, pp. 243–55, 1957–58.

529. DESSLER, A. J. "Large amplitude hydromagnetic waves above the ionosphere" *J. Geophys. Res.*, Vol. 63, pp. 507–11, 1958.

530. DESSLER, A. J. "The propagation velocity of world-wide sudden commencements of magnetic storms" *J. Geophys. Res.*, Vol. 63, pp. 405–8, 1958.

*531. DESSLER, A. J. "Ionospheric heating by hydromagnetic waves" *J. Geophys. Res.*, Vol. 64, No. 4, pp. 397–401, 1959.

*532. DIAMOND, F., GOZZINI, A. and KAHAN, T. "Interaction of cm waves with a plasma in the presence of a magnetic field" *C. R. Acad. Sci., Paris*, Vol. 242, pp. 90–3, 1956 (IRE No. 1691, July 1956).

533. DIBAI, E. A. "Magnetogravitational instability of an infinite cylinder" *Astron. Zh.*, Vol. 35, p. 253, 1958.

*534. DICKERMAN, P. J. and PRICE, C. F. "Flow of a partially ionized gas in an axial magnetic field" *Phys. Fluids*, Vol. 3, No. 1, pp. 137–8, 1960.

535. DICKINSON, H., BOSTICK, W., DIMARCO, J. N. and KOSLOV, S. "Observation of apparent flute type plasma instability" *Phys. Fluids*, Vol. 3, No. 3, pp. 480–1, 1960.

536. DITTMER, A. F. "Experiments on the scattering of electrons by ionized mercury vapour" *Phys. Rev.*, Vol. 28, p. 507, 1926.

537. DOBENECKER, O. "Effect of viscosity upon the conductivity and dielectric constant of electrolytes" *Ann. Phys.*, Vol. 17, p. 699, 1933.

538. DOBINSKIK, S. "Uber den einfluss eines elektrischen feeldes auf des viskositat von flussigkeiten" *Acad. Poln. Bull.*, Vol. 1–2A, p. 42, 1935, *Phys. Z.*, Vol. 36, p. 509, 1935.

*539. DOLDER, K. "The transmission of strong shock waves through magnetic fields". AERE GP/M 199, April 1957.

540. DOLDER, K. and HIDE, R. "An experiment on the interaction between a plane shock and magnetic field" *Nature, Lond.*, Vol. 181, pp. 1116–18, 1958.

541. DOLDER, K. and HIDE, R. "Bibliography on shock waves, shock tubes and allied topics". AERE, G.R. 2055, H.M.S.O., 1957.

542. DOLIQUE, J. M. "Etude d'une colonne de plasma alimentée en continu et soumise à un champ électromagnétique: condition d'existence de solutions maxwelliennes non centrées, equation aux densités" *C. R. Acad. Sci., Paris*, Vol. 250, No. 7, pp. 1221–2, 1960.

543. DOLIQUE, J. M., BERNARD, M. Y. "Etude d'une colonne de plasma alimentée en continu et soumise à un champ magnétique: approximation du premier ordre par rapport aux vitesses de diffusion; mise en evidence d'une zone de frontière" *C. R. Acad. Sci., Paris*, Vol. 250, No. 8, pp. 1458–9, 1960.

*544. DOMBROWSKI, G. E. "A small-signal theory of electron-wave interaction in crossed electric and magnetic fields". Electron Tube Lab. Univ. of Michigan, Ann Arbor (TN No. 22, Rept. n. 2275–2 8T).

*545. DONALDSON, C. "The magneto-hydrodynamics of a layer of fluid having a free surface". *Meeting of the Heat Transfer and Fluid Mechanics Institute*, pp. 55–67, 1959. Stanford U.P., 1959.

546. Dougal, A. A. and Goldstein, L. "Energy exchange between electron and ion gases through Coulomb collisions in plasmas" *Phys. Rev.*, Vol. 109, pp. 615–24, 1958.

*****547.** Dow, D. G. and Knechtli, R. C. "Plasma containment by R.F. and D.C. field combination" *J. Electronics and Control*, Vol. 7, No. 4, pp. 316–43, 1959.

*****548.** Doyle, P. H. and Neufeld, J. "Behaviour of plasma at ionic resonance" *Phys. Fluids*, Vol. 2, p. 391, 1959.

*****549.** Draganu, M. "Sur l'equation de Fokker Plank d'un plasma" *C. R. Acad. Sci., Paris*, Vol. 250, No. 14, pp. 2519–20, 1960.

550. Drawin, H. W. "The cross sections of neutral hydrogen, helium and argon atoms for electron impact" *Z. Phys.*, Vol. 146, p. 295, 1956.

551. Drazin, P. G. "Stability of parallel flow in a parallel magnetic field at small magnetic Reynolds numbers" *J. Fluid Mech.*, Vol. 8, Pt. I, pp. 130–42, 1960.

552. Drazin, P. G. "Stability problem of a broken line jet in a parallel magnetic field" *J. Math. Phys.*, Vol. XXXIX, No. 1, pp. 49–53, 1960.

553. Dricot, G. and Ledoux, P. "Note on the theory of the vibration of an incompressible fluid in the presence of a magnetic field" *Bull. Soc. Roy. Sci., Liège*, Vol. 28, No. 5/6, pp. 115–21, 1959.

554. Drummond, J. E. "Basic microwave properties of hot magneto plasmas" *Phys. Rev.*, Vol. 110, pp. 293–306, 1958.

555. Drummond, J. E. "Microwave propagation in hot magneto plasmas" *Phys. Rev.*, Vol. 112, pp. 1460–4, 1958.

*****556.** Drummond, W. E. and Rosenbluth, M. N. "Cyclotron radiation from a hot plasma" *Phys. Fluids*, Vol. 3, No. 1, p. 45–52, 1960.

557. Druyvesteyn, M. J. "The interaction between an electron beam and a plasma" *Physica*, Vol. 5, p. 561, 1938.

558. Druyvesteyn, M. J. "Low-voltage arc" *Z. Phys.*, Vol. 64, p. 781, 1930.

559. Druyvesteyn, M. J. and Penning, F. M. "The mechanism of electrical discharges in gases of low pressure" *Rev. Mod. Phys.*, Vol. 12, p. 87, 1940.

560. Du Bois, D. F. "Electron interactions; Part I: Field theory of a degenerate electron gas" *Ann. Phys.*, Vol. 7, No. 1, p. 174–238, 1959.

561. Ducati, A. C. "Research in high intensity ionic jets". ARDC conference on Ion and Plasma Research, University of Maryland, 30 Sept.–2 Oct. 1958.

562. Ducati, A. C. and Cann, G. L. "Propulsive properties of high-intensity plasma jets". Giannini Research Lab. ASTIA AD 136736, 21 Feb. 1958.

563. Duff, A. W. "The viscosity of polarized dielectrics" *Phys. Rev.* (1), Vol. 4, p. 23, 1896.

564. Dungey, J. W. "A family of solutions of the magneto-hydrostatic problem in a conducting atmosphere in a gravitational field" *Mon. Not. Roy. Astr. Soc.*, Vol. 113, pp. 180–7, 1953.

565. Dungey, J. W. "Strong hydromagnetic disturbances in a collision-free plasma" *Phil. Mag.*, pp. 585–93, 1959.

566. Dungey, J. W. "The attenuation of Alfvén waves" *J. Geophys. Res.*, Vol. 59, pp. 323–8, 1954.

567. Dungey, J. W. "The motion of magnetic fields" *Mon. Not. Roy. Astr. Soc.*, Vol. 113, pp. 679–82, 1953.

568. Dutt, T. L. and Stainsby, A. G. "Calculation of the electronic density and collision frequency in a decaying plasma" *Ionization Phenomena in Gases*, Vol. II, p. 755. Amsterdam, North-Holland, 1959.

569. Early, H. C. "Electrical means of producing high velocity wind". Univ. of Michigan Final Report, No. 7B 3-001-146.

570. Early, H. C. and Dow, W. G. "Preliminary research on a low pressure ionic wind tunnel". Univ. of Michigan, memo No. 41.

571. EARLY, H. C., SMITH, H. L. and LU, C. D. "Electrical wind phenomena". Univ. of Michigan Summary Rep. No. 1, project n.M 989.

572. EASTMOND, E. J. and TURNER, E. B. "Velocity in small tubes of electrically excited shock waves in deuterium". Fluid Dynamics Meeting, American Physical Society, San Diego, 24–26 Nov. 1958.

573. EASTMOND, E. J. and TURNER, E. B. "Conductivity measurements at magnetic Reynolds number greater than unity". Fluid Dynamics Meeting, American Physical Society, San Diego, 24–26 Nov. 1958.

574. ECKER, G. and WEIZEL, W. "The interaction energy of the charge carrier in a plasma". *Z. Naturforsch.*, Vol. 13a, pp. 1093–4, 1958.

575. ECKERT, E. R. G. "Heat transfer in ionized gas streams". ARDC Conference on Ion and Plasma Research, University of Maryland, 30 Sept.–2 Oct. 1958.

576. ECKERT, E. R. G. and TEWFIK, O. E. "Use of reference enthalpy in specifying the laminar heat-transfer distribution around blunt bodies in dissociated air" *J. Aero/Space Sci.*, Readers' forum, Vol. 27, No. 6, p. 464, 1960.

577. ECKERT, H. U. "A cool mercury plasma tunnel" *J. Aero/Space Sci.*, Vol. 26, No. 8, pp. 515–7, 1959.

578. ECKERT, H. U. "A low temperature plasma tunnel using mercury vapor and radiofrequency excitation". Fluid Dynamics Meeting, American Physical Society, San Diego, 24–26 Nov. 1958.

579. EDMONDS, F. N. "Supersonic motion in vacuum spark plasmas along magnetic fields" *Phys. Fluids*, pp. 30–41, 1958.

*580. EDMONDS, F. N. Jr. "Hydromagnetic stability of a conducting fluid in a circular magnetic field" *Phys. Fluids*, Vol. 1, pp. 30–41 (13 refs.), 1958.

581. EDWARDS, S. F. "A variational calculation of the equilibrium properties of a classical plasma" *Phil. Mag.*, Ser. 8, pp. 119–24, Feb. 1958.

*582. EIDMAN, V. Y. "The radiation from an electron moving in a magneto-active plasma" *J. Exp. Theor. Phys.*, Vol. 34, No. 1, pp. 91–5, 1958.

583. ELLISON, R. "Study of ionization in rocket flames". ARDC Conference on Ion and Plasma Research, University of Maryland, 30 Sept.–2 Oct. 1958.

584. EL MOHANDIS, M. G. S. "Magnetohydrodynamic disturbances due to the sudden introduction of a magnetic dipole in a fluid of finite conductivity" *J. Astrophys.*, Vol. 129, pp. 172–93, 1959.

585. ELMORE, W. C., TUCK, J. L. and WATSON, K. M. "Inertial-electrostatic confinement of a plasma" *Phys. Fluids*, Vol. 2, p. 239, 1959.

*586. ELSASSER, W. M. "Dimensional relations in magneto-hydrodynamics" *Phys. Rev.*, Vol. 95, pp. 1–5, 1954.

587. ELSASSER, W. M. "Earth's interior and geomagnetism" *Rev. Mod. Phys.*, Vol. 22, pp. 1–35, 1950.

588. ELSASSER, W. M. "Earth's magnetism and magneto-hydrodynamics". Univ. Utah Repts., No. 7, 1954.

*589. ELSASSER, W. M. "Hydromagnetism: A review" *Amer. J. Phys.*, Vol. 23, pp. 590–609, 1955; *ibid.*, Vol. 24, pp. 85–110, 1956.

*590. ELSASSER, W. M. "Hydromagnetic dynamo theory" *Rev. Mod. Phys.*, Vol. 28, pp. 135–63, 1956.

591. ELSASSER, W. M. "Induction effects in terrestrial magnetism" (in 3 parts) Part I: *Phys. Rev.*, Vol. 69, pp. 106–16, 1946; Part II: *ibid.*, Vol. 70, pp. 202–12, 1946; Part III: *ibid.*, Vol. 72, pp. 821–3, 1947.

592. ELSASSER, W. M. "On the origin of the earth's magnetic field" *Phys. Rev.*, Vol. 55, p. 482, 1939.

593. ELSASSER, W. M. "Review of magnetohydrodynamics" *Amer. J. Phys.*, Vol. 23, p. 590, 1955; *ibid.*, Vol. 24, p. 85, 1956.

594. ELSASSER, W. M. "Some dimensional aspects of hydromagnetic phenomena". Magnetohydrodynamics (Landshoff R.K.M. Editor). Stanford U.P. 1957.

595. ELSASSER, W. M. "The hydromagnetic equations" *Phys. Rev.*, Vol. 79, p. 183, 1950.

*596. ELSASSER, W. M. "Magnétohydrodynamique" *Uspekhi Fiz. Nauk.*, No. 3, pp. 529–88, March 1958.

597. ELWERT, G. "Uber die Ionisations und Rekombinations-prozesse in einem Plasma und die Ionisationformel der Sonnenkorona". *Z. Naturforsch.*, Vol. 7a, pp. 432–9, 1952.

598. EMELEUS, K. G. "Electron beam scattering and oscillations in plasma". ARDC Conference on Ion and Plasma Research, University of Maryland, 30 Sept.–2 Oct. 1958.

599. EMELEUS, K. G. "Oscillations and fluctuations in gas discharges" *Nuovo Cimento*, Suppl., Vol. 3, No. 3, p. 490, 1956.

600. EMELEUS, K. G. "Plasma Electron Oscillations" *Appl. Sci. Res.* B, Vol. 5, p. 66, 1955.

601. EMELEUS, K. G. and ALLEN, T. K. "Note on plasma-electron oscillations" *Austr. J. Phys.*, Vol. 8, p. 305, 1955.

602. ENGEL, A. *Ionized Gases*, pp. 131–7. Oxford, Clarendon Press, 1955.

603. ENGEL, A. "Propulsion by ions and ionized plasmas" *Nature, Lond.*, Vol. 183, pp. 573–4, 1959.

604. ENGELHARDT, H. and SACK, H. "Effect of magnetic field on viscosity of oxygen" *Z. Phys.*, Vol. 33, p. 724, 1932.

*605. ENGELKE, B. A. "The pressure variation of the electron temperature in the plasma of a positive column in molecular gas glow discharge" *Z. Phys.*, Vol. 158, No. 4, pp. 422–32, 1960 (in German).

*606. ERICSON, W. B. and BAZER, J. "On certain properties of hydromagnetic shock" *Phys. Fluids*, Vol. 3, No. 4, pp. 631–41, 1960.

*607. ERICSON, W. B. and BAZER, J. "Hydromagnetic shocks". Inst. Mathematical Science, N.Y. Univ. Research Rept. No. MH-8, AFCRC TN-58-241.

608. FAIN, V. M. "On the theory of the coherent spontaneous emission" *J. Exp. Theor. Phys.*, No. 3, p. 562, 1959.

609. FAINBERG, Y. B. "The acceleration of particles in a plasma". *Atomnaia Energiia*, Vol. 6, pp. 447–52, 1959.

*610. FAINBERG, Y. B. and TKALICH, U. S. "The reflection of an electromagnetic wave from a plasma moving through a dielectric in a constant magnetic field" *Zh. Tekh. Fiz.*, Vol. 29, No. 4, pp. 491–6, 1959; *Sov. Phys. Tech. Phys., N.Y.*, Vol. 4, pp. 438–43, 1959.

*611. FAINBERG, Y. B. and GORBATENKO, M. F. "Electromagnetic waves in a plasma situated in a magnetic field" *Zh. Tekh. Fiz.*, Vol. 29, No. 6, pp. 549–62, 1959; *Sov. Phys. Tech. Phys., N.Y.*, Vol. 4, No. 5, pp. 487–500, 1959.

612. FAIR, V. M. "Velocity distribution of electrons in the presence of an alternating current and constant magnetic fields" *Zh. Eksp. Teoret. Fiz.*, Vol. 28, p. 422, 1955.

*613. FALK, D. S. "Magnetohydrodynamic distortion of a magnetic field due to a uniform flow". AVCO Res. Lab. RA 29, 30 Apr. 1958, ASTIA AD 201–913.

614. FALKENHAGEN, H. and VERNON, E. L. "The viscosity of strong electrolytic solutions according to electrostatic theory" *Phil. Mag.*, Vol. 14, p. 537, 1932.

615. FANG, P. H. "Conductivity of plasmas to microwaves" *Phys. Rev.*, 113, pp. 13–14, 1959.

*616. FARLEY, D. J. JR. "A theory of electrostatic fields in a horizontally stratified ionosphere subject to a vertical magnetic field" *J. Geophys. Res.*, Vol. 64, No. 9, pp. 1225–33, 1959.

617. FAY, J. A. "Hall effects in a laminar boundary layer of the Hartman type". AFOSR TN 60-291, December 1959.

618. FAY, H., HINTZ, E. and JORDAN, H. L. "Experiments on shock-compression of plasmas" *Ionization Phenomena in Gases*, Vol. 2, p. 1046. Amsterdam, North-Holland, 1959.

*619. FEDORCHENKO, V. D., RUKTEVICH, B. N. and CHERNYI, B. M. "Motion of an electron in a spatially periodic magnetic field" *Zh. Tekh. Fiz.*, Vol. 29, No. 10, pp. 1212–18, 1959; *Sov. Phys. Tech. Phys.*, *N.Y.*, Vol. 4, No. 10, pp. 112–17, 1960.

620. FEINSTEIN, J. "Condition for radiation from a solar plasma" *Phys. Rev.*, Vol. 85, p. 145, 1952.

621. FEIX, M. "Traitment semi-quantique des interactions dans un plasma" *Ionization Phenomena in Gases*, Vol. II, p. 595. Amsterdam, North-Holland, 1959.

*622. FELDMAN, S. "On the hydrodynamic stability of two viscous incompressible fluids in parallel uniform shearing motion" *J. Fluid Mech.*, Vol. 2, pp. 343–70, 1957.

623. FENYES, I. "Analogy between the mechanical and thermodynamical equations of motion and the Onsager reciprocity relation" *J. Exp. Theor. Phys.*, No. 4, p. 725, 1959.

624. FERMI, E. "On the origin of cosmic radiation" *Phys. Rev.*, Vol. 75, p. 1169, 1949.

625. FERMI, E. "Galactic magnetic fields and origin of cosmic radiation" *Astrophys. J.*, Vol. 119, pp. 1–6, 1954.

626. FERRARI, I. "A uniqueness theorem for the field of an alternating current in a wire in the neighbourhood of a conducting medium" *Accad. Sci.*, *Torino*, Vol. 94. No. 1, pp. 77–88, 1959–60 (in Italian).

627. FERRARO, V. C. A. "A discussion on MHD" *Proc. Roy. Soc.* A, Vol. 233, pp. 289–406, 1955; IRE No. 1687, July 1956.

628. FERRARO, V. C. A. "General theory of plasma" *Nuovo Cimento, Suppl.*, Vol. XIII, Ser. X, No. 1, pp. 9–59, 1959.

629. FERRARO, V. C. A. "Hydromagnetic waves in a rare ionized gas and galactic magnetic fields" *Proc. Roy. Soc.* A, Vol. 233, pp. 310–18, 1955.

630. FERRARO, V. C. A. "Magneto-hydrodynamics" *Nature, Lond.*, Vol. 176, pp. 234–7, 1955.

631. FERRARO, V. C. A. "Mean free path in rare ionized gases" *Mon. Not. Roy. Astr. Soc.*, Vol. 93, pp. 416–422, 1933.

632. FERRARO, V. C. A. "Non-uniform rotation of the sun and its magnetic field" *Mon. Not. Roy. Astr. Soc.*, Vol. 97, pp. 458–72, 1937.

633. FERRARO, V. C. A. "On the equilibrium of magnetic stars" *Astrophys. J.* Vol. 119, p. 407, 1954.

*634. FERRARO, V. C. A. "On the reflection and refraction of Alfvén waves" *Astrophys. J.*, Vol. 119, pp. 393–406, 1954.

635. FERRARO, V. C. A. "The theory of the first phase of a magnetic storm". Int. Symposium on M.F.D. Washington, Jan. 1960.

636. FERRARO, V. C. A. and MEMORY, D. J. "Oscillations of a star in its own magnetic field: an illustrative problem" *Mon. Not. Roy. Astr. Soc.*, Vol. 112, p. 361, 1953.

637. FERRARO, V. C. A. and PLUMPTON, C. "Hydromagnetic waves in a horizontally stratified atmosphere" *Astrophys. J.*, Vol. 127, p. 459, 1958.

*638. FETISOV, I. K. "Wall probe in a magnetic field" *J. Exp. Theor. Phys.*, Vol. 36, 1959.

639. FEYER, J. A. "Hydromagnetic wave propagation in the ionosphere" *J. Atmos. Terr. Phys.*, 1960.

640. FIELD, G. B. "Radiation by plasma oscillations" *Astrophys. J.*, Vol. 124, p. 555, 1956.

641. FINADINGSLAND, O. T. and AUSTIN, G. E. "Magnetically controlled ambipolar diffusion" *Phys. Rev.*, Vol. 79, p. 232, 1950.

642. FINKELSTEIN, D. "Megatron scheme for producing relativistic plasma" *Proc. 2nd Geneva Conf.*, Vol. 32, pp. 446–50, 1958.

643. FINKELSTEIN, D. "High-field plasma accelerators" *Bull. Amer. Phys. Soc.*, Vol. 3, pp. 39, 1958.

*644. FINKELSTEIN, D., SAWYER, G. A. and STRATTON, T. F. "Supersonic motion of vacuum spark plasmas along magnetic fields" *Phys. Fluids*, pp. 188–92, May-June 1958.

645. FIORIO, F. "Magneto-plasma-dynamics" *Alata*, No. 174, pp. 53–6, 10 figs., 1959.

646. FISCHER, W. and WALCHER, W. "Für Extraktion von Ionen aus Plasmas und plasmaähnliken Gebilden" *Z. Naturforsch.*, Vol. 10a, p. 4857, 1955.

647. FISCHER, E. D. and MANSUR, W. "Conference on extremely high temperatures". A. F. Cambridge Research Centre, 1958.

*648. FISHMAN, F. "End effects in magnetohydrodynamic channel flow". June 1959, AVCO, RR 78.

*649. FISHMAN, F., LOTHROP, J. W., PATRICK, R. M. and PETSCHEK, H. E. "Supersonic two-dimensional magneto-hydrodynamic flow". AVCO Res. Lab. Res. Rep. 39, Feb. 1959.

*650. FLEISCHMAN, O. and LIPPMANN, B. A. "Remarks on Alfvén's perturbation method". Rep. No. MH-4, AFCRC-TN-55-854, 11 pp., Aug. 1955.

651. FONDA-BONARDI, G. "Litton research on plasma acceleration". ARDC Conference on Ion and Plasma Research, University of Maryland, 30 Sept.–2 Oct. 1958.

652. FONDA-BONARDI, G. "Research study of plasma acceleration". Final Report AFOSR-TR 59-170 (Contract AF 49-638-345).

653. FORRESTER, A. T. and SPEISER, R. C. "Design criteria for an ion rocket". ARDC Conference on Ion and Plasma Research. University of Maryland, 30 Sept.–2 Oct. 1958.

*654. FOURES-BRUHAT, Y. "Fluides chargés de conductivité infinie" *C. R. Acad. Sci.*, *Paris*, Vol. 248, pp. 2558–60, 1959.

655. FOWLER, R. G. "Research in plasmas and optical excitation cross sections in atomic gases". ARDC Conference on Ion and Plasma Research, University of Maryland, 30 Sept.–2 Oct. 1958.

656. FOWLER, W. A. "Thermonuclear reaction; cross-sections" *Phys. Rev.*, Vol. 81, p. 656, 1951.

657. FRADKIN, E. S. "Contribution to the theory of transport processes in a plasma located in a magnetic field" *J. Exp. Theor. Phys.*, Vol. 5, pp. 901–5, 1957.

*658. FRAENKEL, L. E. "A shallow-liquid theory in magneto-hydrodynamics" Aer. Dept. Imperial College, paper 54, *J. Fluid Mech.*, Vol. 7, Pt. I, pp. 81–107, 1960.

659. FRANKL, F. I. "Potential steady relativistic gas flows" *Dokl. Akad. Nauk.*, *SSSR*, Vol. 123, pp. 47–8, 1958 (in Russian).

660. FREEDERICKS, W. and ZWETKOFF, W. "Über Bewegungen die in anysotropen Flussigkeiten unter ein Wirkung des elektrischen Feldes entstehen" *Dokl. Akad. Nauk.*, *SSSR*, Vol. 4, No. 3, p. 131, 1955.

661. FREEDERICKS, W. and ZWETKOFF, W. "Action of the electric field on anisotropic liquids" *Acta Physiochimica*, Vol. 3, p. 879, 1936.

662. FRIED, B. D. "Distortion of axisymmetric, poloidal magnetic fields by uniform flow of a conducting fluid". Fluid Dynamics Meeting; San Diego Cal., American Physical Society, 24–26 Nov. 1958.

663. FRIED, B. D. "Flow through a plane magnetic nozzle". Space Res. Lab. ARL-6-40.

664. FRIED, D. B. "Methods of heating and confining a thermonuclear plasma". ARDC Conference on Ion and Plasma Research, University of Maryland, 30 Sept.–2 Oct. 1958.

665. FRIED, B. D. "Mechanism for instability of transverse plasma waves" *Phys. Fluids*, Vol. 2, p. 337, 1959.

666. FRIED, B. D. "On the mechanism for instability of transverse plasma waves". Space Res. Lab. TR-59-0000-00235.

667. FRIED, B. D. "Similarity solutions for converging and diverging shock waves". Space Res. Lab. ARL-6-8.

*668. FRIEDLANDER, F. G. "Sound pulses in a conducting medium" *Proc. Camb. Phil. Soc.*, Vol. 55, Pt. 4, pp. 341–67, 1959.

*669. FRIEDRICHS, K. O. "Non-linear wave motion in magneto-hydrodynamics". Los Alamos Development Center Report, 1845, 1955; Minister of Supply Report P66286.

670. FRIEDRICHS, K. O. "Observation on pinch buckling". Int. Symp. on M.F.D., Washington, Jan. 1960.

671. FRIEDRICHS, K. O. and KRANZER, H. "Notes on magneto-hydrodynamics. VIII: Non-linear wave motion". AEC Computing and Applied Mathematics Center, N.Y. Univ., NYO-6486, 31 July, 1958.

*672. FRIEMAN, E. A. and KULSRUD, R. M. "Problems in hydromagnetics" *Advances in Applied Mechanics*, Vol. 5, pp. 195–231. N.Y. Academic Press, 1958.

673. FRIEMAN, E. and ROTENBERG, M. "Hydromagnetic stability of stationary equilibria". Int. Symp. on M.F.D. Washington, Jan. 1960.

674. FROEHLICH, H. and DONIACH, S. "Plasma interaction and conduction in semiconductors" *Proc. Phys. Soc.*, Vol. 69B, p. 961, 1956.

675. FÜNFER, E., LEHNER, G. and TUCZEK, H. "Bewengungsvorgänge beim linearen Pincheffekt und Rumaway-elektronen" *Z. Naturforsch.*, pp. 566–74, July 1960.

676. FURTH, P. *et al.* "Strong magnetic fields" *Sci. Amer.*, Vol. 198, pp. 28–33, 1958.

677. FURTH, H. *et al.* "Production and use of high transient magnetic field" *Sci. Instr.*, Vol. 28, pp. 949–58, 1957.

678. GABOR, D. "Wave theory of plasma" *Proc. Roy. Soc.* A, Vol. 213, p. 73, 1952.

679. GABOR, D. "Electrostatic theory of the plasma" *Z. Phys.*, Vol. 84, p. 474, 1933.

680. GABOR, D., ASH, E. A. and DRACOTT, D. "Langmuir's paradox" *Nature, Lond.*, Vol. 176, p. 916, 1955.

681. GABOVICH, M. P. and KYCHENKO, E. T. "Investigation of penetrating plasma during a discharge" *Zh. Tekh. Fiz.*, Vol. 27, p. 299, 1957.

682. GABOVICH, M. P. and KYCHENKO, E. T. "On the influx of flowing plasma on the focusing power of an ion source" *Zh. Tekh. Fiz.*, Vol. 26, p. 991, 1956.

*683. GABOVICH, M. D. and PASECHNIK, L. L. "Anomalous electron scattering and the excitation of plasma oscillations" *J. Exp. Theor. Phys.*, No. 4, p. 727, Oct 1959.

*684. GAILITIS, A. "Influence of a magnetic field on the boundary layer in a diffuser" *Latv. Pr.S. Zinat. Akad. Vestis*, No. 12 (149) pp. 59–60, 1953 (in Russian).

*685. GAJEWSKI, R. "Magnetohydrodynamic waves in wave guides" *Phys. Fluids*, Vol. 2, No. 6, p. 633, 1959.

686. GALLET, R. "Propagation and production of electromagnetic waves in a plasma" *Nuovo Cimento, Suppl.*, Vol. XIII, Ser. X, No. 1, pp. 234–57, 1959.

687. GARDER, J. N. "Pinched discharge and thermonuclear reactors" *Nuovo Cimento*, No. 6, p. 1228, 1957.

688. GARDNER, C. S. and MORIKAWA, G. K. "Similarity in the asymptotic behavior of collision free hydromagnetic waves and water waves". AEC Res. and Rev. Rep. MF2, May 1, 1960. Contract No. AT(30-1) 1480.

*689. GARTENHAUS, S. and TANNENWALD, L. M. "The collapse of an axially symmetric pinch" Lockheed Missiles and Space Division report No. LMSD-48463, 1958.

690. GARTON, W. R. S. and RAJARITNAM, A. "Flash Absorption Spectra of the Plasmas of Arcs and other discharges" *Proc. Phys. Soc.*, Vol. 70A, p. 815, 1957.

*691. GAUGER, J., VALI, V. and TURNER, T. E. "The arc-driven shock tube". Lockheed Missiles and Space Division Report No. LMSD-5178, 17 Sept. 1958.

*692. GAUGER, J., VALI, V. and TURNER, T. "Laboratory experiments in hydro-magnetic propulsion" *Proc. Amer. Astronaut. Soc.*, Western Regional Meeting, pp. 7–1 to 7–11 (illus. graphs. biblio), 18–19 Aug. 1958.

693. GAUTIER, C. "Hydrodynamique et magnétisme" *Rev. Gén. Elect.*, Vol. 21, 5/327, pp. 363–9 (1 fig.); *ibid.*, Vol. 20, pp. 395–400, 1926.

*694. GELLER, R. "Behaviour of a high-frequency plasma in the presence of a magnetic field" *C. R. Acad. Sci., Paris*, Vol. 250, No. 2, pp. 314–16, 1960 (in French).

*695. GELLER, R. "The production of stable high-frequency plasmoids at the plasma resonant frequency" *C. R. Acad. Sci., Paris*, Vol. 249, No. 25, pp. 2749–51, 1959.

*696. GEORGE, K. A. "Plasma heating by current-saturation" *Nature, Lond.*, Vol. 184, p. 1790, 1959.

*697. GEORGHITA, S. I. "Sur le mouvement stationnaires des Fluides incompressibles dans les milieux poreux non homogènes" *Ann. Univ. "C.I. Parhon" Bucaresti Sez. Sci. Nat.*, Vol. 7, No. 17, pp. 33–7, 1958.

*698. GEORGHITA, S. I. "Sur le mouvements non linéaires dans les milieux poreux" *Acad. Rep. Pop. Roumaine.*, Vol. 9, pp. 491–502, 1958.

699. GERMAIN, P. "Contribution à la théorie des ondes de choc en magnéto-dynamique des fluides" ONERA, Pub. No. 97, 33 pp., 7 figs., 1959.

*700. GERMAIN, P. "Introduction à l'étude de l'aéromagnétodynamique". ONERA, M.T. No. 11 (1958) 51 pp. (5 fol. fig.) (SDIT, Me. 270); *Cah. Phys.*, Vol. 13, No. 103, pp. 38–128, 1959.

701. GERMAIN, P. "Shock waves and shock wave structure in magneto-fluid dynamics". Int. Symposium on M.F.D. Washington, Jan. 1960.

*702. GERMAIN, P. "Sur la structure de certaines ondes de choc dans une fluide conducteur en présence d'un champ magnétique" *C. R. Acad. Sci., Paris*, No. 13, pp. 1929–31, 1959.

703. GERMAIN, P. "Sur certains écoulements d'un fluide parfaitement conducteur en présence d'un champ magnetique" Conf. Sorbonne, 21 Dec. 1959 (A paraître: *Astronautica Acta*).

704. GERSHMAN, B.N. "Notes concerning waves in a homogeneous magneto active plasma" *Zh. Eksp. Teoret. Fiz.*, Vol. 31, pp. 707–9, 1956; *J. Exp. Theor. Phys.*, Vol. 4, pp. 582–4, 1957.

705. GERSHMAN, B. N. "Propagation of electromagnetic waves in plasma subjected to a magnetic field, taking account of the thermal motions of electrons" *Zh. Eksp. Teoret. Fiz.*, Vol. 24, pp. 659–72, 1953.

706. GERSHMAN, B. N. "Non-resonant absorption of electromagnetic waves in a magneto-active plasma" *Zh. Eksp. Teoret. Fiz.*, Vol. 37, No. 3(9), pp. 695–704, 1959; *J. Exp. Theor. Phys.*, Vol. 37 (10), No. 3, pp. 497–503, 1960.

707. GERSHMAN, B. N., GINZBURG, Y. L. and DENISOV, N. G. "The propagation of electromagnetic waves in plasma (ionosphere)" *Usp. Fiz. Nauk*, Vol. 61, pp. 561–612, 1957.

*708. GERSHUNI, G. Z. and ZHUKHOVITSKII, E. M. "Stationary convective flow of an electrically conducting liquid between parallel plates in a magnetic field" *J. Exp. Theor. Phys.*, Vol. 7, No. 3, pp. 461–4, 1958.

*709. GERSHUNI, G. Z. and ZHUKHOVITSKII, E. M. "Stability of the stationary con-vective flow of an electrically conducting liquid between parallel vertical plates in a magnetic field" *Sov. Phys. JETP*, Vol. 7, No. 3, pp. 465–70, 1958.

710. GERTSENSHSTEIN, M. E. "On the longitudinal waves in an ionized medium (plasma)" *Zh. Eksp. Teoret. Fiz.*, Vol. 22, p. 303, 1952.

711. GHAI, M. L. "Plasma propulsion for space applications" ARDC Conference on Ion and Plasma Research, University of Maryland, 20 Sept.–2 Oct. 1958.

*712. GHAI, M. L. "Space propulsion engines—A problem in production of high velocity gases". Presented at the ARS-Northwestern Symp. at Northwestern Univ., Evanston, Illinois, 24–26 Aug. 1959.

*713. GIAMBIRASIO, G. "On the electrical behaviour of an ideal plasma" *Phys. Fluids*, Vol. 3, No. 2, pp. 299–303, 1960.

*714. GIANNINI, G. M. "The plasma jet and its applications". Giannini Research Laboratory Report AFOSR TN 57-520 AD 136505, August 1957.

715. GIANNINI, G. M. "The plasma jet" *Sci. Amer.*, Vol. 197, pp. 80–8, 1957.

*716. GIBSON, G. and LAUER, E. S. "Radiation damping of an electron in a uniform magnetic field" *Phys. Rev.*, Vol. 117, No. 5, pp. 1188–90, 1960.

717. GIBSON, G. *et al.* "Injection into thermonuclear machines using beams of neutral deuterium atoms in the range 100 kev. to 1 Mev." *Proc. 2nd Geneva Conf.*, Vol. 32, pp. 275–8.

*718. GIELLESTAD, G. "On equilibrium configurations of oblate fluid spheroids with a magnetic field" *Astrophys. J.*, Vol. 119, pp. 14–33, 1954.

719. GIELLESTAD, G. "On the equilibrium of an oblate liquid spheroid with a magnetic field" *Astrophys. J.*, Vol. 126, p. 565, 1957.

720. GIELLESTAD, G. "Magnetohydrodynamic oscillation of a star" *Ann. Astrophys.*, Vol. 15, p. 276, 1952.

721. GILARDINI, A. L. and BROWN, S. C. "Microwave conductivity of an ionized decaying plasma at low pressures" *Phys. Rev.*, Vol. 105, p. 25, 1957.

722. GILARDINI, A. L. "Microwaves in ionized gas" *Nuovo Cimento, Suppl.*, Vol. XIII, Ser. X, No. 1, pp. 132–66, 1959.

723. GILARDINI, A. L. and BROWN, S. C. "Microwave determinations of the probability of collision of electrons in neon" *Phys. Rev.*, Vol. 105, p. 31, 1957.

724. GINZBURG, M. A. "Surface waves on the boundary of a gyro-tropic medium" *J. Exp. Theor. Phys.*, No. 6, p. 1123, 1958.

725. GINZBURG, V. L. "Magneto-hydrodynamic waves in gases" *Zh. Eksp. Teoret. Fiz.*, Vol. 21, pp. 788–94, 1951; AEC-tr, 2593.

726. GINZBURG, V. L. "Nonlinear interaction of radio waves propagating in a plasma" *J. Exp. Theor. Phys.*, No. 6, p. 1100, 1959.

*727. GINZBURG, V. L. and EIDMAN, V. Y. "The radiation reaction in the motion of a charge in a medium" *J. Exp. Theor. Phys.*, Vol. 36, 1959.

728. GINTZON, E. L. "Microwaves" *Science*, Vol. 127, pp. 341–859, 1958.

729. GLASS, I. I. and HEUCKROTH, L. E. "Head-on collision of spherical shock waves" *Phys. Fluids*, Vol. 2, p. 542, 1959.

*730. GLOBE, S. "Laminar steady state magneto-hydrodynamic flow in an annular channel" *Phys. Fluids*, Vol. 2, No. 4, pp. 404–7, 1959.

*731. GLOBE, S. "Magneto-hydrodynamic pipe flow". Ph.D. Thesis, Harvard University, No. 1958.

*732. GLOBE, S. "The suppression of turbulence in pipe flow of mercury by an axial magnetic field". Heat Transfer and Fluid Mechanics Institute, Univ. of California, Los Angeles, pp. 68–79, June 1959.

733. GLONTI, G. A. "On the theory of the stability of liquid jets in an electric field" *J. Exp. Theor. Phys.*, Vol. 34, No. 5, pp. 1329–30, 1958.

*734. GLOTOVA, G. V. L., GRANOVSKII and V. I. SAVOSKIN, "Comparison of the decay rates of plasma in hydrogen and deuterium" *J. Exp. Theor. Phys.*, Vol. 35, 1959.

735. GOLD, L. "Current-voltage behaviour in a plasma" *J. Electronics and Control*, Vol. 5, p. 432, 1958.

736. GOLD, L. "Non-linear phenomenological theory of plasma oscillations" *J. Electronics and Control*, Vol. 4, p. 219, 1958.

737. GOLD, L. "Oscillations in a plasma with oriented (D.C.) magnetic field" *J. Electronics and Control*, Vol. 4, p. 409, 1958.

738. GOLD, T. "Plasma and magnetic field in the solar system" *J. Geophys. Res.*, Nov. 1959; *Nuovo Cimento*, Suppl., Vol. XIII, Ser. X, No. 1, pp. 318–24, 1959.

*739. GOLD, T. "Motions in the magnetosphere of the Earth" *J. Geophys*, Vol. 64, No. 9, pp. 1219–24, *Res.* 1959.

740. GOLDSTEIN, L. "Nonreciprocal electromagnetic wave propagation in ionised gaseous media" IRE Transactions on Microwave Theory Tech., MTT-6, No. 1, 1958.

741. GOLDSTEIN, L. "Progress and objectives of ARDC sponsored plasma". ARDC, Conference on Ion and Plasma Research, University of Maryland, 30 Sept.–2 Oct. 1958.

742. GOLDSTEIN, L. and SEKIGUCHI, T. "Electron interaction and heat conduction in gaseous plasmas" *Phys. Rev.*, Vol. 109, pp. 625–30, 1958.

743. GOLDSTEIN, N. L., ANDERSON, N. and CLAR, G. L. "Interaction of microwaves transmitted through a gaseous discharge plasma" *Phys. Rev.*, Vol. 90, p. 151, 1953.

*744. GOLITZYNE, G. S. "One-dimensional motion in magneto-hydrodynamics" *J. Exp. Theor. Phys.*, Vol. 35, No. 3, pp. 776–81 (3 figs.), 1958; *ibid.*, pp. 538–40, 3 March 1959.

*745. GOLITZYNE, G. S. "Plane problems in magnetohydrodynamics" *J. Exp. Theor. Phys.*, No. 3, pp. 688–98, 1958.

*746. GOLITZYNE, G. S. and STANIUKOVICH, K. P. "Some problems of magneto gasdynamics with account at finite conductivity" *Zh. Eksp. Teoret. Fiz.*, pp. 1, 417–427, 1957; *ibid.*, pp. 1090–9 (18 refs.) 1958.

*747. GOLITZYNE, G. S. and STANIVKOVICH, K. P. "Some remarks on the structure of shock waves" *J. Exp. Theor. Phys.*, No. 8, pp. 575–6, March 1959; *Zh. Eksp. Teoret. Fiz.*, Vol. 35, pp. 828–30, 1958.

748. GORDEEV, G. V. "Excitation of plasma oscillations" *Zh. Eksp. Teoret. Fiz.*, Vol. 27, pp. 24–8, 1954.

*749. GORDEEV, G. V. "The influence of end boundaries upon the rotation of plasma in a magnetic field" *Soviet Phys.*, Vol. 4, No. 6, pp. 683–6, 1959.

750. GORDEEV, G. V. "The influence of end boundaries upon the rotation of plasma in a magnetic field" *Zh. Tekh. Fiz.*, Vol. 29, No. 6, pp. 759–62, 1959.

751. GORDEEV, G. V. "Plasma oscillation in a magnetic field" *Zh. Eksp. Teoret. Fiz.*, Vol. 23, p. 660, 1952.

752. GORDEEV, G. V. "Low-frequency plasma oscillations" *Zh. Eksp. Teoret. Fiz.*, Vol. 27, p. 19, 1954.

*753. GORDEEV, G. V. and GOUBANOV, A. J. "On the question of the acceleration of a plasma in a magnetic field" *J. Exp. Theor. Phys.*, Vol. 2, pp. 2046–54, 1958.

*754. GORDEEV, G. V. and GOUBANOV, A. J. "On the acceleration of a plasma in a magnetic field" *Soviet Phys.*, Vol. 3, No. 9, pp. 1880–7, 1958.

755. GORDON, E. I. "Plasma oscillations—the interaction of electron beams with gas discharge plasmas". MIT—Ph. D. Thesis, 1957.

*756. GOROWITZ, B. and HARNED, B. W. "Measurements of velocity and momentum with a pulsed T-tube plasma generator". Tech. Inform. series 20, Feb. 59, 1 vol. (incl. illus.) (Aerophysics research memo n. 26, Rept. n. R59SD314).

757. GOROWITZ, B. and HARNED, B. W. "Electric propulsion-measurements with a small thrust plasma generator". SAE National Aeronautical Meeting, Hotel Commodore, New York, Paper 63T, 31 Mar.–3 April 1959.

*758. GOTO, K. "Relativistic magneto-hydrodynamics" *Progr. Theor. Phys. Jap.*, No. 1, pp. 1–14, 1958.

*759. GOTO, T., SATO, M. and UCHIDA, T. "On the mechanism of the pinch effect" *Nuovo Cimento*, Vol. 14, No. 5, pp. 1065–75, 1959.

*760. GOULARD, R. "Optimum magnetic field for stagnation heat transfer reduction at hypersonic velocities" *ARS. J.*, Vol. 29, 604–6, 3 refs., 1949.

761. GOULD, L. "Doppler phenomenon in radiant gaseous atmospheres with velocity and density fields". *Ionization Phenomena in Gases*, Vol. 2, p. 813. Amsterdam, North-Holland, 1959.

762. GOULD, L. and BROWN, S. C. "Microwave determination of the probability of collision of electrons in helium" *Phys. Rev.*, Vol. 95, p. 897, 1954.

763. GRAD, H. "Reducible problems in fluid magnetic steady flows". Int. Symposium, on M.F.D. Washington, Jan. 1960.

764. GRAD, H. "Propagation of magneto-hydrodynamic waves without radial attenuation" *Magnetodynamics of Conducting Fluids*. New York University, Stanford U.P., 1959.

765. GRAD, H. "One-dimensional propagation of three-dimensional transverse magnetohydrodynamic disturbances". Third Magneto-hydrodynamic Symposium, Lockheed Research Lab. Palo Alto, 21–22 Nov. 1958.

766. GRAD, H. "Notes on magnetohydrodynamics; I: General fluid equations". New York University, Aug. 1956.

767. GRAD, H. and ROSE, M. H. "Notes on magnetohydro-dynamics; II: Dimensional considerations". New York University, Aug. 1956.

768. GRAD, H. "Notes on magneto-hydro-dynamics; III: Special solutions". New York University, Aug. 1956.

*769. GRAD, H. "Notes on magneto-hydro-dynamics; IV: Ohm's Law". New York University, Aug. 1956; Report NYO-6486.

*770. GRANOVSKII, V. P., RIUMINA, K. P, SAVOSKIN, V I. and TIMOFEEVA, G. G. "Observations of the pinch effect at decreasing currents" *J. Exp. Theor. Phys.*, Vol. 8, No. 1, pp. 33–6, 1959.

771. GRAVES, J. "Propagation of transverse waves on viscoelastic jets" *Industr. Eng. Chem., U.S.A.*, Vol. 51, No. 7, pp. 885–6, 1959.

772. GREEN, H. S. "Propagation of disturbances at high frequencies in gases, liquids and plasmas" *Phys. Fluids*, Vol. 2, p. 31, 1959.

*773. GREEN, H. S. "Ionic theory of plasmas and magneto-hydro-dynamics" *Phys. Fluids*, Vol. 2, p. 341, 1959.

774. GREEN, H. S. "Statistical mechanics of electrical conduction in fluids" *J. Phys. Chem.*, pp. 714–16, Sept. 1954.

*775. GREENBERG, O. W. and SEN, H. K. "Hydrodynamic model of diffusion effects on shock structure in a plasma" *Phys. Fluids*, Vol. 3, No. 3, pp. 379–87, 1960.

776. GREENBERG, O. W., SEN, H. K. and TREVE, Y. M. "Charge separation effects on shock wave structure in a plasma" *Ionization Phenomena in Gases*, Vol. II, p. 1098. Amsterdam, North-Holland, 1959.

*777. GREENSPAN, H. P. "On the flow of a viscous electrically conducting fluid" ASTIA AD 231877, Oct. 1959.

*778. GREENSPAN, H. P. "Flat plate drag in magnetohydrodynamic flow" *Phys. Fluids*, Vol. 3, No. 4, pp. 581–8, 1960.

*779. GREENSPAN, H. P. and CARRIER, G. F. "The magnetohydrodynamic flow past a flat plate" *J. Fluid Mech.*, Vol. 6, Pt. I, pp. 77–96 (5 figs.), 1959.

780. GREIFINGER, C. "Effect of a transverse magnetic field on the 'escape speed' of a conducting fluid" *Phys. Fluids*, Vol. 3, No. 4, pp. 662–4, 1960.

781. GREYBER, H. D. "Transient temperature variations during the self-heating of a plasma by thermonuclear reactions". Paper presented at the Divisional Meeting of the Division of Fluid Dynamics, American Physical Society, San Diego, California, 24–26 Nov. 1958.

782. GROETZINGER, G. and FREY, R. "Thermal conduction in electrostatic fields" *Z. Phys.*, Vol. 36, p. 292, 1935.

783. Gross, E. P. "Plasma oscillations in a static magnetic field". MIT Lab. for Insulation Research Tech. Rep. No. 39.

784. Gross, E. P. "Plasma oscillations in a static magnetic field" *Phys. Rev.*, Vol. 82, p. 232, 1951.

785. Gross, E. P. and Jackson, E. A. "Kinetic models and the linearized Boltzmann equation" *Phys. Fluids*, Vol. 2, p. 432, 1959.

786. Gross, E. P. and Krook, M. "Model for collision processes in gases—small-amplitude oscillations of charged two component system" *Phys. Rev.*, Vol. 102, pp. 593–604, 1956.

*__787.__ Gross, R. A. "A note on one-dimensional plasma motion" *J. Aero/Space Sci.*, Vol. 25, No. 12, pp. 788–9, 1958.

*__788.__ Gross, R. A., Chinitz, W. and Rivlin, T. J. "Magnetohydrodynamic effects in combustion". Rept. No. AFOSR TN-58-120, 15 Feb. 1958.

*__789.__ Gross, R. A., Chinitz, W. and Rivlin, T. J. "Magnetohydrodynamic effects on exothermal waves" *J. Aero/Space Sci.*, Vol. 27, No. 4, pp. 283–91, 1960; AFOSR TN-58-120, ASTIA AD 152-028, Feb. 1958.

*__790.__ Grubin, E. S., Harrach, W. G. and Orr, W. R. "Feasibility study for a hypervelocity projector". Rept. APGC TR-59-62 15, 143 pp., 1959.

791. Gryolajtys, J. "Application of Langmuir's electrical probe to the determination of plasma parameters in an electrical discharge" *Rozprawy Elektrotech*, Vol. 3, p. 3, 1957.

*__792.__ Guerchman, B. N. "Contribution à l'étude de la théorie cinétique de propagation des ondes magnétohydrodynamiques dans le plasma" *Izv. Vys. Uch. Zav.*, Vol. 1, No. 4, pp. 3–20, 1958.

793. Guess, A. W. and Sen, H. K. "A quasi-similarity solution of a composite radiation-hydrodynamic spherical shock". ARDC, Conference on Ion and Plasma Research, University of Maryland, 30 Sept.–2 Oct. 1958.

794. Guile, A. E. and Secker, P. E. "Arc cathode movement in a magnetic field" *J. Appl. Phys.*, Vol. 29, No. 12, 1662–7, 1958.

*__795.__ Guman, W. J. "Further comments on ionizing shock waves in monoatomic Gases" *J. Appl. Phys.*, Vol. 29, p. 1, 1958.

796. Guman, W. J. "Partition of energy in a pulsed plasma accelerator" *Phys. Fluids*, Vol. 3, No. 3, pp. 483–4, 1960.

797. Guman, W. J. "On the 'escape speed' of a conducting fluid in a transverse magnetic field" *Phys. Fluids*, Vol. 2, No. 6, p. 714, 1959.

798. Gurevich, A. V. "Simplification of the equations for the distribution function of electrons in plasma" *Zh. Eksp. Teoret. Fiz.*, Vol. 32, p. 1237, 1957.

799. Gurevich, A. V. "Certain special features of ohmic heating of electron gas in a plasma" *J. Exp. Theor. Phys.*, Vol. 11, No. 1, pp. 85–8, 1960.

800. Gurevich, A. V. "Velocity distribution function of electrons in alternating electric and constant fields" *Dokl. Akad. Nauk. URSS*, Vol. 104, pp. 201–4, 1955, IRE No. 724, April 1956.

801. Gurevich, A. V. "The temperature of plasma electrons in a variable electrical field" *J. Exp. Theor. Phys.*, No. 2, p. 271, 1959.

802. Gurevich, A. V. "Hysteresis and non-stationary fields in the electron temperature in plasma in inert gases" *Zh. Eksp. Teoret. Fiz.*, Vol. 36, pp. 624–6, 1959.

803. Gurevich, A. V. "On the effect of radio waves on the properties of plasma (ionosphere)" *J. Exp. Theor. Phys.*, Vol. 3, pp. 895–904, 1957.

804. Gurevich, A. V. "Hysteresis and non-stationary effects in the electron temperature in plasma in inert gases" *J. Exp. Theor. Phys.*, No. 2, p. 434, August 1959.

805. Gurevich, P. B. and Prokofiev, V. K. "Temperature distribution in the plasma of low and high-voltage spark discharges" *Optika i Spektrosk*, Vol. 2, p. 417, 1957.

806. Guro, G. "On equilibrium configurations of oblate fluid spheroids with a magnetic field." Yerkes Observatory, University of Chicago, 10 Aug. 1953.

807. Gutton, H. "Ionised gases in high-frequency fields" *C. R. Acad. Sci., Paris,* Vol. 188, p. 156, 1929.

808. Gutton, H. "Effect of a magnetic field on resonance phenomena in ionised gases" *C. R. Acad. Sci., Paris,* Vol. 188, p. 385, 1929.

809. Gutton, H. "Dielectric constant of ionised gases" *C. R. Acad. Sci., Paris,* Vol. 188, p. 1235, 1929.

810. Gutton, H. "Dielectric properties of ionised gas and the high-frequency discharge" *Ann. Phys.,* Vol. 13, p. 62, 1930.

811. Gutton, H. "Dielectric properties of ionised gases" *C. R. Acad. Sci., Paris,* Vol. 184, p. 441, 1927.

*812. Haaland, C. M. "Confinement of charged particles by plane electromagnetic waves in free space" *Phys. Rev. Letters,* Vol. 4, No. 4, pp. 166–70, 1960.

813. Haar, D. *"Introduction to the Physics of Many Bodied Systems"* New York, Interscience Publ. Inc., 1958.

814. Hacques, G. "Ecoulement d'un fluide conducteur en présence du champ magnétique créé par un courant électrique indéfini et en détermination par la méthode des analogies rheéléctrique" *C. R. Acad. Sci., Paris,* No. 2 pp. 284–6, 4 figs., 1960.

815. von Hagenow, K. V. "On the stability of a linear pinch with volume currents" *Ionization Phenomena in Gases,* Vol. II, p. 614. Amsterdam, North-Holland, 1959.

816. Hain, K. *et al.* "Zur stabilität eines plasmas" *Z. Naturforsch.,* Vol. 12a, pp. 833–41, 1957.

817. Hain, K. and Hain, G. "Calculations of the pinch in the hydromagnetic approximation" *Ionization Phenomena in Gases,* Vol. II, p. 843. Amsterdam, North-Holland, 1959.

*818. Hain, K. and Lüst, R. "Stability of axially symmetrical plasma configuration in volume flow" *Z. Naturforsch.,* Vol. 13a, No. 11, pp. 936–40, 1958 (in German).

819. Hain, K., Lüst, R. and Schlüter, A. "Hydromagnetic waves of finite amplitude in a plasma with isotropic and non-isotropic pressure perpendicular to a magnetic field". Int. Symposium on M.F.D. Washington, Jan. 1960.

*820. Haines, M. G. "The joule heating of a stable pinched plasma" *Proc. Phys. Soc.,* Vol. 76, Pt. 2, No. 488, pp. 250–60, 1960.

821. Hains, F. D. "Some exact solutions to the magneto-hydrodynamic equations for incompressible flow" *J. Aero/Space Sci.,* Vol. 26(4), pp. 246–7, 1959.

*822. Hains, F. S., Yoler, Y. A. and Ehlers, E. "Axially symmetric hydromagnetic channel flow". Preprint. Third Biennial Gas Dynamic Symposium, ARS, Northwestern Univ., Illinois, Evanston. 24–26 Aug. 1959.

823. Halbwachs, F., Hillion, P. and Viyiev, J. E. "Lagrangian formalism in relativistic hydrodynamics of rotating fluid masses" *Nuovo Cimento,* p. 817, 1958.

*824. Hall, L. S., Gardner, A. L. and Fundingsland, O. T. "Analysis of the interaction of electromagnetic radiation with a plasma in a magnetic field". Rept. of Radiation Lab. University of California, 34 pp., Sept. 1956.

825. Hamaola, S. "Notes on magneto-hydrodynamic equilibrium" *Progr. Theor. Phys., Jap.,* Vol. 22, No. 1, p. 145, (1959).

*826. Haques, G. "Flow of a conducting fluid in the presence of the magnetic field created by a line electric current, and its determination by the method of rheoelectric analogies" *C. R. Acad. Sci., Paris,* Vol. 250, No. 2, pp. 284–6, 1960.

827. Harned, B. W. "Magnetic effect in a T-tube" *ARS J.,* Vol. 30, No. 7, p. 636, 1960.

828. Harris, E. G. "Relativistic magneto-hydrodynamics" *Phys. Rev.,* Vol. 108, pp. 1357–60, 1957.

829. HARRIS, E. G. "Unstable plasma oscillations in a magnetic field" *Phys. Rev. Letters*, Vol. 2, No. 2, pp. 34–6, 1959.

*830. HARRIS, E. G. and SIMON, A. "Coherent and incoherent radiation from a plasma" *Phys. Fluids*, Vol. 3, No. 2, pp. 255–8, 1960.

831. HARRIS, E. G., THEUS, R. B. and BOSTICK, W. H. "Experimental investigations of the notion of plasma projected from a button source across magnetic fields" *Phys. Rev.*, Vol. 105, pp. 46–50, 1957.

*832. HARRISON, E. R. "Experiments with plasma beams" *Ionization Phenomena in Gases*, Vol. 2, p. 1160. Amsterdam, North-Holland, 1959.

833. HARRISON, E. R. "The run-away effect in a fully ionized plasma" *Phil. Mag.*, Ser. 8, pp. 1318–25, Nov. 1958.

834. HARRISON, E. R. and DAWTON, R. H. "Apparatus for producing plasma beams" *J. Electronics and Control*, Vol. 5, p. 29, 1958.

*835. HART, P. J. "Effect of gas pressure and cone angle on the velocities of electrically excited, shock waves" *J. Appl. Phys.*, Vol. 31, No. 2, pp. 436–7, 1960.

836. HARTMANN, J. V. L. "Hg-Dynamics; 1: Theory of the laminar flow of an electrically conductive liquid in a homogeneous magnetic field" *K. Danske Vidensk. Selsk.*, Vol. 15, No. 6, 1937.

837. HARTMANN, J. V. L. and LAZARUS, F. "Hg-Dynamics; 2: Experimental investigations on the flow of mercury in a homogeneous magnetic field" *K. Danske Vidensk. Selsk.*, Vol. 15, No. 7, 1937.

838. HARTMANN, J. V. L. "Theory and experimental flow of plasma in a magnetic field (mercury flows)" *K. Danske Vidensk, Selsk.*, Vol. 15, Nos. 6 and 7, Copenhagen, 1937.

839. HASIMOTO, H. "Magnetohydronamic waves in a viscous conducting fluid". Int. Symp. on M.F.D. Washington, Jan. 1960.

*840. HASIMOTO, H. "Viscous flow of a perfectly conducting fluid with a frozen magnetic field" *Phys. Fluids*, Vol. 2, No. 3, pp. 337–8, 1959.

841. HASIMOTO, H. "Magnetohydrodynamic wave of finite amplitude at magnetic Prandtl number 1" *Phys. Fluids*, Vol. 2, No. 5, pp. 575–6, 1959.

842. HASIMOTO, H. "Steady longitudinal motion of a cylinder in a conducting fluid" *J. Fluid Mech.*, Vol. 8, Pt. I, pp. 61–81, 1960.

843. HAYAKAWA, S. and HOKKYO, N. "Electromagnetic radiation from electron plasma" *Progr. Theor. Phys.*, Vol. 15, p. 193, 1956.

*844. HELFER, H. L. "Magneto-hydrodynamic shock waves" *Astrophys. J.*, Vol. 117, pp. 177–99, 1953.

845. HELLWIG, G. "Veber die Bewegung geladener Teilchen in schwach veränderlichen Magnetfeldern" *Z. Naturforsch.*, Vol. 10a, pp. 508, 1955.

846. HERDAN, R. and LILEY, B. S. "Dynamical and transport equations for a thermal plasma". Int. Symposium on M.F.D. Washington, Jan. 1960.

847. HERLOFSON, N. "Magneto-hydrodynamic waves in a compressible fluid conductor" *Nature, Lond.*, Vol. 165, pp. 1020–1, 1950.

848. HERLOFSON, N. "Plasma resonance in ionospheric irregularities" *Ark. Fys.*, Vol. 3, p. 247, 1951.

849. HERMAN, R. and RUBIN, R. J. "Modulator vibrational relaxation of diatomic gases behind shock waves" *Phys. Fluids*, Vol. 2, p. 547, 1959.

850. HERMAN, R., WENIGER, S. and HERMAN, L. "The formation of H_2^+ molecules during a discharge plasma in ionized hydrogen" *C. R. Acad. Sci., Paris*, Vol. 244, p. 1746, 1957.

851. HERNQUIST, K. G. "Plasma ion oscillations in electron beams" *J. Appl. Phys.*, Vol. 26, p. 544, 1955.

852. HERNQUIST, K. G. "Plasma oscillations in electron beams" *J. Appl. Phys.*, Vol. 26, pp. 1029–30, 1955.

853. HERNQUIST, K. G. and JOHNSON, E. O. "Retrograde motion in gas discharge Plasmas" *Phys. Rev.*, Vol. 98, p. 1576, 1955.

854. HERTWICK, F. and SCHLÜTER, A. "Die 'adiabatische Invarianz' des magnetichen Bahnmomentes geladener Teilchen" *Z. Naturforsch.*, Vol. 12a, pp. 844–9, 1957.

855. HERZENBERG, A. "Geomagnetic dynamos" *Phil. Trans.* A, Vol. 250, p. 543, 1958.

856. HERZOG, R. O., KUDER, H. and PAERSCH, E. "Electrostatic viscosity effect" *Z. Phys.*, Vol. 35, p. 446, 1934.

857. HERZOG, I. and WESHE, J. R. "Characteristics of the technique of aerodynamic investigation by means of a series of sparks". Univ. of Maryland Tech. Note BN-105, 1957.

858. HESS, R. V. "Plasma acceleration by guided microwaves". Preprint. Third Biennial Gas Dynamic Symposium, A.R.S. Northwestern Univ., 24–26 Aug. 1959.

*859. HESS, R. V. "Some basic aspects of magnetohydrodynamic boundary-layer flows". NASA-MENO, 4-9-59L, 42 pp., April 1959.

860. HESS, R. V. and THOM, K. "National aeronautics and space administration plasma acceleration by guided microwaves". Presented at the ARS. Northwestern Gas Dynamics Symp. Northwestern University, Eranston, Illinois, 24–26 Aug. 1959.

861. HIDE, R. "Waves in a heavy viscous incompressible electrically conducting fluid of variable density in the presence of a magnetic field" *Proc. Roy. Soc.* A, Vol. 233, pp. 376–96, 1955.

862. HIDE, R. and DOLDER, K. "Experiments on the passage of a shock wave through a magnetic field". Int. Symposium on M.F.D. Washington, Jan. 1960.

863. HIDE, R. and ROBERTS, P. H. "On the hydromagnetic flow due to an oscillating plane". Int. Symposium on M.F.D. Washington, Jan. 1960.

864. HILL, R. M. "Investigation of factors affecting microwave breakdown and transmission near missile antennas". ARDC, Conference on Ion and Plasma Research, University of Maryland, 30 Sept.–2 Oct. 1958.

865. HILSENRATH, J., GREEN, M. S. and BECKETT, C. W. "Internal energy of highly ionized gases". 9th Annual Congress of International Astronautical Federation, Aug. 1958.

866. HINES, C. O. "Hydromagnetic resonance in ionospheric waves" Defence Research Telecommunications Establishment (Canada) Radio Physics Laboratory. Project D48-95-11-01, 29 Oct. 1954.

*867. HINES, C. O. "On the rotation of the polar ionospheric regions" *J. Geophys. Res.*, Vol. 65, No. 1, pp. 141–4, 1960.

868. HINES, C. O. "Generalized magnetohydrodynamic formulae" *Proc. Camb. Phil. Soc.*, Vol. 49, p. 299, 1953.

869. HOFFMANN, F. W. and KOHN "Use of flames for plasma research". FA 10, Amer. Phys. Soc., Spring Meeting Washington, D.C., May 1959.

*870. HOFFMANN, F. W. and TELLER, E. "Magneto-hydrodynamic shocks" *Phys. Rev.*, Vol. 80, pp. 692–703, 1960.

871. HÖGBERG, L., SIEGBAHN, K. and BOCKASTEN, K. "Electrodeless generation and acceleration of plasma rings" *Ionization Phenomena in Gases*, Vol. 2, p. 1156. Amsterdam, North-Holland, 1959.

872. HOH, F. C. and LEHNERT, B. "Experiments on diffusion in a plasma column in a longitudinal magnetic field" *Ionization Phenomena in Gases*, Vol. II, p. 604. Amsterdam, North-Holland, 1959.

*873. HOH, F. C. and LEHNERT, B. "Diffusion processes in a plasma column in a longitudinal magnetic field" *Phys. Fluids*, Vol. 3, No. 4, pp. 600–7, 1960.

*874. HOLTER, O., JENSEN, E. *et al.* "Theoretical researches in magnetohydrodynamics". Final Tech. Rep., 19 pp. (AFOSR TH-59-92) contract AF 61 (052) 49, 30 June 1959.

875. HOPSON, J. E., TARG, R., and WANG, C. C. "Coherent microwave oscillations of a beam-plasma system". ARDC, Conference on Ion and Plasma Research, University of Maryland, 30 Sept.–2 Oct. 1958.

876. HORVATH, J. I. "New geometrical methods of the theory of physical fields" *Nuovo Cimento, Suppl.*, Vol. IX, Ser. X, No. 2, pp. 444–96, 1958.

877. HOYLE, F. "The build-up of large magnetic fields inside stars" (editor Landshoff.) *Magnetohydrodynamics Symposium*, Stanford U.P.; Oxford U.P., 1957.

878. HOYLE, F. *Recent Researches in Solar Physics*. Cambridge U.P., 1949.

*****879.** HU, P. N. "An outline of the basic theory of magnetohydrodynamics". 15 Nov. 1958, 62 pp. incl. illus. (MSD rept. n. 206-950-2, A FS WC TR-58-46) (Subcontract to Republic Aviation Corp., Contract AF 29 (601) 1218.

*****880.** HUBBARD, J. "The instabilities of a cylindrical gas discharge with field penetration". AERE T/R 2668. Atom. En. Res. U.K., 1958.

881. HULST, H. C. VAN DE "Problems of cosmical aerodynamics". Chap. 6, p. 52, Dayton, Chicago, Central Air Documents Office, 1951.

*****882.** HUNZIKER, R. R. "The flow about a charged body moving in the lower ionosphere" *J. Aero/Space Sci.*, Vol. 27, pp. 935–42, 1960.

883. HUXLEY, L. G. H. "Free path formulae for the electronic conductivity of a weakly ionized gas in the presence of a uniform and constant magnetic field and a sinusoidal electric field" *Aust. J. Phys.*, pp. 240–5, June 1957 (IRE n. 894, Feb., 1958).

884. HWA, R. C. "Effects of electron–electron interaction on cyclotron resonance in gaseous plasma" *Phys. Rev.*, Vol. 110, pp. 307–13, 1958.

*****885.** IAKOVLEV, L. G. "Wave-front velocity in electrodynamics containing higher derivative" *J. Exp. Theor. Phys.*, No. 3, p. 542, March 1959.

886. IMAI, ISAO "Some remarks on flows of conducting fluids past bodies". Int. Symp. on M.F.D. Washington, Jan. 1960.

*****887.** INGLIS, D. R. "Theories of the earth's magnetism" *Rev. Mod. Phys.*, Vol. 27, pp. 212–48, 1955.

888. IONESCU, T. V. and MIHUL, C. "Free electrons in ionised gases in a magnetic field" *C. R. Acad. Sci., Paris*, Vol. 194, p. 1330, 1932.

889. IONESCU, T. V. "Sur les periodes propres des vibratiores des gas enserrés dans le champ magnétique" *C. R. Acad. Sci., Paris*, Vol. 203, p. 57, 1936.

890. IONESCU, T. V. and MIHUL, C. "Ionised gases in a magnetic field: proof of the existence of the rotating electron" *C. R. Acad. Sci., Paris*, Vol. 194, p. 70, 1932.

891. IORDANSKII, S. V. "On compression waves in magnetohydrodynamics" *Dokl. Akad. Nauk. SSSR*, Vol. 121, pp. 610–12, 1958; *Sov. Phys. Dokl.*, Vol. 3, No. 4, pp. 736–9, 0000.

892. IORDANSKII, S. V. "Zemplem's Theorem in magnetohydrodynamics" *Dokl. Akad. Nauk. SSSR.*, Vol. 121, pp. 610–12, 1958.

893. IVANCHUCK, V. I. "The variability of the sun's magnetic field and the heating of the solar atmosphere" *Dokl. Akad. Nauk. SSSR*, Vol. 117, p. 589, 1957.

*****894.** JACOBS, J. A. and OBAYASHI, T. J. "A dynamo theory of magnetic storms" (Scientific Rept. 4 under USAF Contract AF19 (604) 761) Toronto U. Department of Physics, 19 pp. (5 figs., 526 refs.).

895. JAHN, R. C. "Interaction of electromagnetic waves with ionized gases". TN-59-911, AD 226 365, Aug. 1959, AFI 8 (603)-2 P. 9750 T. 37501.

*****896.** JANCEL, R. and KAHAN, T. "Analysis of the coupling of ordinary and extraordinary electromagnetic waves in a Lorentzian plasma and its applications to the ionosphere" *Physics of the Ionosphere* (Cambridge), Physical Society, London, pp. 374–83, 1955.

897. JANCEL, R. and KAHAN, T. "Propagation des ondes electromagnetique planes dans un plasma homogène (Ionosphere)" *J. Phys. Rad.*, Vol. 15, p. 26, 1954.

898. JANCEL, R. and KAHAN, T. "Conditions for discharge in an electromagnetic cavity and progressive waves in Lorentzian plasmas" *C. R. Acad. Sci., Paris*, Vol. 244, p. 2894, 1957.

899. JANCEL, R. and KAHAN, T. "Théorie magnéto-ionique des gaz faiblement ionisés en presence d'un champ électrique oscillant et d'un champ magnétique constant" *J. Phys. Rad.*, Vol. 10, p. 533, 1953.

900. JANCEL, R. and KAHAN, T. "Théorie non Maxwellienne des plasmas homogènes et anisotropes" *Nuovo Cimento*, Vol. 12, p. 573, 1954.

901. JANCEL, R. and KAHAN, T. "Sur une theorie généralisée d'un plasma Lorentzian soumis d'une force non-périodique et tenant compte des processes de collisions inelastiques" *C. R. Acad. Sci., Paris*, Vol. 244, p. 2583, 1957.

902. JANCEL, R. and KAHAN, T. "Statistical mechanics of Lorentzian electron plasmas and their application to the ionosphere" *Physics of the Ionosphere* (Cambridge) p. 365, 1955.

903. JANCEL, R. and KAHAN, T. "Approximation Maxwellienne de la théorie magnéto-ionique général des plasmas soumis à un champ électrique" *J. Phys. Rad.*, Vol. 15, p. 382, 1954.

904. JANCEL, R. and KAHAN, T. "Étude théorique de la distribution électronique dans un plasma Lorentzian hétérogène et anisotrope" *J. Phys. Rad.*, Vol. 20, pp. 35–42, 1959.

*905. JANCEL, R. and KAHAN, T. "Development of a general solution for Boltzmann's transport equation in the presence of an electric and magnetic field" *C. R. Acad. Sci., Paris*, Vol. 244, pp. 1333–6, 1957 (IRE n. 2420, Sept. 1957).

906. JANES, G. S. "Electrical characteristics of plasma accelerators employing electrodes". Paper presented at American Rocket Society Meeting, Washington, D.C., November 1959.

*907. JANES, G. S. "Production of high velocity shock waves and their interaction with magnetic fields" *Bull. Amer. Phys. Soc.*, Vol. 3, No. 1, p. 66, 1958.

908. JANES, G. S. "Scaling relations for plasma devices". AFOSR TN 60-367, Dec. 1959.

909. JANES, G. S. and KORITZ, H. "Numerical calculation of absolute Bremsstrahlung intensity for a fully ionized fully dissociated hydrogenic gas". Sept. 1959. AFOSR TN 59-1076; ASTIA AD 228 740; *J. Appl. Phys.*, Vol. 31, March 1960.

*910. JANES, G. S. and PATRICK, R. M. "The production of high temperature gas by magnetic acceleration". AVCO Research Laboratory, March 1958, R.R. 27 (AFOSR TN 58–439; ASTIA AD 158–244).

911. JENSEN, E. "Radial pulsations of a cylindrical magnetic tube of force in temperature equilibrium with a plasma" *Astrophys. Norwege*, Vol. 5, p. 209, 1957.

912. JEPHCOTT, D. F. and HARDCASTLE, R. A. "The velocity and damping of Alfvén waves in a gas discharge" *Ionization Phenomena in Gases*, Vol. 2, p. 786, Amsterdam, North-Holland, 1959.

913. JEPHCOTT, D. F. "Magnetohydrodynamic waves" *Contemporary Physics*, Vol. 1, No. 5, pp. 385–9, 1960.

914. JEPHETT, D. F. "Alfvén waves in a gas discharge" *Nature, Lond.*, Vol. 183, pp. 1652–3, 1959.

915. JIGOULEV, V. N. "Analyse de faibles discontinuités en magnéto-hydrodynamique" *Prikl. Mat. Mekh.*, Vol. 23, No. 1, pp. 81–5, 1959.

*916. JIGOULEV, V. N. "Contribution à l'étude d'un espèce de mouvements en magnétohydromécanique" *Prikl. Mat. Mekh.*, Vol. 22, pp. 389–90, 1958.

917. JIGOULEV, V. N. "Théorie de la couche limite magnétique" *Dokl. Akad. Nauk. SSSR*, Vol. 124, No. 5, pp. 1001–4 (2 figs.), 1959.

918. JIRLOV, K. "Experimental investigation of the inhibition of convection by a magnetic field" *Tellus*, Vol. 8, p. 252, 1956.

919. JOHANSSON, C. H. and SELBERG, H. L. "Transient high temperature gas layers in detonation" *Ionization Phenomena in Gases*, Vol. II, p. 1114. Amsterdam, North-Holland, 1959.

920. JOHN, R., SCHWEIGER, R., YOS, J. and MALIN, M. E. "Application of electric arc plasma generators to propulsion". Paper presented at the IX I.A.F. Meeting, Amsterdam, 25–30 Aug. 1958.

921. JOHNSON, E. O. and WALTER, W. M. "Studies of externally heated hot cathode arcs; Part III: Plasma density distributions in the anode slow mode" *RCA Review*, Vol. 16, p. 82, 1955.

922. JOHNSON, E. O. "Studies of externally heated hot cathode arcs; Part IV: The low-voltage form of the ball-of-fire mode" *RCA Review*, Vol. 16, p. 498, 1955.

923. JOHNSON, W. B. "Observations on the plasma produced in a magnetic mirror geometry" *Phys. Rev. Letters*, Vol. 1, p. 333, 1958.

924. JOHNSON, J. L. "Hydromagnetic stability of force-free toroidal fields" *Phys. Fluids*, Vol. 3, No. 4, pp. 658–9, 1960.

*925. JOHNSON, J. L., OBERMAN, C. R., KULSRUD, R. M. and FRIEMAN, E. A. "Some stable hydromagnetic equilibria" *Phys. Fluids*, Vol. 1, p. 281, 1958.

926. JORDAN, H. L. "Hydromagnetic shock waves; Part I: Theory" *Rend. Phys. School "E. Fermi"* corso XIII, pp. 82–90, Varenna, 1959.

927. JORDAN, H. L. "Hydromagnetic shock waves; Part II: Experiment" *Rend. Phys. School "E. Fermi"* corso XIII, pp. 90–7, Varenna, 1959.

928. JORDAN, H. L. "The Boltzmann equation" *Rend. Phys. School "E. Fermi"* corso XIII, pp. 76–82, Varenna, 1959.

929. JORDAN, H. L. "Fast circuit techniques and experiments with fast magnetic compression devices" *Rend. Phys. School "E. Fermi"* corso XIII, pp. 97–107, Varenna, 1959.

930. JORDANSKY, S. V. "Evaluation of Zemplen's theorem in magneto-hydrodynamics" *Dokl. Akad. Nauk. SSSR*, Vol. 121, No. 4, pp. 610–12, 1955.

931. JÖRGENS, K. "Axialsymmetriche Läsungen der magneto hydrodynamische Gleichungen mit Oberflachenstromen" *Z. Naturforsch.*, Vol. 13a, pp. 493–8, 1958.

932. JOSEPHSON, J. "Sur la structure des tourbillons électronvectifs" *C. R. Acad. Sci., Paris*, Vol. 249, No. 8, pp. 876–7, 1959.

933. JOSEPHSON, J. "Plasma containment in a toroidal configuration by a D.C.F.R. field combination". Paper presented at the Divisional Meeting of the Division of Fluid Dynamics, American Physical Society, San Diego, California, 24–26 Nov., 1958.

*934. JUKES, J. D. "The structure of a shock wave in a fully ionized gas" *J. Fluid Mech.*, Vol. 3, Pt. III, pp. 275–85, 1957.

935. JUKES, J. D. "A theory of the fast-pinched discharge". AERE GP/R 2293, 14 pp., 1958.

*936. JUNGCLAUS, G. "Laminar boundary layers in magnetohydrodynamics" *Dtsch. Versuchsanst. Luftf. Ber.*, Vol. 85, p. 25, 1959.

937. JUNGCLAUS, G. "Two-dimensional laminar boundary-layers and jets in magneto-fluid dynamics". Int. Symposium on M.F.D. Washington, Jan. 1960.

*938. JUNGCLAUS, G. "Laminare Grenzschichten in der Magnetohydrodynamik". Westdeutscher Verlag Koln und Opladen, March 1959.

939. KADOMTSEV, B. B. "On hydromagnetic stability of the toroidal low pressure plasma" *Ionization Phenomena in Gases*, Vol. 2, p. 609. Amsterdam, North-Holland, 1959.

940. KADOMTSEV, B. B. "On the hydrodynamic description of plasma oscillation" *Zh. Eksp. Teoret. Fiz.*, Vol. 31, 1956, pp. 1083–4; *Dokl. Akad. Nauk. SSSR*, Vol. 4, pp. 926–7, 1957.

941. KADOMTSEV, B. B., BRAGINSKY, S. I. "Stabilization of plasma by non uniform magnetic field" *Proc. 2nd Geneva Conf.*, Vol. 32, pp. 233–6, 1958.

942. KAEPPELER, H. J. "On the phenomenological equations of fully ionized plasmas derived from a statical description" *Ionization Phenomena in Gases*, Vol. 2, p. 577. Amsterdam, North-Holland, 1959.

943. KAEPPELER, H. J. and BAUMANN, G. "Irreversible stochastic thermodynamics and the transport phenomena in a reaction plasma". Mitteilungen aus dem Forschungsinstitut fur Physik der Strahlantriebe E.V.8. AFOSR TR 57–20, 1956.

*944. KAGAN, U. M. "Le mouvement des ions dans le plasma" *Izv. Akad. Nauk. SSSR*, Ser. Fizitcheskala, Vol. 22, No. 6, pp. 702–7, 1958.

*945. KAHALAS, S. L. "Magnetohydrodynamic wave propagation in the ionosphere" *Phys. Fluids*, Vol. 3, No. 3, pp. 372–9, 1960.

*946. KAHALAS, S. L. and KASHIAN, H. C. "On the approach of electrons to equilibrium" *Phys. Fluids*, Vol. 2, No. 2, pp. 100–2, 1959.

*947. KAHN, F. D. "Velocity changes of charged particles in a plasma" *Astrophys. J.*, Vol. 129, pp. 468–74, 1959.

*948. KAHN, F. D. "The collision of two ionized streams" *J. Fluid Mech.*, Vol. 2, Pt. 6, pp. 601–15, 1957.

949. KAI-HUA CHAO "Surface oscillations of a charged column in a longitudinal magnetic field" *J. Exp. Theor. Phys.*, No. 6, p. 1031, 1959.

*950. KAITMAZOV, S. D. and PROKHOROV, A. M. "Paramagnetic resonance of the free radicals obtained by freezing a plasma of H_2S" *J. Exp. Theor. Phys.*, No. 2, p. 381, 1959.

*951. KAKUTANI, T. "Effect of transverse magnetic field on the flow due to an oscillating flat plate" *J. Phys. Soc., Japan*, Vol. 13, No. 12, pp. 1504–9, 1958.

952. KAMKE, D. and ROSE, H. J. "Die Tragerdichte in Plasma und die Bestimmung mit der Impulse Probe" *Z. Phys.*, Vol. 145, p. 83, 1956.

*953. KANAWAL, R. P. "Flow behind shock waves in conducting gases" *Proc. Roy. Soc.*, A, Vol. 257, No. 1289, p. 263–8, 1960.

*954. KANEKO, S. "The maximum disturbance growth rate for an unstable plasma column" *J. Phys. Soc., Japan*, Vol. 13, pp. 947–53, 1958.

955. KANER, E. A. "Cyclotron resonance in plasma" *J. Exp. Theor. Phys.*, No. 2, Vol. 33, pp. 425–6, 1958.

956. KANTOR, M. "Plasma oscillations in the presence of a magnetic field". Space Res. Lab. GM-TR-0165-00526, 1958.

957. KANTROWITZ, A. R. "Shock waves passing through a magnetic field region" *Magneto-hydrodynamics*, Stanford U.P. (Landshoff, R.K.M., editor), 1957.

958. KANTROWITZ, A. R. "Introducing magneto-hydrodynamics" *Astronautics*, p. 10, Oct. 1958; pp. 18–20 and 74–7 (3 figs. 6 photos).

*959. KANTROWITZ, A. R. "Application of magneto-hydrodynamics to astronautics" Proc. 10th Int. Astronautical Congress, London, 31 Aug.–5 Sept. 1959.

*960. KANTROWITZ, A. R. "Flight magnetohydrodynamics". March 1959, AFBMD-TH 59-27. AFOSR-TN-59-882. ASTIA AD 230 023.

*961. KANTROWITZ, A. R. "Magnetic field alters aerodynamic forces" *Aero. Eng. Rev.*, Vol. 17, p. 63, 1958.

*962. KANTROWITZ, A. R. and JANES, G. S. "On magnetohydrodynamic propulsion" *J. Aero/Space Sci.*, Jan. 1960. ARS 14th Annual Meeting, Washington, 16–20 Nov. 1959, Preprint 1009–59, 17 pp. USAF.

*963. KANTROWITZ, A. R. and PETSCHEK, H. E. "An introductory discussion of magneto-hydrodynamics" *Magneto-hydrodynamics*. Stanford U.P.; Oxford U.P. (Landshoff, R.K.M., editor), 1957.

*964. KANTROWITZ, A. R., PATRICK, R. M. and PETSCHEK, H. E. "Collision free magnetohydrodynamic shock wave" *Ionization Phenomena in Gases*, Vol. 2, p. 1086, Amsterdam, North-Holland, 1959.

965. KANTROWITZ, A. R., RESLER, E. L. and LIN, S. C. "Electrical conductivity of highly ionized argon produced by shock waves" *J. Appl. Phys.*, Vol. 26, pp. 95–109, 1955.

966. KAPLAN, S. A. "A system of spectral equations for magneto-gas-dynamic isotropic turbulence" *Dokl. Akad. Nauk. SSSR*, Vol. 95, pp. 769–71, 1954.

967. KAPLAN, S. A. "On the theory of propagation and decay of hydromagnetic waves in an anisotropic medium". Int. Symposium on M.F.D. Washington, Jan. 1960.

968. KAPLAN, S. A. "On the 'Larmor' Plasma Theory" *J. Exp. Theor. Phys.*, p. 1370, 1959.

969. KAPLAN, S. A. "Spectral theory of gaseous magnetic isotropic turbulence" *Zh. Eksp. Teoret. Fiz.*, Vol. 27, pp. 699–707, 1954.

970. KAPLAN, S. A. "Theory of the acceleration of charged particles by isotropic gas magnetic turbulent fields" *Zh. Eksp. Teoret. Fiz.*, Vol. 29, p. 203–10, 1956.

*971. KAPLAN, S. A. "The effect of anisotropic conductivity in a magnetic field on the structure of a shock wave in magnetohydrodynamics" *Zh. Eksp. Teoret. Fiz.*, Vol. 38, No. 1, pp. 252–3, 1960 (in Russian).

972. KAPLAN. S. A. and KOLODII, B. I. "The functional equations of magneto-hydrodynamics". Dopov. Povidom., No. 7, p. 229–30, 1957.

973. KAPLAN, S. A. and STANYUKOVICH, K. P. "Solution of the equations of magneto-aerodynamics for unidimensional motion" *Dokl. Akad. Nauk. SSSR*, Vol. 95, pp. 769–71, 1954; AEC-TR-3101.

974. KAPLAN, S. A. and STANYUKOVICH, K. P. "The solution of inhomogeneous one-dimensional motion problems in magnetic gas dynamics" *Zh. Eksp. Teoret. Fiz.*, Vol. 30, pp. 382–5, 1956.

*975. KAPUR, J. N. "Superposability in magneto-hydrodynamics I" *Appl. Sci. Res.* A, No. 2–3, pp. 198–208, 1959 (12 refs.).

976. KAPUR, J. N. "Superposability in magnetohydrodynamics II" *Appl. Sci. Res.* A, Vol. 9, No. 2–3, pp. 139–47, 1960.

977. KAPUR, J. N. and JAIN, R. K. "Comments on Laminar steady-state magneto-hydrodynamic flow in an annular channel" *Phys. Fluids*, Vol. 3, No. 4, pp. 664–5, 1960.

*978. VON KÁRMÁN, T. "Applications of magnetofluidmechanics" *Astronautics*, October 1959.

979. VON KÁRMÁN, T. "Magneto-fluid-dynamics in relation to space flight problems". 9th Annual Congress of I.A.F., Amsterdam, Aug. 25–30, 1958.

*980. VON KÁRMÁN, T. "Some comments on applications of magnetofluid-mechanics". Preprint. Third Biennial Gas Dynamics Symposium, ARS, North-western, Univ., 24–26 Aug. 1959.

*981. VON KÁRMÁN, T. "Magnetofluidmechanics: A General Lecture" *Aircr. Engng.*, Vol. 30 (357), Nov. 1958.

982. KARR, H. J. *Experimental Studies of the Pinch-Effect* (The plasma in a magnetic field Symposium), 130 pp., Stanford U.P. Stanford, 1958.

*983. KASH, S. W. "Electrical propulsion systems". Lockheed Missiles and Space Division Report No. LMSD-2448, May 9, 1958, 12 pp. (illus.); also presented at Meeting of the American Astronautical Society on April 10, 1958.

*984. KASH, S. W. "The pinch tube as a device for plasma propulsion". Lockheed Missiles and Space Division Report No. LMSD-5056, 7 pp., July 10, 1958.

*985. KASH, S. W. "Magnetically driven shock waves" (Experiments at Lockheed Missile Systems Division). *Magneto-hydrodynamics*, Stanford U.P. 1957, pp. 92–8, Oxford U.P. (Landshoff, R.K.M. editor).

986. KASH, S. W. "Note of plasma acceleration by means of a rotating magnetic field". Lockheed Missiles and Space Division Report No. LMSD-5117, 2 pp., July 21 1958.

*987. KASH, S. W., GAUGER, J., STARR, W. and VALI, V. "Velocity measurements in magnetically driven shock tubes" *The Plasma in a Magnetic Field Symposium*, 130 pp. (fig.) Stanford U.P., Stanford 1958.

*988. KATO YUSUKE (or: YUSUKE KATO) "Interactions of Hydromagnetic waves" *Progr. Theor. Phys., Japan*, Vol. 21, No. 3, pp. 409–00, 1959.

*989. KATO, Y. and TANIUTI, T. "Hydromagnetic plane steady flow of incompressible ionized gases" *Progr. Theor. Phys., Japan*, No. 4, pp. 606–12 (2 figs.), April 1959.

990. KATZ, L. N. and KOLIN, A. "The flow of blood in the carotid artery of the dog under various circumstances as determined with the electromagnetic flowmeter" *Amer. J. Phys.*, Vol. 122, p. 788, 1938.

*991. KAUFMAN, A. N. "Effect of charge separation on plasma diffusion in a strong magnetic field" *Phys. Fluids*, Vol. 1, p. 252, 1958.

992. KAUFMAN, A. N. "Properties of ionized gas of low density in a magnetic field". CRL Rept. No. 4861.

*993. KAUFMAN, A. N. "Plasma viscosity in a magnetic field" *Phys. Fluids*, Vol. 3, No. 4, pp. 610–17, 1960.

994. KAUFMAN, S. and WILLIAMS, R. V. "The measurement of electron temperature in high temperature plasmas" *Ionization Phenomena in Gases*, Vol. I, p. 824. Amsterdam, North-Holland, 1959.

*995. KELLOGG, P. J. "Possible explanation of the radiation observed by van Allen at high altitudes in satellites". T.R. on Cosmic Ray Program, 27 pp. incl. tables, Sept. 1958, Minnesota Un. School of Physics.

*996. KELLOGG, P. J. and LIEMOHN, H. "Instability of contrastreaming plasmas" *Phys. Fluids*, Vol. 3, No. 1, pp. 40–4, 1960.

*997. KEMP, N. H. "On hypersonic blunt-body flow with a magnetic field". AVCO Research Laboratory, R.R. 19, February 1958. AFOSR TN 58-437; ASTIA AD (158–242); *J. Aero. Sci.*, Vol. 25, June 1958.

998. KEMP, N. H. "A further note on hypersonic stagnation point flow with a magnetic field". April 1959. AFOSR TN 59-445; ASTIA AD 214 807. PB 142–152.

*999. KEMP, N. H. "On hypersonic stagnation-point flow with a magnetic field" *J. Aero. Aci.*, Vol. 25, No. 6, pp. 405–407 (Readers' Forum) (5 ref.), 1958.

*1000. KEMP, N. H. and PETSCHEK, H. E. "Theory of the flow in the magnetic annular shock tube" *Phys. Fluids*, Vol. 2, pp. 599–600, 1959.

*1001. KEMP, N. H. and PETSCHEK, H. E. "Two-dimensional incompressible magnetohydrodynamic flow across an elliptical solenoid". AVCO Research Laboratory, Research Report 26, April 1958. AFOSR TN 58-438; ASTIA AD 158 243; *J. Fluid Mech.*, Vol. 4, Pt. 6, pp. 553–84, 1958.

*1002. KENDALL, P. C. "Hydromagnetic oscillations of a rotating liquid sphere" *Quart. J. Mech. Appl. Math.*, Vol. XIII, Pt. 3, pp. 285, 1960.

1003. KERR, D. E. "Charge removal in low-energy plasmas". ARDC, Conference on Ion and Plasma Research, University of Maryland, 30 Sept.–2 Oct. 1958.

*1004. KERREBROCK, J. L. "Similar solutions for boundary layers in constant temperature magneto-gasdynamic channel flow" Readers' Forum, *J. Aero/Space Sci.*, Vol. 27, No. 2, pp. 156–7, 1960.

*1005. KERREBROCK, J. L. "La diffusion dans les gaz neutres ou ionises à gradients de pression extrêmement élevés". Heat Transfer and Fluid Mechanics Institute Preprints of Papers, pp. 193–206, 4 figs., 1959.

1006. KERREBROCK, J. L. and MARBLE, F. E. "Constant-temperature magnetogasdynamic channel flow". Readers' Forum, *J. Aero/Space Sci.*, Vol. 27, No. 1, p. 78, 1960.

*1007. KHALATNIKOV, I. M. "On magneto-hydrodynamic waves and magneto tangential discontinuites in relativisitic hydrodynamics" *Zh. Eksp. Teoret. Fiz.*, pp. 1092–7, May 1957; *J. Exp. Theor. Phys.*, pp. 901–5, Dec. 1957.

*1008. KIEPENHEUER, K. O. "The observability of hydromagnetic phenomena in the sun" *Nuovo Cimento, Suppl.*, Vol. 13, No. 1, pp. 305–10, 1959.

*1009. KIHARA, T. "Macroscopic foundation of plasma dynamics" *J. Phys. Soc., Japan*, pp. 473–81, May, 1958.

1010. KIHARA, T. "Thermodynamic foundation of the theory of plasma" *J. Phys. Soc., Japan*, pp. 128–33 (14 refs.), Feb. 1959.

1011. KIHARA, T. "Mathematical theory of electrical discharges in gases" *Rev. Mod. Phys.*, Vol. 24, p. 45, 1952.

1012. KIHARA, T. and MIDZUNO, Y. "Ion-electron relaxation of plasmas in a magnetic field". Int. Symposium on M.F.D. Washington, Jan. 1960.

*1013. KILLEEN, J. GIBSON, G. and COLGATE, S. A. "Boundary-layer formation in the pinch" *Phys. Fluids*, Vol. 3, No. 3, pp. 387–95, 1960.

*1014. KIM, Y. B. and PLATNER, E. D. "Flux concentrator for high intensity pulsed magnetic fields". TR, April 1959, 24 pp., illus., Washington Un., Seattle.

1015. KIMURA, O. "Effect of electric fields on the viscosity of liquids, Part I" *Bull. Chem. Soc., Japan*, Vol. 12, p. 147, 1937.

1016. KIPPENHAHN, R., DE VRIES, H. L. "Zur Energieabgabe eines modulierten Ionenstrahls in Plasma mit Magnetfeld" *Z. Naturforsch.*, pp. 506–11, May/June 1960.

1017. KIRILLOV, V. D. "Energy losses from plasma by radiation" *Ionization Phenomena in Gases*, Vol. 2, p. 912. Amsterdam, North-Holland, 1959.

1018. KIRKO, I. M. "Similarity criteria of electrodynamic phenomena in the case of relative motion of the magnetic field of a conductive medium" *Vopr. Energ. Riga*, Vol. 3, pp. 97–109, 1955.

*1019. KIRKO, I. M. "Phenomènes magnétohydrodynamiques à l'echelle mondiale" *Elektritchestvo*, No. 4, pp. 9–16, April 1959.

1020. KIRZHNITS, D. A. "Correlation energy of an inhomogeneous electron gas" *J. Exp. Theor. Phys.*, No. 5, p. 838, May 1959.

1021. KISCHEL, K. "On the theory of electric waves in homogeneous plasmas" *Ann. Phys., Lpz.* (6), Vol. 19, p. 309, 1956.

*1022. KISCOVODSKY, A. D. "Contribution à la théorie des ondes superficielles en magnéto-hydrodynamique". *Messager de l'Université de Moscou* (Vestnik Moskovskoge Ouniversiteta) Série Mathématiques Mécanique, etc., No. 6, pp. 99–106, 1957.

*1023. KISELEV, M. I. "On the calculation of shock waves in magnetohydrodynamics" *Soviet Phys. Dokl.*, Vol. 4, No. 3, pp. 517–20, Dec. 1959 (Translation of *Dokl. Akad. Nauk, SSSR* (M.S.) Vol. 126, No. 3, pp. 524–7, 1959).

*1024. KISELEV, M. I. and TSEPLIAEV, V. I. "Oblique shock waves in a plasma with finite conductivity" *Zh. Eksp. Teoret. Fiz.*, pp. 1605–7, June 1958: *J. Exp. Theor. Phys.*, No. 6, pp. 1104–6, 1958.

1025. KISTENACHER, J. "Potential distribution in mercury arc discharges" *Appl. Sci. Res. B*, Vol. 5, p. 313, 1955.

1026. KIVEL, B. "On the loss of energy of charged particles in a strongly ionized medium" *J. Phys. Radium*, Vol. 12, p. 805, 1951.

1027. KLEIN, M. M. "Plasma propulsion by a rapidly varying magnetic field". Paper presented at the Divisional Meeting of the Division of Fluid Dynamics, American Physical Society, San Diego, California, 24–26 Nov. 1958.

1028. KLEIN, M. M. and BRUECKNER, K. A. "Plasma propulsion by a rapidly varying magnetic field, diamagnetic case". General Electric Co., MSVD Report Aerophysics Operation TM 104.

1029. KLEIN, M. M. and BRUECKNER, K. A. "Plasma propulsion by a rapidly varying magnetic field, non-diamagnetic case". General Electric Co., MSVD Report Aerophysics Operation, TM-107.

1030. KLEIN, M. M. and BRUECKNER, K. A. "Plasma propulsion by a rapidly varying magnetic field" *J. Appl. Phys.*, Vol. 31, No. 8, pp. 1437–48, 1960.

1031. KLIMONTOVICH, Y. L. "Some problems of the theory of the inhomogeneous non-isothermal plasma" *Zh. Eksp. Teoret. Fiz.*, Vol. 21, p. 1284, 1951.

*1032. KLIMONTOVICH, Y. L. "Charged particle energy losses due to excitation of plasma oscillations" *J. Exp. Theor. Phys.*, No. 5, p. 999, 1959.

*1033. KLIMONTOVICH, Y. L. "Relativistic transport equations for a plasma" *Zh. Eksp. Teoret. Fiz.*, Vol. 37, No. 3(9), pp. 735–44, 1959.

1034. KLIMONTOVICH, Y. L. "On a possible statistical description of systems of particles interacting with the field" *J. Exp. Theor. Phys.*, No. 5, May 1959.

*1035. KLIMONTOVICH, Y. L. "Space-time correlation functions for a system of particles with electromagnetic interaction" *J. Exp. Theor. Phys.*, No. 1, Vol. 34, pp. 119–27, July 1958.

*1036. KLINE, M. "Magneto-hydrodynamics". AFCRC-TR-56-461 AD 110241 (NATO) New York Univ. Div. Electromagnetic Res., U.S.A., 1956.

1037. KNOX, K. F. B. "A method of heating matter of low density to temperatures in the range 10^5–10^6" *Aust. J. Phys.*, Vol. 10, pp. 221–5, 1957.

1038. KOCH, O., LESEMANN, K. J. and WALTHER, A. "The radial temperature variations in wall-stabilized high pressure mercury arcs" *Z. Phys.*, Vol. 127, p. 153, 1950.

1039. KOERPER, K. "Oscillations of a plasma cylinder in an electrical magnetic field" *Z. Naturforsch.*, Vol. 12A, p. 815, 1957.

*1040. KOGAN, M. N. "Les ondes de choc en magnétohydrodynamique" *Prikl. Mat. Mekh.*, Vol. 23, No. 3, pp. 557–63, (5 figs.), 1959.

*1041. KOGAN, M. N. "Ondes de choc dans la gazdynamique magnétique". C.N.R.S. Jan. 60; *Prikl. Mat. Mekh. SSSR*, Vol. 23, No. 3, pp. 557–63 (784–92), 1959 (in Russian).

*1042. KOGAN, M. N. "Magnétodynamique des écoulements plans et à symétrie axiale à conductivité électrique infinie" *Prikl. Mat. Mekh.*, Vol. 23, No. 1, pp. 70–80 (9 figs.), 1959.

1043. KOGELNIK, H. "The radiation resistance of an elementary dipole in anisotropic plasmas" *Ionization Phenomena in Gases*, Vol. 2, p. 721. Amsterdam, North-Holland, 1959.

1044. KOJIMA, S., KATO, K. and HAGIWARA, S. "Oscillation in Plasma I" *J. Phys. Soc.*, Japan, Vol. 12, p. 1276, 1957.

1045. KOJIMA, S., TAKAYAMA, K. and SHIMAUCHI, A. "Noise of gas discharge plasma" *J. Phys. Soc., Japan*, Vol. 9, p. 802, 1954.

1046. KOLB, A. C. "Magnetic compression of plasmas". Int. Symposium on M.F.D. Washington, Jan. 1960.

*1047. KOLB, A. C. "Magnetically confined plasmas" *Phys. Rev.*, Vol. 112, pp. 291–5, 1958.

1048. KOLB, A. C. "Magnetically driven shock waves" (Experiments at U.S. Naval Research Laboratory) *Magneto-hydrodynamics Symposium*. Stanford U.P.: (Landshoff, R.K.M., editor), 1957.

*1049. KOLB, A. C. "Production of high-energy plasmas by magnetically driven shock waves" *Phys. Rev.*, Vol. 107, pp. 345–50, 1957.

1050. KOLB, A. C. "Propagation of strong shock waves in pulsed longitudinal magnetic fields" *Phys. Rev.*, Vol. 107, pp. 1197–8, 1957.

1051. KOLB, A. C. "Recent progress in shock wave research" *Ionization Phenomena in Gases*, Vol. 2, p. 1021. Amsterdam, North-Holland, 1959.

*1052. KOLB, A. C. "High temperature plasmas". Prog. Rep. Naval Res. Lab., pp. 1–6, June 1957.

1053. KOLB, A. C., GRIEM, H. R. and FAUST, W. R. "Dense plasmas confined by external fields" *Ionization Phenomena in Gases*, Vol. 2, p. 1037. Amsterdam, North-Holland, 1959.

1054. KOLIN, A. "Mercury Jet Magnetometer" *Rev. Sci. Instrum.*, Vol. 16, p. 209, 1945.

1055. KOLIN, A. "An AC induction flow meter for measurements of blood flow in intact blood vessels" *Proc. Soc. Exp. Biol. Med.*, Vol. 46, p. 235, 1941.

1056. KOLIN, A. "An electromagnetic flowmeter: Principle of the method and its application to blood flow measurements" *Proc. Soc. Exp. Biol. Med.*, Vol. 35, p. 53, 1936.

1057. KOLIN, A. "An alternating field induction flowmeter of high sensitivity" *Rev. Sci. Instrum.*, Vol. 16, pp. 109–16, 1945.

*1058. KOLLER, A. "The confinement of plasma by a magnetic field" *Raketentech. u. Raumfahrtforsch*, Vol. 3(4), pp. 109–15, Oct.–Dec. 1959, Germany Index Aeronauticus, Jan. 1960.

*1059. KOLOMENSKII, A. A. "Radiation emitted by an electron uniformly moving in electron plasma situated in a magnetic field" *Dokl. Akad. Nauk. SSSR*, Vol. 106, pp. 982–5, 1955.

*1060. KOLOMENSKII, A. A. and FONG SOY-CEN "Cyclic motion of charged particles in an electric field" *J. Exp. Theor. Phys.*, No. 1, p. 184, 1959.

1061. KOLOMENSKII, A. A. and LEBEDEV, A. L. "Effect of radiation on the motion of a relativistic electron in a magnetic field" *Soviet Doklady*, Vol. 1, pp. 100–4, 1956.

1062. KOMEL'KOV, V. S., SKVORTSOV, Y. V., TSEREVITINOV, S. S. and VASILIEV, V. I. "A dynamically stable current filament" *Ionization Phenomena in Gases*, Vol. 2, p. 1141. Amsterdam, North-Holland, 1959.

*1063. KOMEL'KOV, V. S. "Self constricting discharges in deuterium at high rates of current growth" *J. Exp. Theor. Phys.*, No. 1, 1959.

1064. KOMEL'KOV, V. S. and ARETOV, G. N. "The production of high-current pulses" *Dokl. Akad. Nauk. SSSR*, Vol. 110, pp. 559–61, 1956.

*1065. KONTOROVICH, V. M. "On the interaction between small disturbances and discontinuities in magneto-hydrodynamics and on the stability of shock waves" *Zh. Exp. Teoret. Fiz.*, pp. 1216–25, Nov. 1958; *J. Exp. Theor. Phys.*, pp. 851–8 (20 refs.), May 1959.

*1066. KONTOROVICH, V. M. "Stability of shock waves in relativistic hydrodynamics" *Zh. Eksp. Teoret. Fiz.*, Vol. 34, pp. 186–94, Jan. 1958; *J. Exp. Theor. Phys.*, Vol. 34(7), No. 1, pp. 127–32, July 1958.

*1067. KONYUKOV, M. V. "Non linear Langmuir electron oscillations in a plasma" *Zh. Eksp. Teoret. Fiz.*, Vol. 37, No. 3(9), pp. 799–801, 1959; *J. Exp. Theor. Phys.*, Vol. 37, No. 3, pp. 570–1, 1960.

*1068. KONYUKOV, M. V. "On the theory of a positive column in a longitudinal magnetic field" *J. Exp. Theor. Phys.*, No. 2, Vol. 33, pp. 316–18, 1958.

1069. KONYUKOV, M. V. "Concentrations of negative ions in the plasma of a positive column" *Zh. Eksp. Teoret. Fiz.*, Vol. 34, p. 908, 1958.

1070. KONYUKOV, M. V. and TERLETSKII, I. D. "Relativistic motion of an electron in an axially symmetric field which moves along the axis of symmetry" *J. Exp. Theor. Phys.*, Vol. 34, No. 4, p. 692, 1958.

1071. KONYUKOV, M. V. and TERLETSKII, I. D. "Electroacoustic waves in a gas discharge plasma with consideration of volume recombination" *Zh. Eksp. Teoret. Fiz.*, Vol. 29, p. 874, 1955.

1072. KONYUKOV, M. V., TERLESKII, I. D. "Electro-acoustic waves in the plasma of a gas discharge" *J. Exp. Theor. Phys.*, Vol. 27, pp. 451–8, 1954.

1073. KORNEFF, T., BOHN, J. and NADIG, F. "Plasma production by exploding wires". ARDC, Conference on Ion and Plasma Research, University of Maryland, 30 Sept.–2 Oct. 1958.

1074. KOROBEINIKOV, V. P. "Study of plane non-stationary adiabatic motion of a perfectly conducting gas with plane and cylindrical waves in the presence of a magnetic field" *Dokl. Akad. Nauk.*, SSSR, pp. 613–561, Aug. 1958 (in Russian).

1075. KOROBEINIKOV, V. P. "Similarity-type one-dimensional motions of a conducting gas in a magnetic field" *Soviet Phys. Dokl.*, Vol. 121(3), pp. 739–42, 1958.

*1076. KOROBEINIKOV, V. P. and RIAZANOV, E. V. "Solution des equations de la magnétohydrodynamique pour a gradient de température égal à zéro" *Dokl. Akad. Nauk., SSSR*, Vol. 124, No. 1, pp. 51–2, 1959.

1077. KOROBEINIKOV, V. P. and RIAZANOV, E. V. "Some solutions of the equations of one-dimensional magnetohydrodynamics and their application to problems of shock wave propagation" *Prikl. Mat. Mekh.*, Vol. 24, No. 1, 1960.

1078. KORPER, K. "Schwingung eines Plasmazylinders in cinem äusseren Magnetfeld" *Z. Naturforsch.*, Vol. 12a pp. 815–21, 1956–7.

*1079. KOTCHINA, N. N. "Solutions exactes des equations de mouvement en magnétohydrodynamique, à la limite des mouvements analogiques" *Dokl. Akad. Nauk., SSSR*, Vol. 126, No. 3, pp. 528–31 (2 figs.), 1959.

*1080. KOTCHINA, N. N. "Shape-preserving, exact solution of the equations of megnetohydrodynamics" *Soviet Phys. Dokl.*, Vol. 4, No. 3, pp. 521–5, 1959.

1081. KOULIKOVSKI, A. G. "Les ondes de Riemann en magnétohydrodynamique" *Dokl. Akad. Nauk., SSSR*, Vol. 121, No. 6, pp. 987–90 (2 figs.), 1959.

1082. KOULIKOVSKI, A. G. "Flow of conducting liquid past magnetized bodies" *Dokl. Akad. Nauk., SSSR*, Vol. 117, pp. 199–202, 1957.

*1083. KOULIKOVSKI, A. G. "Mouvements à déformation homogène en magnétohydrodynamique" *Dokl. Akad. Nauk., SSSR*, Vol. 120, No. 5, pp. 984–6, 1958.

*1084. KOULIKOVSKI, A. G. and LUBIMOV, G. A. "Les problèmes les plus simples comportant une onde de choc ionisant un gaz dans un champ électromagnétique" *Dokl. Akad. Nauk., SSSR*, Vol. 129, No. 3, pp. 525–8, 2 figs., 1959.

*1085. KOULIKOVSKI, A. G. and LUBIMOV, G. A. "Remarques concernant la structure d'une onde de choc magnétohydrodynamique orthogonale" *Prikl. Mat. Mekh.*, Vol. XXIII, No. 6, pp. 1146–7, 1959.

1086. KOULIKOVSKI, A. G. and YAVORSKAYA, I. M. "The oscillations of an infinite gas cylinder with its own gravitation in magnetic field" *Dokl. Akad. Nauk., SSSR*, Vol. 114, p. 998, 1957.

1087. KOVASZNAY, L. S. G. "Plasma turbulence". Int. Symposium on M.F.D. Washington, Jan. 1960.

1088. KOVNER, M. S. and GERECHMAN, B. N. "Particularités de la propagation quasi transversale des ondes magnéto-hydrodynamiques dans le plasma". Bull. Ec. Sup. Section Radiophisique (Izv. Vys. Ouich. Zav.), No. 3, pp. 19–24 (1 fig.), 1958.

*1089. KOVRIZHNYKH, L. M. "Effect of inelastic collisions on the velocity distribution of electrons" *Zh. Eksp. Teoret. Fiz.*, Vol. 37, No. 2(8), pp. 490–500, 1959; *J. Exp. Theor. Phys.*, Vol. 37(10), No. 2, pp. 347–53, 1960.

*1090. KOVRIZHNYKH, L. M. "Velocity distribution of electrons in a strong electric field" *Ionization Phenomena in Gases*, Vol. 2, p. 627. Amsterdam, North-Holland, 1959; *Zh. Eksp. Teoret. Fiz.*, Vol. 37, No. 5(11), pp. 1394–400, 1959.

*1091. KOVRIZHNYKH, L. M. "Motion of a plasma loop in an axially symmetric magnetic field" *J. Exp. Theor. Phys.*, No. 6, p. 1038, Dec. 1959.

*1092. KOVRIZHNYKH, L. M. "Oscillations of a completely ionized plasma in a cylindrical cavity" *J. Exp. Theor. Phys.*, No. 3, p. 592, Sept. 1959.

*1093. KOVRIZHNYKH, L. M. "On the dynamics of a bounded plasma in an external field" *J. Exp. Theor. Phys.*, Vol. 33, No. 1, pp. 54–8, 1958.

1094. KRACIK, J. "The complex conductivity of the plasma of a D.C. sustained arc discharge" *Czech. J. Phys.*, Vol. 6, p. 376, 1956.

1095. KRAEMER, R. S. and LARSON, V. R. "Comparison of several propulsion systems for a Mars mission". ASME Aviation Conf. Los Angeles, Calif., March 1959, Pap. 59-AV-40, 56 pp.

1096. KRAICHNAN, R. N. "Irreversible statistical mechanics of incompressible hydromagnetic turbulence" *Phys. Rev.*, Vol. 109, pp. 1407–22, 1958; *ibid.*, Vol. 111, p. 1747, 1958.

1097. KRAICHNAN, R. N. "Statistical mechanics of many-body system". ARDC Conference on Ion and Plasma Research, University of Maryland, 30 Sept.–2 Oct. 1958.

*1098. KRAICHNAN, R. N. "Relation of fourth to second moments in stationary homogeneous hydromagnetic turbulence". Res. Rep. MH-6, AD 110217 (NATO). New York Univ., Inst. of Math. Sci. Electromagnetic Div., U.S.A., Jan. 1957.

1099. KRAPIVINA, I. V. "Extension of plasma beyond the limits of the discharge space". Moscow, Vseoinz. Elehtrotekh. Inst. Trudy, No. 63, pp. 38–47, 1958.

1100. KRAUS, L. "Electrohydrodynamic properties of satellites". Paper presented at the Divisional Meeting of the Division of Fluid Dynamics, American Physical Society, San Diego, Calif., 24–26 Nov. 1958.

*1101. KRAUS, L. and YOSHIHARA, H. "Electro-gasdynamic motion of a charged body in a plasma" *J. Aero/Space Sci.*, Vol. 27, No. 3, p. 229, 1960.

*1102. KRAUS, L. and WATSON, K. M. "Plasma motions induced by satellites in the ionosphere. Appendix: Damping when the density is high" *Phys. Fluids*, Vol. 1, p. 480, 1958.

1103. KRAVTCHENKO, V. Y. and DAMBOURG, R. Y. "Excitation des ondes hydromagnétiques dans le plasma par une charge en mouvement" *Latv. Pr.S. Zinat. Akad. Vestis*, No. 6, pp. 87–92 (1 fig.), 1959.

1104. KRIMCHIK, G. S. and CHEKTIN, M. V. "The problem of determining the dielectric permittivity and magnetic permeability tensors of a medium" *J. Exp. Theor. Phys.*, No. 6, p. 1368, Dec. 1959.

1105. KRISTOV, K. I. "On the diffusion of charged particles in a uniform electromagnetic field" *Trans. Dokl.*, Vol. 2, pp. 437–9, 1957.

1106. KRONIG, R. "A collective description of electron interaction" *Phys. Rev.*, Vol. 86, p. 795, 1952.

*1107. KROOK, M. "Structure of shock fronts in ionized gases" *Ann Phys.*, Vol. 6, No. 2, pp. 188–207, 1959.

*1108. KRUMIGUE, U. "Rotation d'une sphère conductrice dans un fluide visqueux conducteur en présence d'un champ magnétique" *Izv. Akad. Nauk. Lat. SSR*, No. 2 (127), pp. 97–102, 1958.

1109. KRUSKAL, M. D. "The spiraling of a charged particle" *Proc. Venice Conf. 1957*, pp. 562–8.

*1110. KRUSKAL, M. D. and KULSRUD, R. M. "Equilibrium of a magnetically confined plasma in a toroid" *Phys. Fluids*, Vol. 1, p. 265, 1958.

1111. KRUSKAL, M. D. and OBERMAN, C. R. "On the stability of a plasma in static equilibrium" *Phys. Fluids*, Vol. 1, p. 275, 1958.

1112. KRUSKAL, M. D. and SCHWARZSCHILD, M. "Some instabilities of a completely ionized plasma" *Proc. Roy. Soc.* A, Vol. 223, p. 348, 1954.

*1113. KRUSKAL, M. D. and TUCK, J. L. "The instability of a pinched fluid with a longitudinal magnetic field" *Proc. Roy. Soc.* A, pp. 222–37, 1958.

*1114. KRUSKAL, M. D., JOHNSON, J. L. GOTTLIEB, M. B. and GOLDMAN, L. M. "Hydromagnetic instability in a stellarator" *Phys. Fluids*, Vol. 1, No. 5, pp. 421–9, 1958.

1115. KRUSKAL, M. D. "Validity of MHD plasma models". Paper JA3, Symp. High Temp. Plasma, Amer. Phys. Soc., Annual Meeting, New York, 1958.

*1116. KRUSKAL, M. D. and OBERMAN, C. R. "On the stability of plasma in static equilibrium". Paper No. EI, Meeting of American Physical Society (Division of Fluid Dynamics), San Diego, Calif., 24–26 Nov. 1958.

1117. KRZYWOBLOCKI, M. Z. E. "On the equations of isotropic turbulence in magnetohydrodynamics of a compressible medium" *Acta Phys. Austr.*, Vol. 6, p. 157, 1952.

1118. KRZYWOBLOCKI, M. Z. E. "On the fundamentals of locally isotropic turbulence in magnetohydrodynamics of a compressible medium" *Acta Phys. Austr.*, Vol. 6, p. 250, 1953.

1119. KRZYWOBLOCKI, M. Z. and MARTIN, J. T. "Canonical forms, Beltrami flows, and certain exact solutions in magneto-gas-dynamics" *Proc. Sixth Midwest. Conf. Fluid Mech., Austin, Tex., Sept. 1959*, Austin, Tex. Univ. Press, pp. 427–45, 1959.

*1120. KRZYWOBLOCKI, M. Z. and NUTANT, J. "On the similarity rule in magneto-gas-dynamics" *Acta. Phys. Austr.* Vol. 13, No. 1, pp. 1–18, 1960.

1121. KUARTZHAVA, I. P., KERVALIDZE, K. N. and GVALADZE, J. S. "Some magnetohydrodynamic effects by the impulse plasma confinement, I" *Ionization Phenomena in Gases*, Vol. 2, p. 876. Amsterdam, North-Holland, 1959.

1122. KUDOMTZIE, B. B. "Hydromagnetic description of plasma oscillations" *Zh. Eksp. Teoret. Fiz. SSSR*, Vol. 31, p. 1083, 1956.

*1123. KUDRIAVTSEV, V. S. "Energy diffusion of fast ions in an equilibrium plasma" *J. Exp. Theor. Phys.*, pp. 1075–9, Dec. 1958.

1124. KUIPER, G. (Editor) *The Sun.* Chapter 8. Chicago U.P., 1954.

*1125. KULIKOVSKII, A. G. "On the flow of a conducting fluid along magnetized bodies" *Dokl. Akad. Nauk., SSSR*, Vol. 117, p. 199, 1957.

*1126. KULIKOVSKII, A. G. "Study concerning Riemann wave in magnetohydrodynamics". *Soviet Doklady*, Vol. 3, pp. 743–6, 1959.

1127. KULIKOVSKII, A. G. "The problem of the pulsation of a plasma thread" *Dokl. Akad. Nauk., SSSR*, Vol. 5, pp. 984–7, 1957.

*1128. KULIKOVSKII, A. G. and LYUBIMOV, G. A. "The simplest problems involving shock wave which ionize gases in an electromagnetic field" *Dokl. Akad. Nauk., SSSR*, Vol. 129, No. 3, pp. 525–8, 1959.

*1129. KULSRUD, R. M. "Effect of magnetic fields on generation of noise by isotropic turbulence" *Astrophys, J.*, pp. 461–80, 1955.

*1130. KULSRUD, R. M. "General behavior of hydromagnetic fluids". ARS Preprint, 705–58 (11/58), 11 pp., (8 figs.).

1131. KULSRUD, M. D. and SCHWARZSCHILD, M. "Some instabilities of a completely ionised plasma" *Proc. Roy. Soc.* A, Vol. 233, p. 348, 1954.

*1132. KUNEN, A. E. and McILROY, W. "The electromagnetic pinch effect applied to a space propulsion system". Preprint Third Biennial Gas Dynamics Symposium, ARS, Northwestern Univ., Aug. 24–26, 1959.

*1133. KUNKEL, W. B. "Some considerations concerning magnetohydrodynamic exhaust control for rocket guidance". Space Tech. Labs., Inc. Los Angeles Rept. n. TR 59-0000-00608, 1959.

1134. KWO, Y. H. "Dissociation effects in hypersonic viscous flow" *J. Aero/Space Sci.*, Vol. 24, No. 5, pp. 345–50, 1957.

1135. KUPER, C. G. "On the Bohm–Pines theory of a quantum mechanical electron plasma" *Proc. Phys. Soc.*, Vol. 69A, p. 492, 1956.

1136. KURCHATOV, I. V. "On the possibility of producing thermonuclear reactions in a gas discharge" *J. Nucl. Energy*, Vol. 4, 1957, p. 193–202.

1137. KURCHATOV, I. V. "Research on controlled thermonuclear reactions at the Atomic Energy Institute of the URSS Acad. of Sci." *J. Nucl. Eng.*, Vol. 8, pp. 168–75, 1958.

1138. LACOMBE, E. *et al.* "Evolution énergétique d'un plasma thermonucléaire de deuterium" *C. R. Acad. Sci., Paris*, Vol. 246, pp. 744–6, 1958.

*1139. LADYJENSKAIA, O. A. and SOLONNIKOV, V. A. "Étude de la possibilité de résolution des problèmes instationnaires de la magnétohydrodynamique" *Dokl. Akad. Nauk. SSRR*, Vol. 124, No. 1, pp. 25–8, 1959.

*1140. LADYZHENSKII, M. D. "Problémes de l'écoulement autour de corps en magnétohydrodynamique" *Prikl. Mat. Mekh.*, Vol. 23, No. 2, pp. 292–8, 1959.

1141. LADYZHENSKII, M. D. "Flow problems in magnetohydrodynamics" *Prikl. Mat. Mech.*, Vol. 23, No. 2, pp. 419–27, 1959.

*1142. LAI, W., SLOAN, D. H. and TALBOT, L. "Preliminary design and tests of a plasma jet". T.R. No. HE-150-153, 15 Nov. 1957. Inst. of Engineering Res., Un. of California, Berkeley.

1143. LAMB, L. and LIN, S. C. "Electrical conductivity of thermally ionized air produced in a shock tube" *J. Appl. Phys.*, Vol. 28, pp. 754–9, 1957.

1144. LAMPERT, M. A. "Plasma oscillations and extremely high temperatures" *J. Appl. Phys.*, Vol. 27, 1956.

1145. LAMPERT, M. A. "Incidence of an electromagnetic wave on a Cerenkov electron gas" *Phys. Rev.*, Vol. 102, pp. 299–304, 1956.

1146. LANDAU, L. "On the vibrations of the electronic plasma" *Zh. Tekh. Fiz., SSSR*, Vol. 10, p. 25, 1946.

1147. LANDAU, L. "Oscillations of an electron plasma" *J. Exp. Theor. Phys.*, Vol. 7, pp. 574–86, 1866.

1148. LANDAU, L. "Kinetic equation for the Coulomb effect" *Z. Phys. Zeib. d. Sowjetumum*, Vol. 10, p. 154, 1936.

1149. LANDQUIST, K. C. "Plasma oscillations in electron beams" *J. Appl. Phys.*, Vol. 26, p. 1029, 1955.

*1150. LANDSHOFF, R. K. M. "Scaling laws as aid to experimental studies of magnetically driven shock waves". *Magnetohydrodynamics,,* Stanford U.P., (Landshoff, R.K.M., editor), 1957.

*1151. LANDSHOFF, R. K. M. *Magneto-hydrodynamics.* Stanford U.P., 1957, Proceedings of a symposium.

*1152. LANDSHOFF, R. K. M. "The plasma in a magnetic field". Stanford Univ. Press. 1958. Stanford.

1153. LANDSHOFF, R. K. M. "Transport phenomena in a completely ionized gas in presence of a magnetic field" *Phys. Rev.*, Vol. 76, p. 904, 1949.

1154. LANDSHOFF, R. K. M. "Magneto-hydrodynamics". Heat Transfer and Fluid Mech. Inst. Preprints of Papers, pp. 253–64, 1958.

*1155. LANDSHOFF, R. K. M. "A review of magneto-hydrodynamics". Lockheed Missiles and Space Division Report No. LMSD-49702, 33 pp. (biblio.), April 15, 1959.

1156. LANGMUIR, I. "Oscillations in ionized gases" *Proc. Nat. Acad. Sci.*, Vol. 14, p. 627, 1928.

1157. LANGMUIR, I. "The interaction of electron and positive ion space charges in cathode sheaths" *Phys. Rev.*, Vol. 33, p. 954, 1929.

1158. LANGMUIR, I. "Scattering of electrons in ionized gases" *Phys. Rev.*, Vol. 26, p. 585, 1925.

*1159. LARENZ, R. W. "On the magneto-hydrodynamics of compressible media" *Z. Naturforsch.*, Vol. 10A, pp. 761–5, 1955.

*1160. LARENZ, R. W. "Plasma flows of large amplitude and charge separation" *Z. Naturforsch.*, Vol. 10A, pp. 766–76, 1955.

1161. LARISH, E. "Possibilité de conception d'un réacteur thermonucléair non-stationnaire" *Atom. Energia*, Vol. 5, pp. 646–7, 1958.

*1162. LARISH, E. and SHEKHTMAN, I. "Propagation of detonation waves in the presence of a magnetic field" *J. Exp. Theor. Phys.*, No. 1, p. 139, 1959.

1163. LARISH, E. and SHEKHTMAN, I. "Production of two temperatures in an ionized gas in a magnetic field" *J. Exp. Theor. Phys.*, No. 2, p. 355, 1959.

1164. LARMOR, J. "Magnetic field of sunspots" *Mon. Not. Roy. Astr. Soc.*, Vol. 94, p. 469, 1934.

1165. VON LAVE, M. "Der Einfluss eines Magnetfeldes auf Warmleitung und Reibung in paramagnetischen Gasen" *Ann. Phys.*, Vol. 23, p. 1, 1935.

1166. VON LAVE, M. "Der Einfluss eines Magnetfeldes auf Warmleitung und Reibung in paramagnetischen Gasen II" *Ann. Phys.*, Vol. 26, p. 474, 1936.

1167. LAWSON, J. D. "Some criteria for power producing thermonuclear reactors" *Proc. Phys. Soc.*, B, Vol. 70, pp. 5–10, 1957.

1168. LAZLER, D., BROOK, M. and MENZEL, D. H. "Torsional oscillations and solar magnetic fields" *Proc. Roy. Soc.* A, Vol. 233, pp. 302–10, 1955.

*1169. LAZUKIN, V. A. "Oscillations of a plasma in a magnetic field at frequencies close to the cyclotron frequency" *J. Exp. Theor. Phys.*, No. 4, p. 685, 1959.

*1170. LAZUKIN, V. A. "Some features of multiplet ferromagnetic resonance in ferrites" *J. Exp. Theor. Phys.*, Vol. 36, No. 3, pp. 477–82, 1959.

*1171. LEADON, B. M. "Plane Couette flow of a conducting gas through a transverse magnetic field". Conv. Sci. Res. Lab., Res. Note 13, Dec. 1957.

1172. LEDOUX, P. and SIMON, R. "On the oscillation of a gaseous star possessing a weak magnetic field" *Ann. Astrophys.*, Vol. 20, p. 185, 1957.

1173. LEDRUS, R. A. "An apparatus for studying electron plasma" *Appl. Sci. Res.* B, Vol. 5, p. 151, 1955.

1174. LEDRUS, R. A., HOYAUX, M., VAN AVERMALTE, A. and GAUS, P. "Synchronized plasmograph" *Rev. Gen. Elect.*, Vol. 66, p. 513, 1957.

1175. LEDRUS, R. A., HOYAUX, M. and VAN AVERMALTE, A. "The plasmograph: A novel device for the investigation of periodically variable electrical discharges" *Rev. Gen. Elect.*, Vol. 64, p. 391, 1955.

1176. LEENOV, D. and KOLIN, A. "Theory of electromagnetophoresis; I: Magneto-hydrodynamic forces experienced by spherical and symmetrically oriented cylindrical particles". Chicago U., (Final Rept. AD-81 120), 6 pp., 20 July 1953.

*1177. LEEUW DE, J. H. "The interaction of a plane strong shock wave with a steady magnetic field (Interaction d'une forte onde de choc plane et d'un champ magnetique uniform)." University of Toronto, Institute of Aerophysics. Report No. 49, March 1958, 47 pp. (29 figs. and photos, 3 tables).

1178. LEHNERT, B. "Confinement of charged particles by a magnetic field" *Nature, Lond.*, Vol. 181, pp. 331–2, 1958.

1179. LEHNERT, B. *Electromagnetic Phenomena in Cosmical Physics*. Cambridge Univ. Press, 1958.

1180. LEHNERT, B. "MHD waves in the ionosphere and their application to grant pulsations" *Tellus*, Vol. 8, pp. 241–51, 1956.

*1181. LEHNERT, B. "Magneto-hydrodynamic waves in liquid sodium" *Phys. Rev.*, Vol. 94, pp. 815–24, 1954.

*1182. LEHNERT, B. "Magneto-hydrodynamic waves under the action of Coriolis force" *Astrophys. J.*, Vol. 119, pp. 647–753, 1954; *ibid.*, Vol. 121, pp. 481–9, 1955.

*1183. LEHNERT, B. "The decay of magneto-turbulence in the presence of a magnetic field and Coriolis force" *Quart. Appl. Math.*, Vol. 12, pp. 321–41, 1955.

1184. LEHNERT, B. "An experiment on axisymmetric flow of liquid sodium in a magnetic field" *Ark. Fys.*, Vol. 13, pp. 109–16, 1958.

1185. LEHNERT, B. "Experiments on non-laminar flow of mercury in the presence of a magnetic field" *Tellus*, Vol. 4, pp. 63–7, 1952.

1186. LEHNERT, B. "An instability of laminar flow of mercury caused by an external magnetic field" *Proc. Roy. Soc.* A, Vol. 233, pp. 299–302, 1955.

1187. LEHNERT, B. *Magneto-hydrodynamics on Cosmical and Laboratory Scale*. Uppsala, Almquist and Wiksells, 1955.

1188. LEHNERT, B. "Plasma physics on cosmical and laboratory scale" *Nuovo Cimento*, Suppl., Vol. XIII, Ser. X, No. 1, pp. 59–111, 1959.

1189. LEHNERT, B. "On the behaviour of an electrically conductive liquid in a magnetic field" *Ark. Fys.*, Vol. 5, pp. 69–90, 1952.

1190. LEHNERT, B. "Magnetohydrodynamics on cosmical and laboratory scale" *K. Tekh. Hogskd. Handl.*, No. 100, 1955.

1191. LEHNERT, B. and LITTLE, N. C. "Experiments on the effect of inhomogeneity and obliquity of a magnetic field in inhibiting convection" *Tellus*, Vol. 9, pp. 97–103, 1957.

1192. LEIGH, D. C. and SUTTON, G. W. "An analogy between magnetohydrodynamics and heat transfer" *J. Aero/Space Sc.*, Vol. 27, No. 6, p. 469, 1960.

1193. LEIPMANN, H. W. "Hydromagnetic effects in Couette and Stokes flow" *The Plasma in a Magnetic Field Symposium.* Stanford U.P., Stanford, 130 pp. (fig.) (Cp 1536), 1958.

1194. LENARD, A. and BERNSTEIN, I. B. "Plasma oscillations with diffusion in velocity space" *Phys. Rev.*, Vol. 112, pp. 1456–9, 1958.

*__1195.__ LENCHEK, A. M. "Radiowave propagation in interplanetary magnetic field". Maryland U., College Park, 18 pp. incl. illus. table (Physics Dept. TN No. 113; AFOSR TN 59-165).

1196. LEONARD, S. L., JOSEPHSON, V., MASEK, G. E. and PENNING, J. R. "Magnetic channeling and reflection of high velocity shocks". Paper presented at the Divisional Meeting of the Division of Fluid Dynamics, American Physical Society, San Diego, Calif., 24–26 Nov. 1958.

*__1197.__ LEONTOVICH, M. A. and OSOVETS, S. M. "On the mechanism of current constriction in high-current gas discharges" *J. Nucl. Energy*, Vol. 4, pp. 209–12, 1956; *Atomnaya. Energiia*, Vol. 1, p. 81, 1956.

1198. LEVENGOOD, W. C. "Influence of a magnetic field on thermal convection patterns" *Nature, Lond.*, Vol. 177, pp. 631–2, 1956.

1199. LEVERETT, D., LÜST, R. and SCHLÜTER, A. "The structure of hydromagnetic shock waves in a cold gas". Paper presented at the Divisional Meeting of the Division of Fluid Dynamics, American Physical Society, San Diego, California, 24–26 Nov. 1958.

1200. LEVINE, M. A. "Stability in a magnetic field". ARDC, Conference on Ion and Plasma Research, University of Maryland, 30 Sept.–2 Oct., 1958.

*__1201.__ LEWELLEN, W. S. "An inviscid boundary layer of magnetohydrodynamics". AFORS TN-59-927. Contract AF 18(600) 1523, 1959.

*__1202.__ LI, H. MICHELSON I. and RABINOWICZ, J. "Studies in magneto-aerodynamics; I: One-dimensional flows; II: Stability of laminar boundary layer". Odin Assoc. TR 102–1 (AFOSR TR 5B–2B), 43 pp., Dec. 1957.

1203. LIBOFF, R. L. "Transport coefficients determined using the shielded Coulomb potential" *Phys. Fluids*, Vol. 2, p. 40, 1959.

1204. LIEPMANN, H. W. and COLE J. D. *Magnetohydrodynamics.* California Inst. of Technology, Pasadena, California, 1957.

1205. LIN, S. C. "Ionization phenomenon of shock waves in oxygen-nitrogen mixtures". AVCO Research Laboratory, RR33, 23 pp., 1958.

*__1206.__ LIN, S. C. "Note on class of exact solutions in magnetohydrodynamics". *Arch. Rational Mech. Anal.*, Vol. 1, No. 5, pp. 391–395, 1958.

*__1207.__ LIN, S. C. and CAMBEL, A. B. "Magnetohydrodynamic flow regimes" *ARS J.*, Vol. 29 (11), pp. 871–3, 1959; U.S.A. Index Aeronautics, Jan. 1960.

*__1208.__ LIN, S. C. and LAMB, L. "Electrical conductivity of a thermally ionized air produced in a shock tube". AVCO Research Laboratory Report 5, February 1957.

1209. LIN, S. C., RESLER, E. L. and KANTROWITZ, A. "Electrical conductivity of highly ionized argon produced by shock waves" *J. Appl. Phys.*, Vol. 26, pp. 95–109, 1955.

*__1210.__ LINDBERG, L. WITALIS, E. and JACOBSEN, C. T. "Experiments with plasma rings" *Nature, Lond.*, Vol. 185, pp. 452–3, 1960.

1211. LINDER, E. G. "Effect of electron pressure on plasma electron oscillations" *Phys. Rev.*, Vol. 49, p. 753, 1936.

*1212. LINHART, J. G. "Accelerated self-constricted electron streams in plasma" *Proc. Roy. Soc.* A, Vol. 249, pp. 318–34 (14 refs.), 1959.

*1213. LINHART, J. G. "Plasma confinement by external magnetic fields" *Nuovo Cimento, Suppl.*, Vol. 13, No. 1, pp. 257–80, 1959.

1214. LINHART, J. G. "Power from thermonuclear reactions" *Nuclear Engineering*, Vol. 2, pp. 60–5, 1957.

1215. LINHART, J. G. "Plasma betatron" *Ionization Phenomena in Gases*, Vol. 2, p. 981. Amsterdam, North-Holland, 1959.

1216. LINHART, J. G. and ORNSTEIN, L. T. M. "Compression of radiation fields by a magnetically driven plasma shell" *Ionization Phenomena in Gases*, Vol. 2, p. 774. Amsterdam, North-Holland, 1959.

1217. LINHART, J. G. and ORNSTEIN, L. T. M. "Production of plasma in a toroidal vessel by means of a spiral electron beam". C.E.R.N. Report 59–2, Jan. 1959.

1218. LINHART, J. G., PERSICO, E. "Plasma loss from magnetic bottles" *Nuovo Cimento*, Vol. 8, pp. 740–53, 1958.

1219. LINHART, J. G. and ZYCH, W. "Plasma wave-guides and resonators for cm-waves" *Ionization Phenomena in Gases*, Vol. 2, p. 778. Amsterdam, North-Holland, 1959.

1220. LIU, CHING-SHI and CAMBEL, A. B. "Magnetogasdynamic flow regimes" *ARS J.*, Vol. 29, pp. 871–3, 1959; Index Aeronautics Jan. 1960.

*1221. LIUBARSKII, G. J. and POLOVIN, R. V. "The disintegration of instable shock waves in magnetohydrodynamics" *J. Exp. Theor. Phys.*, Vol. 9, No. 4, pp. 902–6, 1959; *Zh. Eksp. Teoret. Fiz. USSR*, Vol. 36, pp. 1272–8, Apr. 1959.

1222. LIUBARSKII, G. J. and POLOVIN, R. V. "On the piston problem in magnetic hydrodynamics" *Dokl. Akad. Nauk.*, SSSR, Vol. 128, No. 4, pp. 684–7, 1959.

*1223. LIUBARSKII, G. J. and POLOVIN, R. V. "Dissociation des ondes de choc instables en magnétohydrodynamique" *J. Exp. Theor. Phys.*, No. 4, pp. 302–6, 1959.

*1224. LIUBARSKII, G. J. and POLOVIN, R. V. "Simple magnetoacoustic waves" *J. Exp. Theor. Phys.*, No. 2, p. 351, 1959.

1225. LIUBARSKII, G. J. and POLOVIN, R. V. "The splitting of a small discontinuity in magneto-hydrodynamics" *J. Exp. Theor. Phys.*, Vol. 35, No. 5, pp. 901–2, 1959.

*1226. LOCK, R. C. "The stability of the flow of an electrically conducting fluid between parallel planes under a transverse magnetic field" *Proc. Roy. Soc.* A, Vol. 233, pp. 105–25, 1955.

*1227. LODIJENSKY, M. D. "Ecoulement hipersonique autour de corps en Magnetohydrodynamique". *Prikl. Mat. Mekh.*, Vol. XXIII, No. 6, pp. 993–1005 (6 figs.), 1959.

1228. LOM, T. and PLECITY, M. "On the interaction between an electron wave and free electrons" *Slab. Obz.*, Vol. 18, p. 191, 1957.

*1229. LONG, R. R. "Steady finite motions of a conducting liquid" *J. Fluid Mech.*, Vol. 7, Pt. I, pp. 108–14, 1960.

1230. LONGMIRE, C. L. "The static pinch" *Proc. 2nd Geneva Conf.*, Vol. 31, p. 84, 1958.

1231. LONGMIRE, C. L. and ROSENBLUTH, M. N. "Diffusion of charged particles across a magnetic field" *Phys. Rev.*, Vol. 103, pp. 507–10, 1956.

1232. LOONEY, P. H. and BROWN, S. C. "The excitation of plasma oscillations" *Phys. Rev.*, Vol. 93, pp. 365–9, 1954.

*1233. LOOS, H. G. "The 'punch' method of compressing, heating and confining of a plasma". Plasmadyne Corp., Santa Ana, Cal., T-ITN 128-335 AFOSR TN 58-1130, 1958.

*1234. Loos, H. G. "Some dynamics problems of the 'punch' method of reacting and acceleration of plasmas". Plasmadyne Corp. Calif., Feb. 1959; AFOSR TN-59-256; ASTIA 212256.

1235. Loos, H. G. "Heating and confinement of a plasma by a magnetic field of external origin with a short rise time". Plasmadyne, Report n. PLR 6, Feb. 1959.

1236. Loughhead, R. E. "Eigen oscillations of compressible ionized fluids" *Aust. J. Phys.*, Vol. 8, pp. 416–18, 1955.

1237. Loughhead, R. E. "Hydromagnetic stability of a current layer" *Aust. J. Phys.*, Vol. 8, pp. 319, 328, 1955.

*1238. Loughhead, R. E. "Solution of flow problems in unidimensional Lagrangian hydromagnetics" *Aust. J. Phys.*, Vol. 10, pp. 213–16, 1957.

1239. Loughhead, R. E. "Solution of problems involving the hydromagnetic flow of compressible ionized fluids" *Phys. Rev.*, Vol. 99, pp. 1678–81, 1955.

1240. Lovberg, R. H. "The use of magnetic probes in plasma diagnostics" *Ann. Phys.*, Vol. 8, No. 3, pp. 311–25, 1959.

*1241. Low, F. E. "A Lagrangian formulation of the Boltzmann–Vlasov equation for plasmas" *Proc. Roy. Soc.* A, 1958, pp. 282–7, 1958.

*1242. Lowry, E. S. "Geometrical representation of the Maxwell field in Minkowski space" *Phys. Rev.*, Vol. 117, No. 2, pp. 616–18, 1960.

1243. Lozzi, M., Jancel, R. and Kahan, T. "Absorption of electromagnetic waves in weakly ionised gases (Ionospheric and Lorentzian Plasmas)" *Appl. Sci. Res.* B, Vol. 5, p. 327, 1955.

1244. Ludford, G. S. S. and Murray, J. D. "Further results on the flow of a conducting fluid past a magnetized sphere". Un. of Maryland, Inst. for Fluid Dyn. and Appl. Math. TN BN-174, 1959.

*1245. Ludford, G. S. S. "The structure of a hydromagnetic shock in steady plane motion" *J. Fluid Mech.*, Vol. 5, Pt. 1, pp. 67–80, 1959; AFOSR 49 (638) 154, Selected Topics in Magnetohydrodynamics Univ. Maryland 1958, ASTIA AD 162274.

*1246. Ludford, G. S. S. "The propagation of small disturbances in hydromagnetics". AFOSR 49 (638) 154, Abstracts of Papers presented at Conference on Ion and Plasma Research Univ. Maryland, 30 Sept.–2 Oct. 1958; *J. Fluid Mech.*, Vol. 5, Pt. 3, pp. 387–400 (1 fig.), 1959.

1247. Ludford, G. S. S. "The transmission of electromagnetic waves in the presence of a conducting layer of gas". AFOSR 49 (638) 154, Ab. Conf. Ion and Plasma Res. Univ. Maryland, 30 Sept.–2 Oct., 1958; ASTIA AD 162274.

*1248. Ludford, G. S. S. "Rayleigh's problem in hydrodynamics; the impulsive motion of a pole-piece". AFOSR (638) 154 Ab. Conf. Ion and Plasma Res. Univ. Maryland, 30 Sept.–2 Oct. 1958; *Arch. Rat. Mech. and Anal.* (to be published); ASTIA AD 162274.

1249. Ludford, G. S. S. "Flow past a body at low magnetic Reynolds number". Int. Symposium on M.F.D. Washington, Jan. 1960.

1250. Ludford, G. S. S. "On initial conditions in hydromagnetics (selected Topics in Magneto-hydrodynamics)". Univ. Maryland, 30 Sept.–2 Oct. 1958; *Proc. Camb. Phil. Soc.*, Vol. 55, 1959; ASTIA AD 162274.

*1251. Ludford, G. S. S. and Murray, J. D. "On the flow of a conducting fluid past a magnetized sphere" *J. Fluid. Mech.*, Vol. 7, Pt. 4, pp. 516–28, 1960.

*1252. Ludloff, H. F. "Magnetic boundary layer" *ARS J.*, Vol. 29, Aug. 1959.

*1253. Luk'yanov, S. Yu. and Sinitsyn, V. I. "Spectroscopic investigation of an intense pulsed discharge in hydrogen; III: Determination of the parameters of a high-temperature plasma" *J. Exp. Theor. Phys.*, No. 6, p. 1155, Dec. 1959.

1254. Luk'yanov, S. Y. and Sinitsyn, V. I. "Spectroscopic studies of a high-power pulsed discharge in hydrogen" *J. Nuclear Energy*, Vol. 4, p. 216, 1957.

1255. LUNDQUIST, S. "Experimental demonstration of magnetohydrodynamic waves" *Nature, Lond.*, Vol. 164, p. 145, 1949.

1256. LUNDQUIST, S. "Run-away phenomena and relaxation effects" *Rend. Phys. School "E. Fermi"* corso XIII, pp. 20–5, Varenna, 1959.

1257. LUNDQUIST, S. "Experimental investigations of magnetohydrodynamic waves" *Phys. Rev.*, Vol. 76, pp. 1805–9, 1949.

1258. LUNDQUIST, S. "Plasma stability" *Rend. Phys. School "E. Fermi"* corso XIII, pp. 25–34, Varenna, 1959.

1259. LUNDQUIST, S. "Motion of charged particles in electrical magnetic fields" *Rend. Phys. School "E. Fermi"* corso XIII, pp. 9–15, Varenna, 1959.

1260. LUNDQUIST, S. "Magneto-hydrostatic fields" *Ark. Fys.*, Vol. 2, pp. 361–5, 1950.

*1261. LUNDQUIST, S. "Oh the stability of magneto-hydrostatic fields" *Phys. Rev.*, Vol. 83, pp. 307–11, 1951.

1262. LUNDQUIST, S. "Particle view compared with hydrodynamics" *Rend. Phys. School "E. Fermi"* corso XIII, pp. 15–20, Varenna, 1959.

1263. LUNDQUIST, S. "Mercury experiments" *Rend. Phys. School "E. Fermi"* corso XIII, pp. 34–8, Varenna, 1959.

1264. LUNDQUIST, S. "Studies in magneto-hydrodynamics" *Ark. Fys.*, Vol. 5, No. 297, p. 347, 1952.

1265. LÜST, R. "Plasmaschwingungen in einem äusserem Magnetfeld" *Z. Astrophys.* Vol. 37, p. 567, 1955.

1266. LÜST, R. "Magneto-hydrodynamische Stosswellen in einem Plasma unendlicher Leitfühigkeit" *Z. Naturforsch.*, Vol. 8a, No. 5, pp. 277–84, 1953.

1267. LÜST, R. "Stationary magneto-hydrodynamic shock waves of arbitrary strength" *Z. Naturforsch.*, Vol. 10a, pp. 125–35, 1955.

*1268. LÜST, R. "Some theoretical aspects of magnetohydrodynamics and thermonuclear fusion" *Nuovo Cimento, Suppl.*, Vol. 13, No. 1, pp. 330–5, 1959.

1269. LÜST, R. and SCHLÜTER, A. "Force-free magnetic fields" *Z. Astrophys.*, Vol. 34, pp. 263–82, 1954.

1270. LÜST, R. and SCHLÜTER, A. "Die Bewegung geladener Teilchen in rotations-symmetrichen Magnetfeldern" *Z. Naturforsch.*, Vol. 122, pp. 841–3, 1957.

1271. LÜST, R. and SCHLÜTER, A. "Axialsymmetrische magnetohydrodynamische Gleichgewichtskonfigurationen" *Z. Naturforsch.*, Vol. 12a, pp. 850–4, 1957.

1272. LYKOUDIS, P. S. "A discussion of magnetic boundary conditions assimilating combustion blowing or sublimation at the wall" Symposium on Rarefied Gas Dynamics and Aerothermodynamics, Nice, France, July 1958.

*1273. LYKOUDIS, P. S. "Channel turbulent flow of an electrically conducting fluid in the presence of a magnetic field". Pardue U. Rept. A-59-4, 19 pp., Mar. 1959.

1274. LYKOUDIS, P. S. "On a class of compressible laminar boundary layers with pressure gradient for an electrically conducting fluid in the presence of a magnetic field". Paper presented at the IX I.A.F. Meeting, Amsterdam, 25–30 Aug. 1958.

1275. LYKOUDIS, P. S. "The matching of the viscid and inviscid regions for the stagnation magnetic flow" *J. Aero/Space Sci.*, p. 315, May 1959.

1276. LYSOV, B. A. "Particle energy losses due to the excitation of longitudinal waves" *J. Exp. Theor. Phys.*, No. 1, p. 221, July 1959.

*1277. LYUBIMOV, G. A. "Onde de choc d'un gaz à coefficient de conductivité discontinu dans un champ électromagnétique" *Dokl. Akad. Nauk., SSSR*, Vol. 126, No. 2, pp. 291–4 (2 figs.), 1959.

1278. LYUBIMOV, G. A. "Gas steady flow conditions assimilating combustion, blowing or sublimation at the wall". Proc. Symposium on Rarefied Gas Dynamics and Aerothermodynamics, Nice, France, July 1958.

*1279. LYUBIMOV, G. A. "Stationary Flow of an ideally conducting gas around a corner" *Soviet Phys. Dokl.*, Vol. 4, No. 3, pp. 529–631, 1959; *Dokl. Akad. Nauk., SSSR*, Vol. 126, No. 4, pp. 733–5, 1959.

1280. MACHE, H. "Application of laws of similarity to streaming of electricity in gases" *Z. Phys.*, Vol. 33, p. 43, 1932.

1281. MAECKER, H. "Plasma stream produced by self magnetic compression and its importance for the mechanism of high current arcs" *Appl. Sci. Res.* B, Vol. 5, p. 231, 1955.

*1282. MAECKER, H. "Plasma streams in arcs due to self-magnetic compression". TIL/OT/2459, 1955, AEI T/895, *Z. Physik.*, Vol. 141, pp. 198–216.

1283. MAECKER, H. and PETERS, T. "Messung der Plasmalleitfuhigkeit in Hochleistunsbogen" *Z. Phys. Chem.*, Vol. 198, No. 5/6, pp. 319–28, 1951.

1284. MAJUMDAR, S. "A note on force-free field" *Z. Astrophys.*, Vol. 47, pp. 44–49, 1959.

1285. MALKUS, W. V. R. "Magneto-convection in a viscous fluid of infinite electrical conductivity". Paper presented at the Divisional Meeting of the Division of Fluid Dynamics, American Physics Society, San Diego, California, 24–26 Nov. 1958.

1286. MALMFORS, K. G. "Unstable oscillation in an electron gas" *Ark. Fys.*, Vol. 1, p. 569, 1950.

1287. MALTER, L. and WEBSTER, W. M. "Rapid determination of gas discharge constant from probe data" *RCA Rev.*, Vol. 12, p. 191, 1951.

1288. MALTER, L., JOHNSON, E. O. and WEBSTER, W. M. "Studies of externally heated hot cathode arcs; Part I: Modes of the discharge" *RCA Rev.*, Vol. 12, p. 415, 1951.

1289. MAMIYSIN, B. A. "Measurements of plasma parameters by the pulse method in high density discharge currents" *Zh. Tekh. Fiz.*, Vol. 23, p. 1915, 1953.

*1290. MANHEIMER TIMNAT, Y. and LOW, W. "Electron density and ionization rate in thermally ionized gases produced by medium straight shock waves" *J. Fluid Mech.*, Vol. 6, Pt. 3, pp. 449–61, 4 figs., 5 tables., 1960.

1291. MARCUVITZ, N. "Plasma program". ARDC, Conference on Ion and Plasma Research, University of Maryland, 30 Sept.–2 Oct. 1958.

1292. MARGENAU, H. "The structure of spectral lines from plasmas" *Ionization Phenomena in Gases*, Vol. 2, p. 791. Amsterdam, North-Holland, 1959.

1293. MARGENAU, H. "Conductivity of plasma to microwaves" *Phys. Rev.*, Vol. 100, pp. 6–9, 1958.

1294. MARGENAU, H. "Conduction and dispersion of ionized gases at high frequencies" *Phys. Rev.*, Vol. 69, p. 508, 1946.

*1295. MARGENAU, N., DEZLODZH, E. and STILLINGER, D. "Conductivity of weakly ionized air" *Izv. Akad. Nauk., SSSR*, Ser. fiz., Vol. 23, No. 8, pp. 1040–9, 1959.

1296. MARIANI, F. "The world-wide distribution of the F_2 layer electron density: seasonal and non-seasonal variations and correlations with solar activity" *Nuovo Cimento*, Vol. XII, No. 3, pp. 218–40, 1959.

1297. MARKHAM, J. R. "Comprehensive theory on plasma states and phenomena". ARDC, Conference on Ion and Plasma Research, University of Maryland, 30 Sept.–2 Oct. 1958.

1298. MARKS, G. "The variational principle for dielectrics" *Byull. Pol'skii Akad. Nauk. Otd.*, Vol. 111, 4, No. 1, pp. 29–35, 1956 (in Russian); *Ref. Zh. Mekh.*, No. 3, Rev. 2884, 1958.

1299. MARMO, F. F., ASCHENBRAND, L. M. and PRESSMAN, J. "Physics of artificial electron clouds" *ARS J.*, Vol. 30, No. 6, p. 523, 1960.

*1300. MARONI, P. "Phénomenès de décharge dans les plasmas Lorentziens: Etude de la distribution électronique en presence d'un champ magnetique" *C. R. Acad. Sci., Paris*, Vol. 249, pp. 881–3, 1959.

*1301. MARSHALL, W. "The growth in time of a hydromagnetic shock". Harwell, AERE Memo T/M 135, 1956.

1302. MARSHALL, W. "The structure of magneto-hydrodynamic shock waves" *Proc. Roy. Soc.* A, Vol. 233, pp. 367–76, 1955.

1303. MARSHALL, W. "Structure of magneto-hydrodynamic shock waves in a plasma of infinite conductivity" *Phys. Rev.*, Vol. 103, p. 1900(L), 1956.

*1304. MARSHALL, W. "The structure of magneto-hydrodynamic shock". Harwell, AERE Rept. T/R 1718, 1955.

1305. MARSHALL, J. "Acceleration of plasma into a vacuum". A/Conf. 15/p/355, U.S.A., 4 August 1958.

*1306. MARSHALL, J. "Performance of a hydromagnetic plasma gun" *Phys. Fluids*, Vol. 3, No. 1, pp. 134–5, 1960.

1307. MARSHALL, L. "Production of the sun's non-thermal radio emission by Cherenkov radiation" *Astrophys. J.*, Vol. 124, p. 469, 1956.

1308. MARTIN, A. V. J. and YOUNG, E. J. "Confinement magnétique des réactions thermonucléaires non-stationnaires" *J. Phys. Rad.*, suppl., No. 4, 20, Vol. 1A–4A, 1959.

*1309. MATSUSHITA, S. "On artificial geomagnetic and ionospheric storms associated with high-altitude explosion" *J. Geophys. Res.*, Vol. 64, No. 9, pp. 1149–61, 1959.

*1310. MAWARDI, O. K. "Magneto-hydrodynamics. A survey of literature" *Appl. Mech. Rev.*, Vol. 12, No. 7, pp. 443–6, 1959.

1311. MCCREA, W. H. "On the equation of the state of an ionized gas" *Proc. Camb. Phil. Soc.*, Vol. 26, p. 107, 1929–30.

*1312. MCCUNE, J. E. "On the motion of thin airfoils in fluids of large but finite electrical conductivity" *J. Fluid Mech.*, Vol. 7, Pt. 3, pp. 449–68, 1960.

1313. MCCUNE, J. E. and RESLER, E. L. Jr. "Compressibility effects in the magneto-aerodynamic theory of thin airfoils" *J. Aero/Space Sci.*, Vol. 27, No. 7, p. 493, 1960.

1314. MCCUNE, J. E. and SEARS, W. R. "On magnetohydrodynamic channel flow". Reader's forum, *J. Aero/Space Sci.*, Vol. 27, No. 2, pp. 139–40, 1960.

1315. MCCUNE, J. E. and SEARS, W. R. "On the concept of moving electric and magnetic fields in magneto-hydro-dynamics" *J. Aero/Space Sci.*, Vol. 26, pp. 674–5, 1959.

1316. MCILROY, W. "Magneto-hydrodynamics" *J. Soc. Automot. Engrs.*, Vol. 4, pp. 90–3, 1958.

*1317. MCILROY, W. "Magnetohydrodynamics is an old field with new implications for engineers" *J. Soc. Automot. Engrs.*, pp. 90–3, April 1958.

*1318. MCILROY, W. "Research in magnetohydrodynamics" *J. Soc. Automot. Engrs.* (National Aeronautical Meeting Preprint N. 39C), p. 7, April 1958; *SAE Trans.*, Vol. 67, pp. 39–43 (6 figs.), 1959.

1319. MEDICUS, G. "Diffusion and elastic collision losses of the fast electrons in plasmas" *J. Appl. Phys.*, Vol. 29, p. 903, 1958.

1320. MEDICUS, G. "Simple way to obtain the velocity distribution of the electron gas discharge plasmas from probe curves" *J. Appl. Phys.*, Vol. 27, p. 1242, 1956.

1321. MEDICUS, G. "Energy spectrum of plasma electrons". ARDC, Conference on Ion and Plasma Research, University of Maryland, 30 Sept.–2 Oct. 1958.

*1322. MEECHAM, W. C. "Some exact solutions of the Navier–Stokes and the hydromagnetic equations" *Phys. Fluids*, Vol. 2, pp. 121–4, 1959.

1323. MEHAFFEY, D. W. and EMELEUS, K. G. "Suppression of plasma oscillations" *J. Electronics and Control*, Vol. 4, p. 301, 1958.

1324. MENZEL, D. H. Report of Conference on the dynamics of ionized media 1951.

1325. MERRILL, H. J. and Webb, H. W. "Plasma oscillations and scattering in low pressure discharges" *Phys. Rev.*, Vol. 55, p. 597, 1939

1326. MERRILL, H. J. and WEBB, H. W. "Electron scattering and plasma oscillations" *Phys. Rev.*, Vol. 55, p. 1191, 1939.

*1327. MEYER, F. "The stability of a plasma in crossed magnetic fields" *Z. Naturforsch*, Vol. 13a, No. 12, pp. 1016–20, Dec. 1958 (in German).

*1328. MEYER, F. and SCHMIDT, H. U. "Toruslike configurations of a plasma in equilibrium with an exterior magnetic field without azimuthal current" *Z. Naturforsch*, Vol. 13a, No. 12, pp. 1005–15, 1958 (in German).

*1329. MEYER, R. C. "On reducing aerodynamic heat transfer rates by magnetohydrodynamic techniques". IAS Preprint 816 Jan. 1958; *J. Aero/Space Sci.*, Vol. 25, No. 9, pp. 561–6, 1958.

1330. MEYER, R. C. "Magneto-hydrodynamic techniques" *J. Aero/Space Sci.*, Vol. 25, No. 9, 1958.

1331. MEYER, R. X. "Rate of heat transfer near the stagnation point of a blunt body of revolution in the presence of a magnetic field". Phys. Res. Lab. Rept. GM-TR-0127-00016. The Ramowooldridge Corp. Lo.́ Angeles, 1958.

*1332. MEYER, R. X. "Magneto-hydrodynamics and aerodynamic heating" *ARS J.*, Vol. 29, No. 3, 1959.

*1333. MEYER, R. X. "Magneto-hydrodynamics in the limit of small inertial forces". Preprint Third Biennial Gas Dynamic Symposium. ARS Northwestern Univ., 24–26 Aug. 1959.

*1334. MEYER, R. X. "Magneto-hydrodynamics and its application to propulsion re-entry". 10th Int. Astronautical Congress; London, 5 Sept., 1959.

*1335. MEYER, R. X. "The quasi-Newtonian approximation". Int. Symposium on M.F.D. Washington, Jan. 1960.

*1336. MEYER, R. X. "A magnetohydrodynamic model for a two-dimensional magnetic piston" *J. Aero/Space Sci.*, Jan. 1960; Space Tech. Lab. PRL TR 59-0000-00617, 4 Mar., 1959, 12 pp. U.S.A.F.

*1337. MEYER, R. X. "Magnetohydrodynamic-Hypersonic flow in the quasi-Newtonian approximation". 21 May, 1959, 12 pp., incl. illus. 12 refs. (Rept. N. TR-59-0000-00690); Contract AF 04(647)309.

1338. MICHAEL, D. H. "Stability of plane parallel flows of electrically conducting fluids" *Proc. Camb. Phil. Soc.*, Vol. 49, pp. 166–8, 1953.

1339. MICHAEL, D. H. "The stability of a combined current and vortex sheet in a perfectly conducting fluid" *Proc. Camb. Phil. Soc.*, Vol. 51, 528–32, 1955.

1340. MICHAEL, D. H. "A two-dimensional magnetic boundary layer problem" *Mathematika*, Vol. 1, pp. 131–42, 1954.

1341. MICHAEL, D. H. "The stability of an incompressible electrically conducting fluid rotating about an axis when current flows parallel to the axis" *Mathematika*, Vol. 1, pp. 45–50, 1954.

1342. MIERDAL, G. "Potential conditions in a decaying plasma" *Wiss. Z. Tech. Hochsch., Dresden*, Vol. 4, p. 611, 1954–55.

1343. MIESOWICZ, M. "Influence of the magnetic field on the viscosity of liquids in the Nemantic Phase" *Bull. Acad. Polon. Sci. et lettres*, Vol. 5–6A, p. 228, 1936.

1344. MIESOWICZ, M. and JEZEWSKI, M. "Uber den thermischen, von magnetischen Felden hervogerufenen Effekt in anisotropen Flussigkeiten und den Einfluss des elektrischen Feldes auf denselben" *Z. Phys.*, Vol. 36, p. 107, 1935.

1345. MIKHAILOV, G. and ZWETTKOF, V. "Influence of electric fields on flow of p. azoxyanisole in capillary tubes" *Zh. Eksp. Teoret. Fiz. SSSR*, Vol. 9, p. 208, 1939.

1346. MIKHAILOV, G. and ZWETTKOFF, V. "Action of magnetic and electric fields on flow of p. Azoxyanisole" *Zh. Eksp. Teoret. Fiz. SSSR*, Vol. 9, p. 597, 1939.

1347. MILHOUD, A. "EMF produced by a flow of water vapor" *C. R. Acad. Sci., Paris*, Vol. 198, p. 1586, 1934.

1348. Millan, G. "Du fluide parfait au plasma" *Ingen. Aeronaut. Astronaut.*, No. 49, pp. 1–18, 21 figs., 1 photo., Oct. 1959.

1349. Millar, W. "On a moving boundary problem in electromagnetic theory". Harwell, AERE Memo GP. M 172, 1955.

1350. Miller, D. B. "An electromagnetic accelerator and its applicability to acceleration of an electrical discharge plasma". ARDC, Conference on Ion and Plasma Research, University of Maryland, 30 Sept.–2 Oct. 1958.

1351. Miller, M. A. "Reflection of electrons from a high-frequency potential barrier" *J. Exp. Theor. Phys.*, No. 1, p. 206, 1959.

*1352. Miller, M. A. "Acceleration of plasmoids by high-frequency electric fields" *J. Exp. Theor. Phys.*, No. 6, p. 1358, 1959.

1353. Miller, M. A. "Several possibilities associated with the separation of charged particles in an inhomogeneous high-frequency electromagnetic field" *J. Exp. Theor. Phys.*, Vol. 35 (8), pp. 561–2, 1959.

1354. Mitchner, M. "Steady two-dimensional flow with a transverse magnetic field". Lockheed Missiles and Space Division Rept. No. LMSD-48423, 20 Jan. 1959.

*1355. Mitchner, M. "Magneto-hydrodynamic flow in a shock tube" *Phys. Fluids*, Vol. 2, p. 62, 1959.

1356. Mitchner, M. "Magnetohydrodynamic flow in a shock tube". Lockheed Missiles and Space Division Rept. No. LMSD-80777, 1958.

*1357. Mitchner, M. "Steady two-dimensional flow with a transverse magnetic field". Lockheed Missiles and Space Division Rept. No. LMSD-48423, 20 Jan. 1959.

1358. Mitchner, M. "Magneto-hydrodynamic flow in a shock tube. Magneto-dynamics of conducting fluids" *Symposium on M.H.D.*, Stanford U.P., 1959; *Phys. Fluids*, Vol. 2, No. 1, pp. 52–71, 1959.

1359. Mitsuk, V. E. and Koz'minykh, M. D. "Electric field in a microwave plasma as a function of time" *J. Exp. Theor. Phys.*, No. 5, p. 1139, 1959.

1360. Model, I. S. "Measurement of high temperatures in strong shock waves in gases" *J. Exp. Theor. Phys.*, Vol. 5, pp. 589–601, 1957.

1361. Moeglich, F. "On the hydrodynamics of an electron gas" *S.B. Dtsch. Akad. Wiss., Ber.*, Kl. Math. Phys. Tech. No. 1, 1957.

1362. Montgomery, D. "Nonlinear Alfvén waves in a cold ionized gas" *Phys. Fluids*, Vol. 2, p. 585.

1363. Montgomery, D. "Development of hydromagnetic shock from large amplitude Alfvén waves" *Phys. Rev. Letters*, Vol. 2, No. 2, pp. 36–7, 1959.

1364. Morita, T. "High-altitude voltage breakdown investigation". ARDC, Conference on Ion and Plasma Research, University of Maryland, 30 Sept.—2 Oct. 1958.

*1365. Morozov, A. I. and Solov'ev, L. S. "The integrals of drift equations" *Dokl. Akad. Nauk., SSSR*, Vol. 128, No. 3, pp. 506–9, 1959.

1366. Morozov, A. I. "Plasma acceleration by a magnetic field" *J. Exp. Theor. Phys.*, Vol. 5, pp. 215–20, 1957; *Zh. Eksp. Teoret. Fiz.*, Vol. 32, pp. 305–10, 1957 (IRE N. 3450, Dec. 1957).

1367. Mott-Smith, H. M. and Langmuir, I. "The theory of collisions in gaseous discharges" *Phys. Rev.*, Vol. 28, p. 722, 1926.

1368. Mugibayashi, N. "An example of one-dimensional oscillatory motion in magnetohydrodynamics" *Progr. Theor. Phys.*, Vol. 20, p. 241, 1958.

1369. Murgatroyd, W. "Damping of turbulence by a magnetic field" *Nature, Lond.*, Vol. 171, p. 217, 1953.

1370. Murgatroyd, W. "An experiment on magneto-hydrodynamic channel flow" *Phil. Mag.*, Vol. 44, pp. 1348–54, 1955.

1371. Murgatroyd, W. "The theory of the ideal A.C. conduction pump". Great Britain AERE Rep. ED/R, 1566 (1956).

1372. MYAKISHEV, G. Y. and LUCHINI, A. A. "Longitudinal plasma oscillations II" *Zh. Eksp. Teoret. Fiz.*, Vol. 28, p. 28, 1955.

1373. NAGAO, S. "A possible mechanism of particle acceleration in high current spark discharges" *Proc. Venice Conf. 1957*, pp. 736–8, 1955.

1374. NAKAGAWA, Y. "An experiment on the inhibition of thermal convection by a magnetic field" *Proc. Roy. Soc.* A, Vol. 240, pp. 108–13, 1957; *Nature, Lond.*, Vol. 175, pp. 417–19, 1955.

*1375. NAKAGAWA, Y. "Heat transport by convection in presence of an impressed magnetic field" *Phys. Fluids*, Vol. 3, No. 1, pp. 87–94, 1960.

*1376. NAKAGAWA, Y. "Experiments on the instability of a layer of mercury heated from below and subject to the simultaneous action of a magnetic field and rotation". Part II, *Proc. Roy. Soc.* A, Vol. 249, 1256, pp. 138–45, 1959.

1377. NAKAGAWA, Y. "Some results on heat-transport by convection in presence of impressed magnetic fields". Int. Symposium on MFD, Washington, Jan. 1960.

*1378. NAKAGAWA, Y. *Theoretical and Experimental Study of Heat Transfer by Cellular Convection in the Presence of Impressed Magnetic Fields*", pp. 417–26, Texas, Univ. Press, 1959.

*1379. NAPOLITANO, L. G. "Contributo alla magnetofluidodinamica" *Missili*, No. 1, pp. 15–34, 1959.

1380. NAPOLITANO, L. G. "Onde in un mezzo magnetofluidodinamico". Centro di Studi di Fisica dello Spazio (Università di Napoli) Sez. Magnetofluidodinamica, 1960, C.F.S. M2.

*1381. NAPOLITANO, L. G. "Discontinuity surfaces in magneto-fluid-dynamics". Fifth Annual Meeting of the American Astronautical Society, Washington, 1958.

1382. NAPOLITANO, L. G. "La magnetofluidodinamica nelle comunicazioni spaziali". VII Convegno Internazionale delle Comunicazioni, Genova, Boll. n. 2, Ottobre 1959.

1383. NAPOLITANO, L. G. "Some properties of shock surfaces in magneto-fluid-dynamics". First Int. Space Science Symp. Nice, France, Jan. 1960.

1384. NAPOLITANO, L. G. "Strato limite turbolento in magnetofluidosinamica". Proc. XVI Congresso Nazionale di Aerotecnica Pisa, Italia, Ottobre 1959.

1385. NAPOLITANO, L. G. "On turbulent magneto-fluid dynamic boundary layers". Int. Symposium on M.F.D. Washington, Jan. 1960.

*1386. NAPOLITANO, L. G. "Magneto-fluid-dynamics of two interacting streams" *Proc. IX I.A.F. Meeting, Amsterdam, Aug.* 1958. Wien, Springer Verlag, 1959.

1387. NAPOLITANO, L. G. "Magneto-fluid-dynamic interaction of two compressible streams". Proc. 1959 Int. Symp. on Rockets and Astronautics, Tokyo, Japan, May 1959.

1388. NAPOLITANO, L. G. "On the turbulent flow of an electric conducting stream in the presence of a magnetic field". Fluid Dynamics Meeting, Amer. Phys. Soc. San Diego, Calif., 24–26 Nov. 1958.

*1389. NAPOLITANO, L. G. "Superfici di discontinuità in magnetofluidodinamica" *L'Aerotecnica*, No. 4, pp. 210–20 (1 table), 1958.

1390. NAPOLITANO, L. G. and CONTURSI, G. "Bibliography on magneto-fluid-dynamic waves". Centro di Studi di Fisica dello Spazio (Università di Napoli), Sez. magnetofluidodinamica, C.F.S. M3, 1960.

1391. NAPOLITANO, L. G. and POZZI, A. "Compressible flat plate boundary layer of an electrically conducting fluid in the presence of magnetic fields". Proc. Xth Int. Astr. Congress, London, 1959.

1392. NAPOLITANO, L. G. and POZZI, A. "Alcune considerazioni sulla magneto-fluidodinamica dei getti" *Missili*, No. 3, p. 17, giugno, 1959.

1393. NARDINI, R. "Su un gruppo di casi relativi ad onde magnetoidrodinamiche non omogenee" *Ann. Mat. Pura Appl.* (4), Vol. 43, pp. 371–97, 1957.

*1394. NARDINI, R. "Sulla mutua azione fra fenomeni acustici ed idromagnetici" *J. Math. Mech. U.S.A.*, Vol. 7, No. 1, p. 1–15, 1958.

1395. NARDINI, R. "Remarks on an energy relation in magneto-hydrodynamics" *Accad. Lincei, Roma*, Vol. 18, pp. 376, 1955.

1396. NARDINI, R. "On particular alternating fields in magnetohydrodynamics" *Atti Acad. Sci. Torino*, Vol. 89, p. 17–36, 1954–55.

1397. NARDINI, R. "On the asymptotic behavior of the solution of a problem in magnetohydrodynamics". Nota I, *Accad. Lincei, Roma*, Vol. 16, pp. 225–31, 1954.

1398. NARDINI, R. "On the asymptotic behavior of the solution of a problem in magnetohydrodynamics II" *Accad. Lincei, Roma*, Vol. 16, pp. 341–8, 1954.

1399. NARDINI, R. "On some second order effects in magneto-hydro-dynamics" *Accad. Lincei, Roma*, Vol. 20, Nota I, pp. 457–62; Nota II, p. 591–6, 1956.

*1400. NAZE, J. "Sur certains écoulements quasi-rectilignes d'un fluide doué de conductivité électrique finie" *C. R. Acad. Sci., Paris*, Vol. 4, pp. 525–8 (2 figs.), 1959.

*1401. NAZE, J. "Etude de la stabilité des écoulements de Resler-Sears" *C. R. Acad. Sci., Paris*, Vol. 248, pp. 362–5, 1959.

1402. NEDDERMAYER, S. H. "Problem of generating high circulating currents of relativistic electrons" *J. Appl. Phys.*, Vol. 30, pp. 16–21, 1959.

1403. NEILL, T. R. and EMELEUS, K. G. "Plasma electron oscillations" *Proc. Roy. Irish Acad.*, Vol. 31, p. 354, 1956.

1404. NEITZEL, R. E. "On the possibilities of electrical power generation by magnetohydrodynamic devices". General Electric Co. DF 58A G853.

1405. NELSON, H. K. "On hypersonic stagnation-point flow with a magnetic field" *J. Aero/Space Sci.*, Vol. 25, No. 6, 1958.

1406. NEUERT, N. "Some effects in inductivity coupled electrodeless HF gas discharges with superimposed magnetic field" *Z. Agnew. Math. Phys.*, Vol. 6, pp. 303–10, 1954 (IRE n. 410, March 1955).

*1407. NEUFELD, J. and RITCHIE, R. H. "Passage of charged particles through plasma" *Phys. Rev.*, Vol. 98, pp. 1632–42, 1955.

*1408. NEURINGER, J. L. "Optimum power generation using a plasma as the working fluid". Amer. Phys. Soc. Washington, D.C. Meeting, April–May 1959; *J. Fluid Mech.*, Feb. 1960.

1409. NEURINGER, J. L. "Two dimensional flow in the vicinity of the stagnation point of an incompressible, viscous electrically conducting fluid in the presence of a magnetic field". Republic Aviation Corp. Report, June 1957.

*1410. NEURINGER, J. L. and McILROY, W. "Incompressible two-dimensional point flow of an electrically conducting viscous fluid in the presence of a magnetic field". IAS Preprint 764, of the 25th Annual Meeting, Jan. 1958.

*1411. NEURINGER, J. L. and McILROY, W. "Hydromagnetic effects on stagnation-point heat transfer" *J. Aero. Sci.*, Vol. 25, No. 5, pp. 332–4, Readers' Forum, 1958.

1412. NEWCOMB, W. A. "The hydromagnetic wave guide" *Magneto hydrodynamics Symposium*, Stanford U.P. (Landshoff, R.K.M. editor), 1957.

1413. NEWCOMB, W. "Electron oscillations in a magnetic field". Princeton U.P., Tech. Mem. 13, NYO-7887 (AEC), 14 Dec. 1954.

*1414. NEWCOMB, W. A. "Magnetic differential equations" *Phys. Fluids*, Vol. 2, p. 362, 1959.

1415. NEWCOMB, W. A. "Motion of magnetic lines of force". Princeton Univ. Press. Observatory, Tech. Rep. No. 1, 1955, Adv. Appl. Mech.

*1416. NGUYEN, X. X. "The electromagnetic energy-momentum tensor in the presence of charged matter in the case of the non-linear coupling equations of the Born Infeld theory" *C. R. Acad. Sci., Paris*, Vol. 250, No. 3, pp. 468–70, 1960.

*1417. NIBLETT, E. R. "The stability of Couette flow in an axial magnetic field" *Canad. J. Phys.*, No. 11, pp. 1509–25 (8 figs. and photos., 5 tables), Nov. 1958.

1418. NIBLETT, G. B. F. "Rapid compression of a plasma with azimuthal current" *Proc. Inst. Elect. Engr.*, Paper 2882 (Convention in thermonuclear processes) Vol. 106A, Suppl. 2, pp. 152–7, 182–5, April 1959.

*1419. NIBLETT, G. B. F. and BLACKMAN, V. H. "An approximate measurement of the ionization time behind shock waves in air" *J. Fluid Mech.*, Vol. 4, Pt. 2, pp. 191–4 (4 figs.), 1958.

*1420. NIBLETT, G. B. F. and GREEN, T. S. "Radial hydromagnetic oscillations" *Proc. Phys. Soc.*, Vol. 74, Pt. 6, pp. 737–43, 1959.

*1421. NIBSBET, I. C. T. "Interfacial instability of fluids of arbitrary electrical conductivity in uniform magnetic fields". Cornell University, 1958.

*1422. NIGAM, S. D. and SING, S. N. "Heat transfer by laminar flow between parallel plates under the action of transverse magnetic field" *Quart. J. Mech. Appl. Math.*, Vol. XIII, Feb. 1960.

1423. NIKONOVA, E. I. and PROKOFIEV, V. K. "Determination of the concentrations of metal atoms in the plasma of an arc burning under a reduced pressure" *Optika Spektrosk*, Vol. 1, p. 298, 1956.

*1424. NISHIYAMA, T. "Electrostatic interaction in an electron-ion gas at high density" *Progr. Theor. Phys.*, Vol. 21, No. 3, p. 389–408, 1959.

1425. NOELLE, E. "Ein neues Verfahren zur Messung des Raumpotentials in Niederdruckentladungen" *Ann. Phys.*, Vol. 18, p. 328, 1956.

1426. NORTHROP, T. G. "Helmholtz instability of a plasma" *Phys. Rev.*, Vol. 103, pp. 1150–4, 1956.

*1427. NOSTICK, W. H. "Experimental study of ionized matter projected across a magnetic field". P. 63210-10-5-56, UCRL 4695, U.S.A.

*1428. NOTCHEVKINA, I. I. "Méthode approchée de calcul des ecoulements tourbillonnaires plans en magnétohydrodynamique". C.N.R.S., Jan. 1960; *Dokl. Akad. Nauk., SSSR*, Vol. 126, No. 6, pp. 1220–3, (1 fig.), 1959.

*1429. NOTCHEVKINA, I. I. "On the approximation method in investigation of plane rotational flow in magnetohydrodynamics" *Soviet Phys. Dokl.*, Vol. 4, No. 3, pp. 549–53, 1959.

1430. NOTTINGHAM, W. and STAFF, F. *Bibliography on Physical Electronics*, Research Lab. of Electronics, MIT, Addison-Wesley, Cambridge, 1954.

1431. OBERMAN, C. R. and KRUSKAL, M. D. "On the stability of plasma in static equilibrium". Fluid Dynamics Meeting, Am. Phys. Soc., San Diego, California, 24–26 Nov. 1958.

*1432. OGUCHI, K. "Blunt body viscous layer with and without magnetic field" *Phys. Fluids*, Vol. 3, No. 4, pp. 567–81, 1960.

1433. OHLIN, P., SIEGBAHN, K. "Fusion experiments in linear deuterium pinches" *Proc. Venice Conf.* 1957, pp. 808–12, 1957.

1434. OKAMURA, T. "Effect of magnetic field and of temperature on the specific heats of gases" *Tohoku Univ. Sci. Rep.*, Vol. 22, pp. 519, 1933.

1435. OKHAWA, T. and KIHARA, T. "Externally pinched plasma" *J. Phys. Soc., Japan*, Vol. 13, pp. 473–81, 1958.

1436. OKHAWA, T., MIYAMOTO, G., YAMATO, H. and MARSUDA, N. "Toroidal magnetic bottle" *Ionization Phenomena in Gases*, Vol. 2, p. 11. Amsterdam, North-Holland, 1959.

1437. OKUDA, T. and YAMATO, K. "Disturbance by probe in a plasma" *J. Phys. Soc., Japan*, Vol. II, p. 177, 1956.

1438. OLSEN, H. N. "Thermal and electrical properties of an argon plasma" *Phys. Fluids*, Vol. 2, p. 614, 1959.

*1439. ONG, R. S. and NICHOLLS, J. A. "On the flow of a hydromagnetic fluid near an oscillating flat plate" Reader's Forum, *J. Aero/Space Sci.*, Vol. 26, p. 313, 1959; *Math. Rev.* No. 1, p. 100, 1960.

*1440. ONG, R. S. "Characteristic manifolds in three-dimensional unsteady magneto-hydrodynamics" *Phys. Fluids*, Vol. 2, p. 247, 1959.

1441. OPIK, E. J. and SINGER, S. F. "Distribution of density in a planetary exosphere" *Phys. Fluids*, Vol. 2, p. 653, 1959.

*1442. OSBORN, A. B. "Plasma jet for laboratory use" *J. Sci. Instrum.*, Vol. 36, No. 7, pp. 317–19, 1959.

1443. OSKAM, H. J. "Tentative research program on gaseous electronics". ARDC, Conference on Ion and Plasma Research, University of Maryland, 30 Sept.– 2 Oct. 1958.

1444. OSTER, S. B. "The plasma characteristics of a low-pressure mercury discharge with several electron groups" *Akad. Wiss*, IIa, Vol. 164, p. 311, 1955.

*1445. OSTER, L. "Linearized theory of plasma oscillations" *Rev. Mod. Phys.*, Vol. 32, No. 1, pp. 141–68, 1960.

1446. OWENS, O. G. "One dimensional compressible flow of magnetohydrodynamics". Technical memorandum of Sandia Corporation 1955.

1447. OWENS, O. G. "Ecoulements simples unidimensionels en magnétohydrodynamiques" *Proc. IX Congrés International Mec. Appl.*, t. III, Université de Bruxelles, pp. 17–48, 1957.

1448. PACHOLCZYC, A. G. "Sulla instabilità magneto gravitazionale di un mezzo compressibile non uniforme con rotazione anche non uniforme" *Accad. Lincei, Roma*, Vol. XXVIII, Fasc. 3, pp. 357–63, 1960.

*1449. PAI, S. I. "Cylindrical shock waves produced by instantaneous energy release in magneto-gasdynamics". TN BN-120, Inst. Fluid Dyn. & Appl. Math. Univ. Maryland, Feb. 1958. Proc. of 4th Indian Congress for Theoretical and Applied Mech., Hourath, India, 1958.

*1450. PAI, S. I. "Shock wave propagation in an infinitely electrically conductive gas with transverse magnetic field and gravitation". TN BN-109 Inst. Fluid Dyn. and Appl. Math. Univ. Maryland, Sept. 1957, *Z. Angew Math. Mech.*, pp. 40–9, Jan.–Feb. 1959.

*1451. PAI, S. I. "Energy equation of magneto-gas dynamics" *Phys. Rev.*, Vol. 105, pp. 1424–6, 1957.

1452. PAI, S. I. "Laminar flow of an electrically conducting incompressible fluid in a circular pipe" *J. Appl. Phys.*, Vol. 25, pp. 1205–7, 1954.

1453. PAI, S. I. "Magneto-hydrodynamics and magneto-gas-dynamics". Univ. Maryland Inst. Fluid Dynamics and Appl. Math., TN BN-59, Sept. 1955.

*1454. PAI, S. I. "On exact solutions of one-dimensional flow equations of magnetohydrodynamics". Univ. Maryland Inst. Fluid. Dynamics and Appl. Maths. TN BN-2, Sept. 1956, Univ. Bruxelles, Actes du IX Congres Inst. de Mech. Appl. t. III.

*1455. PAI, S. I. "One dimensional unsteady flow of magneto-gasdynamics". Univ. Maryland Inst. Fluid Dynamics and Appl. Maths. TN BN-86, AFOSR TN 56–537. *Fifth Midwestern Conference on Fluid Mechanics*, Ann Arbor, pp. 251–61, 1957.

1456. PAI, S. I. *Viscous Flow Theory*, Vol. 2, Chap. XIV. "Turbulence in a compressible fluid flow and in magneto-hydrodynamics" Van Nostrand 1957; Proc. 5th Midwestern Conference on Fluid Mech., Univ. Mich., 1957.

1457. PAI, S. I. "Fundamental aspects of magneto-gasdynamics". Lecture series on Space Technology, WADC 1958.

1458. PAI, S. I. "Dynamics from gas dynamic point of view". TN-BN-154, Inst. Fluid Dyn. & Appl. Math. Univ. Maryland, Dec. 1958, Proc. of 1st. Int. Symposium on Rarefied Gases, Nice (France), July 1958.

1459. PAI, S. I. "Some considerations on the fundamental equations of electro-magneto-gasdynamics". Proc. of Golden Jubilee Celebration, Calcutta Mathematical Soc. Calcutta, India, 1958.

*1460. PAI, S. I. "Laminar jet mixing of electrically conducting fluid in a transverse magnetic field". Readers' Forum, *J. Aero/Space Sci.*, Vol. 26, pp. 254–5, April 1959.

1461. PAI, S. I. "The wave motions of small amplitude in a fully ionized plasma". Int. Symposium on M.F.D. Washington, Jan. 1960.

1462. PAI, S. I. "Plasmadynamics from the gasdynamics point of view". Univ. of Maryland Techn. Note BN-154.

*1463. PAI, S. I. and SPETH, A. I. "The wave motions of small amplitude in radiation-electro-magneto-gas dynamics" *Proc. Sixth Midwest. Conf. Fluid Mech. Austin, Tex., Sept. 1959*, Austin Tex. Univ. Press., pp. 446–56, 1959.

*1464. PALMER, J. L. "Laminar flow in magnetically focused cylindrical electron beams". AFOSR TN 58–990 Univ. of California.

1465. PALOVIN, R. V. "Non-linear theory of longitudinal plasma oscillations" *Zh. Eksp. Teoret. Fiz.*, Vol. 31, p. 354, 1956.

1466. PANTCHEV, S. "Sur la théorie statistique de la turbulence" *C. R. Acad. Sci., Paris*, No. 4, pp. 661–2, Jan. 1960.

1467. PAO, S. C. "On the effect of fluid motion on the initial decay of a magnetic field in a sphere" *Astrophys. J.*, Vol. 124, 266–71, 1956.

1468. PAPAS, C. H. "On the index of refraction of spatially periodic plasma" *Ionization Phenomena in Gases*, Vol. 2, p. 718. Amsterdam, North-Holland, 1959.

1469. PARDUE, L. A. and WEBB, J. S. "Ionic oscillations in the glow discharge" *Phys. Rev.*, Vol. 32, p. 946, 1928; *Bull. Amer. Phys. Soc.*, Vol. 3, p. 19, 1928.

1470. PARKER, E. N. "Dynamical instability in anisotropic ionized gas of low density" *Phys. Rev.*, Vol. 109, pp. 1874–6, 1958.

*1471. PARKER, E. N. "The generation of acoustic and hydromagnetic waves and the acceleration of cosmic rays". 1 Dec. 1955, Recd. in TIB 14 May 1955, Univ. of Utah Tech. Rept. No. 12, Contr. No. 1288 (00).

1472. PARKER, E. "Hydromagnetic waves and the acceleration of cosmic rays" *Phys. Rev.*, Vol. 99, pp. 241–53, 1955.

*1473. PARKER, E. N. "The propagation of hydromagnetic waves and the acceleration of cosmic rays". Univ. of Utah Tech. Rept. No. 13 Contr. No. 1288 (00).

*1474. PARKER, E. N. "Hydromagnetic dynamo models" *Astrophys. J.*, Vol. 122, pp. 293–314, 1955.

*1475. PARKER, E. N. "Mechanics of the geomagnetic dynamo" Univ. of Utah Tech. Rept. No. 5 on Earth's Magnetism and Magneto-hydrodynamics, 36 pp. (illus. 12 refs.), June 1954.

1476. PARKER, E. N. "Newtonian development of dynamical properties of ionized gases of low density" *Phys. Rev.*, Vol. 107, No. 4, 1957.

1477. PARKER, E. N. "Plasma instability in the interplanetary magnetic field" *The Plasma in a Magnetic Field*, Symposium, Stanford U.P., Stanford, pp. 130, fig. (CE 1536), 1958.

*1478. PARKER, E. N. "A study of Cowling's Theorem" Univ. of Utah Tech. Rept. No. 3 on Earth's Magnetism and Magneto-hydrodynamics, 22 pp. (illus.), 10 April 1954.

*1479. PARKER, E. N. "A theory of the solar magnetic field, earth's magnetism and magneto-hydrodynamics". Univ. of Utah Tech. Rept. No. 6, 8 Jan. 1954.

1480. PARKER, E. N. "Interaction of the solar wind with the geomagnetic field" *Phys. Fluids*, Vol. 1, p. 171, 1958.

1481. PARKER, E. N. "Origin and dynamics of cosmic rays" *Phys. Rev.*, Vol. 109, p. 1328, 1958.

1482. PARKER, E. N. "Sweet's mechanism for merging magnetic fields in conducting fluids" *J. Geophys. Res.*, Vol. 62, p. 509, 1957.

*1483. PARKER, E. N. and KROOK, M. "Diffusion and severing of magnetic lines of force" *Astrophys. J.*, Vol. 124, pp. 214–31, 1956; Harvard Coll. Observatory Cambridge Mass. Sci. Rept. No. 41, AFCRC TN-56-678.

*1484. PARKER, E. N. and TIDMAN, D. A. "Radio emission from plasma shocks" *Phys. Fluids*, Vol. 3, No. 3, pp. 369–72, 1960.

*1485. PARTEL, G. "Qu'est ce que la magnétohydrodynamique?" *Riv. Aeronaut.*, pp. 887–902 (7 figs.), April 1959.

1486. PARTIDGE, W. S. and HARRIS, E. G. "Feasibility of the electromagnetic accelerator". AD-158330, OSR-14, AFOSR, JN 58-517, 1958.

1487. PARGAMANIK, L. E. "On the kinetic theory of an electron gas in the presence of boundaries" *J. Exp. Theor. Phys.*, No. 1, Vol. 33, pp. 194–7, 1958.

*1488. PATRICK, R. M. "A description of a propulsive device which employs a magnetic field as the driving force". AVCO Research Laboratory, May 1958, R.R. 28 (AFOSR TN 58-684 ASTIA AD 162 217) *Vistas in Astronautics* (ed. by M. Alperin and H. F. Gregory), Vol. 2, N.Y., Pergamon Press, 1959.

*1489. PATRICK, R. M. "High speed shock waves in a magnetic annular shock tube" *Phys. Fluids*, Vol. 2, No. 6, pp. 389–598, 1959.

*1490. PATRICK, R. M. "Magneto-hydrodynamics of compressible fluids". Ph. D. Thesis. Cornell University, 1956.

1491. PATRICK, R. M. "Experimental dependence of the collision-free shock thickness upon Alfvén Mach number" *Phys. Fluids*, Vol. 3, No. 2, pp. 321–3, 1960.

*1492. PATRICK, R. M. and BROGAN, T. R. "One dimensional flow of an ionized gas through a magnetic field". AVCO Research Laboratory Research Report 13, Oct. 1957; *J. Fluid Mech.*, Vol. 5, pp. 289–309, 1959.

1493. PATTERSON, G. N. "Molecular approach to problems of high-altitude, high-speed flight". Univ. of Toronto, TN 57-311, 1957.

1494. PEASE, R. S. "Equilibrium characteristics of a pinched gas discharge coded by bremstrahlung radiation" *Proc. Phys. Soc.*, Vol. 70B, pp. 11–23, 1957.

1495. PEASE, R. S. "Sputtering of solids by penetrating ions" *Rend. Phys. School "E. Fermi"* corso XIII, pp. 158–65, Varenna, 1959.

1496. PEASE, R. S. "Phenomena at plasma-solid boundaries" *Rend. Phys. School "E. Fermi"* corso XIII, pp. 151–8, Varenna, 1959.

1497. PENNING, F. M. "Scattering of electrons in ionized gases" *Nature, Lond.*, Vol. 118, p. 301, 1926.

*1498. PENROSE, O. "Electrostatic instabilities of a uniform non-Maxwellian plasma" *Phys. Fluids*, Vol. 3, No. 2, pp. 258–65, 1960.

*1499. PESCHKA, W. "Contribution to the vortex laws in magnetohydrodynamics" *Öst. Tng. Arch.*, Vol. 13, No. 1, pp. 17–23, 1959.

*1500. PETSCHEK, H. E. "Aerodynamic dissipation". AVCOMfg. Corps. Res. Lab. Research Report No. 23, June 1957 (Cont. AF 04 (645)-18); *Rev. Mod. Phys.*, Vol. 30, July 1958.

1501. PETSCHEK, H. E. "Experiments at AVCO" *Magneto-hydrodynamics*, Stanford U.P.: Oxford U.P. (Landshoff R.K.M., editor), 1957.

1502. PETSCHEK, H. E. "Magnetohydrodynamics". ARDC, Conference on Ion and Plasma Research, University of Maryland, 30 Sept.–2 Oct. 1958.

1503. PETSCHEK, H. E. "Supersonic two-dimensional magneto-hydrodynamic magnetodynamics of conducting fluids". Symposium on M.H.D. Stanford U.P., 1959.

1504. PETSCHEK, H. E. *et al.* "Spectroscopic studies of highly ionized argon produced by shock waves" *J. Appl. Phys.*, Vol. 26, pp. 83–95, 1955.

1505. PETSCHEK, H. E., KANTROWITZ, A. and FISHMAN, F. J. "Magnetohydrodynamic shock waves in a collision-free plasma". Int. Symposium on M.F.D. Washington, Jan. 1960.

*1506. PEYRET, P. "Sur une correspondance entre certains écoulements de magnéto-dynamique des fluides et ceux de la dynamique des gaz" *C. R. Acad. Sci., Paris*, Vol. 250, No. 11, pp. 1971–3, 1960.

*1507. PFIRSCH, D. and BIERMANN, L. "Kooperative Phänomene und Diffusion eines Plasmas quer zu einem Magnetfeld (II)" *Z. Naturforsch.*, pp. 14–18, Jan. 1960.

1508. PFISTER, C. G. and DUNHAM, R. J. D. "Magnetic flowmeter for liquid sodium loops" *Nucleonics*, Vol. 15, p. 122, 1957.

*1509. PHILLIPS, N. J. "Ionization by ion impact in a collapsing current sheet" *Proc. Phys. Soc.*, Vol. 75, Pt. 2, pp. 316–17, 1960.

1510. PIDDINGTON, J. H. "Electromagnetic field equations for a moving medium with Hall conductivity" *Mon. Not. Roy. Astr. Soc.*, Vol. 114, pp. 638–50, 1954.

1511. PIDDINGTON, J. H. "The four possible waves in ionized gas in a magnetic field" *Nature, Lond.*, Vol. 176, pp. 875–6, 1955.

1512. PIDDINGTON, J. H. "The four possible waves in a magneto-ionic medium" *Phil. Mag.*, Vol. 46, pp. 1037–50, 1955.

1513. PIDDINGTON, J. H. "Hydromagnetic waves in ionized gas" *Nature, Lond.*, Vol. 176, p. 508, 1955.

1514. PIDDINGTON, J. H. "Solar atmospheric heating by hydromagnetic waves" *Mon. Not. Roy. Astr. Soc.*, Vol. 116, p. 314, 1956.

1515. PIDDINGTON, J. H. "Galactic turbulence and the origins of cosmic rays and the galactic magnetic field" *Aust. J. Phys.*, Vol. 10, p. 515, 1957.

1516. PIDDINGTON, J. H. "The motion of ionized gas in combined magnetic, electric and mechanical fields of force" *Mon. Not. Roy. Astr. Soc.*, Vol. 114, pp. 651–3, 1954.

1517. PIDDINGTON, J. H. "The Crab Nebula and the origin of interstellar magnetic fields" *Aust. J. Phys.*, Vol. 10, p. 530, 1957.

1518. PIDDINGTON, J. H. "Cosmical electrodynamics" *Proc. IRE*, Vol. 46, p. 349, 1958.

*1519. PIDDINGTON, J. H. "The transmission of geomagnetic disturbances through the atmosphere and interplanetary" *Geophys. J.*, Vol. 2, No. 3, pp. 173–89, 1959.

1520. PIERCE, J. R. "Possible fluctuations in electron streams due to ions" *J. Appl. Phys.*, Vol. 19, p. 231, 1948.

*1521. PIKELNER, S. B. "Principes de base de la magnétoaérodynamique" *Bull. Acad. Sci., URSS*, Sécie Géophysique, No. 1, pp. 46–53, Jan. 1958.

*1522. PIKELNER, S. B. "Structure of a magnetohydrodynamic shock wave in a partially ionized gas" *J. Exp. Theor. Phys.*, Vol. 9, No. 5, pp. 1089–93 (4 figs.), 1959.

1523. PINES, D. and BOHM, D. "A collective description of electron interaction; II : Collective vs. individual particle aspects of the interactions" *Phys. Rev.*, Vol. 85, p. 338, 1952.

*1524. PINTE, R. and SIMON, R. "The radial oscillations and stability of cylindrical plasma" *Bull. Acad. Roy. Belg. Cl. Sci.*, Vol. 45, No. 6, pp. 595–610.

1525. PRENDERGAST, K. H. "The equilibrium of a self-gravitating incompressible fluid sphere with a magnetic field" *Astrophys. J.*, Vol. 123, pp. 498–507, 1956.

*1526. PLUMPTON, C. and FERRARO, V. C. A. "On toroidal magnetic fields in the sun and stars" *Astrophys. J.*, Vol. 121, pp. 168–74, 1955.

1527. PNEUMANN, G. W. and LYKOUDIS, P. S. "Magneto-fluid-mechanics of a viscous, electrically conducting fluid contained within two finite, concentric, rotating cylinders in the presence of a magnetic field". Purdue Univ. School of Aeronautical Engineering, Rep. N.A.-5913, Aug. 1959.

1528. PODOLSKY, B. "Magnetohydrodynamics". General Electric Company, FPD-FPLD, Report R 58 AGT, 967.

*1529. POKALITOV, E. P. "The resonance of charge carriers produced by ultrasonic wave" *J. Exp. Theor. Phys.*, No. 5, p. 1057, Nov. 1959.

1530. Polovin, R. V. "Zemplen's theorem in relativistic hydrodynamics" *J. Exp. Theor. Phys.*, Vol. 36, No. 3, p. 675, 1959.

1531. Polovin, R. V. "Non-linear theory of longitudinal plasma oscillations" *J. Exp. Theor. Phys.*, Vol. 4, p. 290, 1957.

*1532. Polovin, R. V. and Tsintsadze, N. L. "Theory of longitudinal oscillations in an electron-ion beam" *Zh. Tekh. Fiz.*, Vol. 29, No. 7, pp. 831–2, 1959; *Soviet Phys. Tech. Phys.* (New York), Vol. 4, No. 7, pp. 751–2, 1960.

1533. Polovin, R. V. and Liubarskii, G. I. "Impossibility of rarefaction shock waves in magnetohydrodynamics" *J. Exp. Theor. Phys.*, No. 2, p. 351, Feb. 1959.

*1534. Popescu, I. "Kinetics of ions in gases" *Rev. Physique* (Bucarest), Vol. 4, No. 2, pp. 199–209, 1959.

1535. Post, R. F. "Controlled fusion research. An application of the physics of high temperature plasmas" *Rev. Mod. Phys.*, Vol. 28, p. 338, 1956.

1536. Post, R. F. "Acceleration of a plasma by time-varying magnetic fields". AEC Rep. UCRL-4407, 1958.

1537. Post, R. F. "Summary of U.C.R.L. pyrotron (mirror machine) program" *Proc. 2nd Geneva Conf.*, Vol. 32, pp. 245–65, 1958.

*1538. Post, R. F., Ellis, R. E., Ford, F. C. and Rosenbluth, M. "Stable confinement of a high-temperature plasma" *Phys. Rev. Letters*, Vol. 4, No. 4, pp. 166–70, 1960.

1539. Pozzi, A. "Getti di fluidi elettricamente conduttori in presenza di campi magnetici". Atti del VII Convegno Internazionale delle Comunicazioni Genova 1959.

*1540. Pradhan, T. "Plasma oscillations in a steady magnetic field: Circularly polarized electromagnetic modes" *Phys. Rev.*, Vol. 107, pp. 1222–7, 1957.

*1541. Prakash, S. and Tandon, J. N. "On the reflection and refraction of magneto-hydrodynamic waves" *Proc. Nat. Inst. Sci., India*, A, Vol. 23, No. 4, pp. 264–73, 1957 (IRE No. 423, March 1958).

1542. Prendergast, K. H. "The equilibrium of a self-gravitating incompressible fluid sphere with a magnetic field" *Astrophys. J.*, Vol. 123, pp. 498–508, 1956.

*1543. Prevot, F., Hubert, P. and Gourdon, C. "Sur la possibilité de formation d'un plasma thermonucléaire par injection d'ions accélérés dans une configuration magnétique à miroirs" *C. R. Acad. Sci., Paris*, Vol. 249, pp. 987–93, 1959.

*1544. Prokof'ev, V. K., Gurevich, D. B., Belusova, I. H. and Snigirev, Y. A. "The time required for establishment of thermodynamic equilibrium in the plasma of an arc discharge" *Optika i Spetrosk*, Vol. 7, No. 1, pp. 14–20, 1959 (in Russian).

1545. Pütter, P. S. and Sauter, F. "Über die statistiken von Plasmas" *Ann. Phys.*, Vol. 1, p. 4, 1958.

*1546. Pupke, H. and Thom, H. G. "The rotation of plasmoids in a magnetic field". TIL/OT/2653 AEI T/1190, Aug. 1957.

1547. Raha, P. K. and Chatterjee, S. D. "Influence of a magnetic field on the coefficient of viscosity of liquids" *Indian J. Phys.*, Vol. 9, p. 445, 1935.

1548. Raizer, Y. P. "A simple method of calculating the degree of ionization and thermodynamic functions of a multiple ionized ideal gas" *J. Exp. Theor. Phys.*, No. 9, pp. 1124–5, Nov. 1959.

*1549. Raizer, M. D. and Shpigel, I. S. "Etude du plasma à l'aide des ondes radioélectriques ultracourtes" *Prog. Sci. Phys.* (*Usp. Fiz. Nauk.*), Vol. 44, No. 4, pp. 641–67, 1958.

*1550. Ramamoorty, P. "Superposability of two axi-symmetric flows under axi-symmetric magnetic fields" *Appl. Sci. Res.* A., Vol. 9, No. 2–3, pp. 153–6, 1960.

1551. Ramer, J. D. "Bibliography on plasma physics and magnetohydrodynamics and their applications to controlled thermonuclear reactions". Un. of Maryland, Eng. and Phys. Sciences Library, 105 pp. Oct. 1959.

1552. RAND, S. "Magnetic drag on small satellites". AEC Rep. ZPH-024, 1958.

1553. RAND, S. "Electrostatic field about an ion moving slowly in a plasma" *Phys. Fluids*, Vol. 2, p. 649, 1959.

*1554. RAWER, K. and SUCHY, K. "La quatrième condition de réflexion des ondes électromagnétiques dans un plasma" *C. R. Acad. Sci., Paris*, Vol. 246, No. 25, p. 3428, 1958.

1555. RAWER, K. and SUCHY, K. "Statistical derivation of the dispersion formula of a Lorentz plasma of finite temperature" *Ann. Phys.*, Vol. 7, p. 313–25, 1958.

1556. RAWER, K. and SUCHY, K. "Longitudinal and transversal waves in Lorentz plasma" *Ann. Phys.*, Vol. 7, pp. 103–11, 1959.

1557. RAWER, K. and SUCHY, K. "Equivalence theorem on the wave absorption in the plasma" *Ann. Phys., Lpz.*, Vol. p. 255, 1958.

1558. REAGAN, D. "Some compression waves in plasmas" *Phys. Fluids*, Vol. 2, p. 93, 1959.

*1559. REAGAN, D. "Transverse compression waves in a stabilized discharge" *Phys. Fluids*, Vol. 3, No. 1, pp. 33–9, 1960.

*1560. REGIRER, S. A. "Sur le mouvement de convection d'un liquide conducteur entre deux plaques paralleles verticales dans un champ magnétique" *J. Exp. Theor. Phys.*, Vol. 37 (10) No. 1, pp. 149–52, 1960; *Zh. Eksp. Teoret. Fiz. SSSR*, Vol. 37, pp. 212–6, 1959.

*1561. REGIRER, S. A. "Problème non-stationnaire de la magnétohydrodynamique pour un demi-espace". C.N.R.S., Jan. 1960; *Dokl. Akad. Nauk., SSSR*, Vol. 127, No. 5, pp. 983–6, 1959 (in Russian).

*1562. REID, W. H. "The stability of non-dissipative Couette flow in the presence of an axial magnetic field" *Proc. Nat. Acad. Sci., U.S.A.*, Vol. 46, No. 3, pp. 370–3, 1960.

1563. REIFFEL, L. "Structural damage and other effects of solar plasmas" *ARS J.*, Vol. 30, No. 3, p. 258, 1960.

1564. RESLER, E. L. Jr. and McCUNE, J. E. "Some exact solutions in linearized magneto-aerodynamics for arbitrary magnetic Reynolds numbers". Int. Symposium on M.F.D. Washington, Jan. 1960.

1565. RESLER, E. L. and McCUNE, J. E. "Electromagnetic interaction with aerodynamic flows". (Cornell University) Third Magnetohydrodynamic Symposium, Lockheed Res. Lab. Palo Alto, 22–27 Nov. 1958.

1566. RESLER, E. L. Jr. and McCUNE, J. E. "Third Annual Lockheed Symposium on MHD". Cornell University.

*1567. RESLER, E. L. and SEARS, W. R. "Magneto-gasdynamic channel flow" *Z. Angew. Math. Phys.*, No. special, 5–6, pp. 509–518, March 1958.

1568. RESLER, E. L. and SEARS, W. R. "The prospects for magnetoaerodynamics" *J. Aero. Sci.*, No. 4, pp. 235–45 and 258, April 1958; IAS Meeting, Los Angeles, 1957.

*1569. RESLER, E. L. Jr. and SEARS, W. R. "The prospects for magneto-aerodynamics —Correction and addition" *J. Aero/Space Sci.*, Vol. 26, No. 5, p. 313, 1959.

1570. REVANS, R. W. "The transmission of waves through an ionized gas" *Phys. Rev.*, Vol. 44, p. 798, 1933.

*1571. RHUDE, D. P. "Transmission of an electromagnetic wave through a hypersonic shock wave". AF Inst. of Tech. Wright-Patterson Air Force, Master's thesis, March 1959, 64 pp. incl. (Rept. No. GE-59 A-9).

*1572. RIBE, F. L. "Recent experimental results on fast-compression plasma heating and rotating plasmas" *Ionization Phenomena in Gases*, Vol. 2, p. 1032. Amsterdam, North-Holland, 1959.

1573. RICHTER, E. "Die Theorie magnetohydrodynamischer Wellen bei Verwendung der Energie Impuls-Tensors von Abraham" *Z. Phys.*, Vol. 148, p. 253, 1957.

1574. RICHTER, E. "On the theory of magneto-hydrodynamic waves" *Z. Naturforsch.*, Vol. 11a, p. 251, 1956.

1575. RICHTER, E. "Extension of the theory of hydromagnetic waves and application to inhomogeneous layers" *Z. Naturforsch.*, Vol. 11a, pp. 901–12, 1956.

1576. RICHTER, E. "Application of Abraham's energy-momentum tensor in the theory of hydromagnetic waves" *Z. Phys.*, Vol. 148, pp. 253–61, 1957.

1577. RIEGER, E. "Der Einfluss magnetischer Felder auf des Warmeleitvermögen von Gasen" *Ann. Phys.*, Vol. 31, p. 453, 1938.

1578. RIKITAKE, T. "Magneto-hydrodynamic oscillations of a perfectly conducting fluid sphere placed in a uniform magnetic field" *J. Phys. Soc., Japan*, Vol. 13, No. 10, pp. 1224–30, 1958.

*1579. RJAZANOV, E. V. "Quelques solutions précises des équations de la magnéto-gazdynamique en présence des forces de gravitation propre et d'un gradient nul de la température". C.N.R.S. Jan. 1960; *Dokl. Akad. Nauk., SSSR*, Vol. 126, No. 6, pp. 1224–6, 1959 (in Russian).

1580. RJAZANOV, E. V. "Résolution des équations de magnétohydrodynamique définissant les mouvements unidimensionnels à symétrie axiale d'un gaz pesant" *Prikl. Mat. Mekh.*, Vol. 22, No. 1, pp. 187–9. 1959.

*1581. ROBERTS, P. H. "On the equilibrium of magnetic stars" *Astrophys. J.*, Vol. 122, pp. 508–12, 1955.

1582. ROBERTS, P. H. "Twisted magnetic fields" *Astrophys. J.*, Vol. 124, pp. 432–42, 1956.

1583. ROBERTS, P. H. "Hydromagnetic disturbances in a fluid of finite conductivity" *Astrophys. J.*, Vol. 126, pp. 418–28, 1957.

*1584. ROBERTS, P. H. "Propagation of induced fields through the core" *Ann. Geophys.*, Vol. 15, No. 1, pp. 75, 86, 1959.

*1585. ROBERTS, P. H. "On the reflection and refraction of hydromagnetic waves" *Astrophys. J.*, Vol. 121, pp. 720–30, 1955.

*1586. ROBERTS, P. H. "Hydromagnetic disturbances in a fluid of finite conductivity" *Astrophys. J.*, Vol. 122, pp. 315–26, 1955.

1587. ROBSON, A. E. "Controlled thermonuclear fusion" *Nucl. Power*, pp. 486–9, 1958.

1588. ROMELL, D. "Radio reflections from a column of ionized gas" *Nature, Lond.*, Vol. 167, p. 243, 1951.

1589. RON, A. "Penetration of a magnetic field into a one-dimensional Plasma" *Nuovo Cimento*, Vol. 10, No. 5, pp. 659–74, 1958.

1590. ROSA, R. J. "Engineering magneto-hydrodynamics". Ph. D. Thesis, Cornell University, 1956.

1591. ROSA, R. J. "Shock wave spectroscopy and engineering magneto-hydrodynamics". Ph. D. Thesis, Cornell University, 1956.

1592. ROSA, R. J. "Magnetohydrodynamic power generation using nuclear fuel". AVCO RR 87, March 1960.

*1593. ROSA, R. J. "An experimental magnetohydrodynamic power generator" *J. Appl. Phys.*, Vol. 31, No. 4, pp. 735–6, 1960.

1594. ROSA, R. J. and KANTROWITZ, A. R. "Magnetohydrodynamic energy conversion techniques". AVCO RR 86, April 1959.

1595. ROSE, M. "On the structure of a steady hydromagnetic shock. One fluid theory". New York University Institute of Mathematical Sciences. ARC Computing Facility, Oct. 1956.

*1596. ROSE, P. H. "Physical gas dynamics research of the AVCO research laboratory (pp. 44–9 Magneto-hydrodynamics)". AVCO Research Laboratory Research Note 37. Paper presented at 7th Meeting, AGARD wind tunnel and model testing panel, AGARD Report 145, 1957.

*1597. ROSEN, P. "Variational approach to magneto-fluid-dynamics" *Phys. Fluids*, Vol. 1, No. 3, p. 251, 1958.

*1598. ROSEN, P. "Scattering of electromagnetic waves by longitudinal plasma waves" *Phys. Fluids*, Vol. 3, No. 3, pp. 416–18, 1960.

1599. ROSENBLUTH, M. N. "Dynamics of a pinched gas". *Magneto-hydrodynamics Symposium.* Stanford U.P.: Oxford U.P. (Landshoff, R.K.M., editor), 1957.

*1600. ROSENBLUTH, M. N. "Transport properties of ionized gases in a magnetic field". American Rocket Society, New York, Preprint, No. 484-57, 7 pp., Aug. 1957.

1601. ROSENBLUTH, M. N. "Hydrodynamic basis for treatment of plasmas" *The Plasma in a Magnetic Field*: Symposium. Stanford U.P., Stanford 1958, 130 pp. (fig.) (Ce. 1536).

1602. ROSENBLUTH, M. N. *et al.* "Relaxation of a system of particle with Coulomb interactions" *Phy. Rev.*, Vol. 107, p. 350, 1957.

1603. ROSENBLUTH, M. N., McDONALD, W. M. "Fokker-Planck equation for an inverse square force" *Phys. Rev.*, Vol. 107, p. 1, 1957.

*1604. ROSENBLUTH, M. and LONGMIRE, C. L. "Stability of plasmas confined by magnetic fields" *Ann. Phys.*, Vol. 1, pp. 120–40, 1957.

*1605. ROSENBLUTH, M. N. and KAUFMAN, A. N. "Plasma diffusions in a magnetic field" *Phys. Rev.*, Vol. 109, pp. 1–5, 1958.

*1606. ROSENBLUTH, M. N. and ROSTOKER, N. "Theoretical structure of plasma equations" *Phys. Fluids*, Vol. 2, pp. 23–30, 1959.

1607. ROSENBLUTH, M. N. and ROSTOKER, N. "Test particles in a plasma" *Ionization Phenomena in Gases*, Vol. 2, p. 566. Amsterdam, North-Holland, 1959.

*1608. ROSNER, D. E. and CALCOTE, H. F. "Generation of supersonic dissociated and ionized non-equilibrium streams". Aero. Chem. Res. Lab. TM 10 (AFOSR TN 58–1080) AD 207590, 30 pp. (10 refs.), Oct. 1958.

1609. ROSSELUND, *Astrophysik.* Berlin, Springer Verlag, 1931.

*1610. ROSSOW, V. J. "Boundary-layer stability diagrams for electrically conducting fluids in the presence of a magnetic field". TN N.A.C.A., No. 4282, 32 pp. (4 figs., 3 tables), MP 52, August, 1958.

*1611. ROSSOW, V. J. "On flow of electrically conducting fluids over a flat plate in the presence of a transverse magnetic field". TR N.A.C.A., No. 1358, 20 pp. (11 figs., 3 tables), MP 51, 1958.

*1612. ROSSOW, V. J. "Magnetohydrodynamic analysis of heat transfer near a stagnation point" *J. Aero. Sci.*, Vol. 25, No. 5, pp. 334–5 (Readers' Forum), 1958.

*1613. ROSSOW, V. J. "On magneto-aerodynamic boundary layers" *Z. Angew. Math. Phys.*, No. special, 5–6, pp. 519–27, March 1958.

*1614. ROSSOW, V. J. "On series expansions in magnetic Reynolds number". ASTIA, Jan. 60—NASA, TN n. D-10.

*1615. ROSSOW, V. J. "On Rayleigh's problem in magnetohydrodynamics" *Phys. Fluids*, Vol. 3, No. 3, pp. 395–9, 1960.

1616. ROSSOW, V. J. "On flow through direct-current electromagnetic pumps". Int. Symposium on M.F.D. Washington, Jan. 1960.

1617. ROSTOKER, N. and ROSENBLUTH, M. N. "Test particles in a completely ionized plasma" *Phys. Fluids*, Vol. 3, No. 1, pp. 1–15, 1960.

1618. ROTHER, H. "Zum Problem nichtlinearer Plasmaschwingungen" *Ionization Phenomena in Gases*, Vol. II, p. 704. Amsterdam, North-Holland, 1959.

*1619. ROTT, N. "A simple construction for the determination of the magneto-hydrodynamic wave speed in a compressible conductor" *J. Aero/Space Sci.*, Vol. 26, No. 4, pp. 249–50, 1959.

*1620. RUDAKOV, L. I. and SAGDEEV, R. Z. "Oscillations of an inhomogeneous plasma in a magnetic field" *Zh. Eksp. Teoret. Fiz.*, Vol. 37, No. 5 (11) pp. 1337–41, 1959.

1621. RUDI, S. O. "Characteristic manifolds in three-dimensional unsteady magneto-hydrodynamics" *Phys. Fluids*, Vol. 2, p. 247, 1959.

*1622. RUDIN, M. "Magnetic channelling and the nozzle". ARS-Northwestern gas dynamics Symposium—Northwestern Univ., 24–26 August, 1959.

1623. RYDBECK, O. E. H. "Plasma resonance coupling in ionized media" *Ionization Phenomena in Gases*, Vol. 2, p. 726. Amsterdam, North-Holland, 1959.

1624. RYDBECK, O. E. H. "On the interaction between space charge waves and electromagnetic waves in a cold plasma" *Ionization Phenomena in Gases*, Vol. 2, p. 681. Amsterdam, North-Holland, 1959.

1625. RYDBECK, O. E. H. and FISCHER, M. "Raumladungswellen in einem Elektronenstrahl veränderlicher radialer Dichte" *Ionization Phenomena in Gases*, Vol. 2, p. 657. Amsterdam, North-Holland, 1959.

1626. RYDBECK, O. E. H. and THOMASSON, A. R. "Low frequency waves in magneto ionic media" *Ionization Phenomena in Gases*, Vol. 2, p. 707. Amsterdam, North-Holland, 1959.

1627. RYDBECK, O. E. H. and WILHELMSSON, H. "Influence of the electron velocity distribution upon the space charge wave properties of electron beams" *Ionization Phenomena in Gases*, Vol. 2, p. 653. Amsterdam, North-Holland, 1959.

*1628. SACERDOTI, G. "Studio di un contenitore magnetico a forma di otto" *Atti Accad. Sci. Torino*, Vol. 93, pp. 62–81, 1958–59.

*1629. SACERDOTI, G. "Studio del moto di una particella carica in un campo magnetico di un solenoide toroidale" *Atti Accad. Sci. Torino*, Vol. 33, pp. 72–83, 1958–59.

*1630. SACERDOTI, G. "Studio di moto di una particella carica in un campo magnetico in presenza di un'onda elettromagnetica piana che si propaga nella direzione del campo nel caso non relativistico" *Atti Accad. Sci. Torino*, Vol. 93, pp. 530–56, 1958–59.

1631. SAGDEYEN, R. Z. "Shock waves in rarefied plasma" *Ionization Phenomena in Gases*, Vol. 2, p. 1081. Amsterdam, North-Holland, 1959.

1632. SAHA, M. N. "Ionization in the solar chromosphere" *Phil. Mag.*, Vol. 40, p. 472, 1920.

*1633. SAKKURAI, T. "Two-dimensional hypersonic flow of an ideal gas with infinite electric conductivity past a two-dimensional magnetic dipole" *J. Aero/Space Sci.*, Vol. 26, No. 12, p. 841, 1959.

1634. SALMON, J. "Etude des plasmas en regime transitiore" *J. Phys. Radium*, Vol. 17, p. 931, 1956.

1635. SAWADA, K., BRUECKNER, K. A., FUKUDA, N. and BROUT, R. "Correlation energy of electron gas at high density: plasma oscillations" *Phys. Rev.*, Vol. 108, pp. 507–14, 1957.

*1636. SAWYER, G. A., SCOTT, P. L. and STRATTON, T. F. "Experimental demonstration of hydromagnetic waves in an ionized gas" *Phys. Fluids*, Vol. 2, No. 47, p. 51, 1959.

1637. SAWYER, G. A. and STRATTON, T. F. "Low gradient pinch program". Controlled Thermonuclear Conf., Naval Research Lab., Washington, 1958.

1638. SCHATZMAN, E. "On the stability of a periodic force-free field with neutral lines". Int. Symposium on M.F.D. Washington, Jan. 1960.

1639. SCHATZMAN, E. "Le plasma stellaire" *Nuovo Cimento*, Suppl. Vol. XIII, Ser. X, No. 1, pp. 166–89, 1959.

1640. SCHEIBE, M. "Interaction between a strong shock and an inhomogeneous magnetic field". Paper presented at the Divisional Meeting of the Division of Fluid Dynamics, American Physical Society, San Diego, Calif., 24–26 Nov., 1958.

1641. SCHIFF, F. I. "Nucleon structure and electro-magnetic interaction theory" AFOSR-TN-59-900, Stanford University, Sept. 1959.

1642. SCHILLING, P. O. and LOCHTE-HOLTGREVIN, W. "Magnetfelder in turbulent strömenden Plasma" *Z. Naturforsch*, Vol. 9a, p. 520, 1954.

1643. SCHIRMER, I. H. "On the calculations of the electrical conductivity and the thermal conductivity of plasmas, with application to a Xeon high-pressure discharge" *Appl. Sci. Res.* B, Vol. 5, p. 196, 1955.

1644. SCHIRMER, I. H. "Theorie der Elektrischen Leitfähigkeit eines Plasmas" *Z. Phys.*, Vol. 142, p. 1, 1955.

1645. SCHIRMER, I. H. and FRIEDRICH, J. "Die Elektrischen Leitfähigkeit eines Plasmas" *Z. Phys.*, Vol. 1151, pp. 174–86, 1958.

1646. SCHIRMER, I. H. and FRIEDRICH, J. "Die Warmeleitfähigkeit eines Plasmas" *Z. Phys.*, Vol. 153, pp. 563–70, 1959.

1647. SCHLAPP, D. M. "An attempt to measure the collision frequency of electrons in the F-region of the ionosphere" *J. Atmos. Terr. Phys.*, Vol. 17, No. 3, 1960.

1648. SCHLÜTER, A. "The Gyro-relaxation effect" *Z. Naturforsch.*, Vol. 12a, pp. 822–5, 1957.

1649. SCHLÜTER, A. "Dynamics of plasma, I: Fundamental equations of a plasma in crossed fields" *Z. Naturforsch.*, Vol. 5a, pp. 72–8, 1950.

1650. SCHLÜTER, A. and BIERMANN, L. "Dynamics of plasmas, II: Plasma with neutral gas" *Z. Naturforsch.*, Vol. 6a, pp. 73–8, 1951.

*1651. SCHLÜTER, A. "On magneto-fluid-dynamics" *Combustion and Propulsion* Third AGARD Colloquium, March, 1958. London, Pergamon Press, 1958.

1652. SCHLÜTER, A. "Kraftfreie Magnetfelder" *Z. Naturforsch.*, Vol. 12a, pp. 855–9, 1957.

1653. SCHLÜTER, A. and BIERMANN, L. "Interstellar magnetic fields" *Z. Naturforsch.*, Vol. 5a, pp. 237–51, 1950.

1654. SCHMIDT, G. "Virial theorem for plasmas" *Phys. Fluids*, Vol. 3, No. 3, pp. 481–2, 1960.

1655. SCHMIDT, G.. "Investigation on plasma in external magnetic field, I; Steady states" *Nuovo Cimento*, Vol. 1, p. 55, 1959.

1656. SCHMIDT, G. "An investigation on plasmas in external magnetic fields, II: Varying fields" *Nuovo Cimento*, No. 10, pp. 659–74, 1958.

1657. SCHMIDT, G. and BOSTICK, W. *et al.* "Acceleration of a plasma by means of a rail-type gun". Paper FA 13, Amer. Phys. Soc. Spring Meeting, 1959, Washington, D.C., 30 April–2 May, 1959.

1658. SCHNEIDER, F. "Collision-free heating of a plasma" *Z. Angew. Phys.*, Vol. 12, No. 1, pp. 5–7, 1960 (in German).

1659. SCHNITZER, H. "Helix type gaseous discharge noise sources at low plasma densities" *J. Electronics*, Vol. 2, p. 368, 1957.

1660. SCHULTZ, D. L. "Microwave studies of the properties of ionized air in a shock tube" *Ionization Phenomena in Gases*, Vol. 2, p. 1118. Amsterdam, North-Holland, 1959.

1661. SCHULTZ-DU-BOIS, E. "Elementare Prozesse der Elektronenrekombination in Discharge Plasmas" *Z. Angew. Math. Phys.*, Vol. 8, p. 267, 1956.

1662. SCHUMANN, W. O. "On the propagation of electrical waves along a dielectrically bounded plasma layer with longitudinal magnetic field" *Z. Angew. Math. Phys.*, Vol. 10, p. 26, 1958.

1663. SCHUMANN, W. O. "Wave propagation in the plasma between two perfectly conducting planes in the direction of an applied magnetic field" *Z. Angew. Math. Phys.*, Vol. 8, pp. 482–5, 1956 (IRE n. 1881, July 1957).

1664. SCHUMANN, W. O. "Über longitudinal und transversale elektrische Wellen in homogenen bewegten Plasma" *Z. Angew. Math. Phys.*, Vol. 3, p. 178, 1951.

1665. SCHUMANN, W. O. "Über elektrische Wellen in bewegten Plasma" *Z. Angew. Math. Phys.*, Vol. 2, p. 393, 1950.

*1666. SCHUMANN, W. O. "Sur les ondes hydromagnétiques dans les plasmas" *Z. Angew. Math. Phys.*, No. 7, pp. 259–264, 1959.

1667. SCHUMANN, W. O. "Wave propagation and oscillations in plasma bodies". ARDC, Conference on Ion and Plasma Research, University of Maryland, 30 Sept.–2 Oct. 1958.

1668. Schumann, W. O. "Der Plasma Kondensator" *Z. Naturforsch.*, Vol. 13a, pp. 888–95, 1958.

1669. Schumann, W. O. "On plasma transit time oscillation" *Z. Phys.*, Vol. 121, p. 7, 1943.

1670. Schwartz, S. B. and Zirin, H. "Ionization of Fe XIV in a hot plasma" *Phys. Fluids*, Vol. 2, p. 94 (1959).

1671. Schwartzschild, M. "Magnetic oscillation of a highly idealized star" *Ann. Astrophys.*, Vol. 12, p. 148, 1949.

1672. Schwartzschild, M. and Kruskal, M. A. "Some instabilities of a completely ionized plasma" *Proc. Roy. Soc.* A, Vol. 123, pp. 348–60, 1954.

1673. Scott, F. R. and Wenzel, R. F. "Moving magnetic field behind a strong deuterium shock" *Phys. Fluids*, Vol. 2, p. 609, 1959.

1674. Scott, F. R., Wenzel, R. F. "Experimental plasma flow into a vacuum cusp field" *Phys. Rev.*, Vol. 119, No. 4, pp. 1189–92, 1960.

1675. Scott, F. R., Basman, W. P., Little, E. M. and Thomson, D. B. "Magnetic channelling of a strong shock" *The Plasma in a Magnetic Field*: Symposium, 140 pp. (fig.), Stanford U.P., Stanford, 1958. (Ce. 1536.)

1676. Sears, W. R. "Recent developments in magneto-aerodynamics IAS summer meetings". Los Angeles, June, 1957.

*****1677.** Sears, W. R. "Magneto-hydrodynamics in aeronautics" American Rocket Society. Preprint No. 709/58, No. 1958.

*****1678.** Sears, W. R. "Magnetics may aid return of satellites, missiles and rockets" *Astronautics*, Vol. 3, No. 3, p. 148, 1959.

*****1679.** Sears, W. R. "Some solutions of the macroscopic equation of magneto-gas dynamics". Preprint Third Biennial Gas Dynamic Symposium, ARS Northwestern Univ., 24–26 Aug., 1959.

*****1680.** Sears, W. R. and Resler, E. L. "Theory of thin airfoil in fluids of high electrical conductivity" *J. Fluid Mech.*, Vol. 5, Pt. 2, pp. 257–73, 1959.

*****1681.** Sears, W. R. "Magneto-hydrodynamic effects in aerodynamic flows" *J. Amer. Rocket Soc.*, No. 6, pp. 397–406 (7 figs.), 1959.

1682. Sears, W. R. "Magnetohydrodynamics". ARDC, Conference on Ion and Plasma Research, University of Maryland, 30 Sept.–2 Oct., 1958.

1683. Segre, S. "On the formation of magneto hydrodynamic shock waves" *Nuovo Cimento*, Vol. 9, p. 1504–7, 1958.

1684. Sehoguchi, J. and Hermcha, R. C. "Thermal conductivity of an electron gas in a gaseous plasma" *Phys. Rev.*, Vol. 112, pp. 1–10, 1958.

1685. Seifert, H. S. (editor) "Space technology" *Magnetohydrodynamics* by Clauser M. U., Chapter 18, Wiley, 1959.

1686. Self, S. A. "Comments on confinement of plasma by standing electromagnetic waves" *Phys. Fluids*, Vol. 3, No. 3, pp. 488–9, 1960.

1687. Sen, H. K. "Solar 'enhanced radiation' and plasma oscillations" *Phys. Rev.*, Vol. 88, p. 816, 1952.

*****1688.** Sen, H. K. "Structure of a magnetohydrodynamic shock wave in a plasma of infinite conductivity" *Phys. Rev.*, Vol. 102, pp. 5–11, 1956.

1689. Senftleben, H. "Magnetic influence on thermal conductivity of a paramagnetic gas" *Z. Phys.*, Vol. 31, p. 961, 1931.

1690. Senftleben, H. "Influence of magnetic and electric fields on heat transmission through gases" *Z. Phys.*, Vol. 74, p. 757, 1932.

1691. Senftleben, H. "Influence of electric fields on heat transmission through gases" *Z. Phys.*, Vol. 35, p. 661, 1934.

1692. Senftleben, H. and Gladisch, H. "Der Einfluss magnetischer Felder auf der innere Reibung von Gases" *Ann. Phys.*, Vol. 30, p. 713, 1937.

1693. Sentfleben, H. and Gladisch, H. "Der Einfluss magnetischer Felder auf der innere Reibung von Gasen" *Ann. Phys.*, Vol. 33, p. 471, 1938.

1694. Senftleben, H. and Pietzner, J. "Influence of magnetic fields on heat conduction in paramagnetic gases" *Z. Phys.*, Vol. 34, p. 834, 1933.

1695. Senftleben, H. and Pietzner, J. "Die Einwirkung magnetischer Felder auf des Warmeleitvermögen von Gasen" *Ann. Phys.*, Vol. 5, p. 907, 1933.

1696. Senftleben, H. and Pietzner, J. "Die Einwirkung magnetischer Felder auf den Warmstrom in Gasen" *Z. Phys.*, Vol. 35 pp. 986, 1934.

1697. Senftleben, H. and Pietzner, J. "Die Einwirkung magnetischer Felder auf des Warmeleithermögen von Gasen II, III" *Ann. Phys.*, Vol. 27, p. 108, 1936.

1698. Senftleben, H. and Pietzner, J. "Die Einwirskung magnetischer Felder auf des Warmeleitvermogen von Gasen IV" *Ann. Phys.*, Vol. 30, p. 541, 1937.

*1699. Senior, T. B. A. "Diffraction by an imperfectly conducting wedge" *Comm. Pure Appl. Math.*, Vol. 12, No. 2, pp. 337–72, 1959.

1700. Severnyl, A. B. "Magnetohydrodynamic motions in solar protuberances" *Dokl. Akad. Nauk.*, SSSR, Vol. 91, p. 1051, 1953.

*1701. Seymour, P. W. "Drift of a charged particle in a magnetic field of constant gradient" *Aust. J. Phys.*, Vol. 12, No. 4, pp. 309–14, 1959.

1702. Shaphranov, V. D. "An annular magneto-vortex" *Zh. Eksp. Teoret. Fiz.*, Vol. 33, p. 831, 1957.

1703. Shaphranov, V. D. "On equilibrium magnetohydrodynamical configuration" *Zh. Teoret. Eksp. Fiz.*, Vol. 33, p. 710, 1957.

*1704. Shaphranov, V. D. "On the stability of a cylindrical gaseous conductor in a magnetic field" *Sov. J. Atomic Energy*, No. 5, pp. 709–13, 1956; *J. Nuclear Energy*, Vol. 5, No. 1, pp. 86–91, 1957.

1705. Shaphranov, V. D. "The structure of a shock wave in a plasma" *Zh. Eksp. Teoret. Fiz.*, Vol. 32, June 1957.

*1706. Shaphranov, V. D. "On magneto-hydrodynamical equilibrium configurations. Appendix: criteria for the stability of a perfectly conducting cylinder with a surface current" *Zh. Eksp. Teoret. Fiz.*, pp. 710–22, Sept. 1957; *J. Exp. Theor. Phys.*, No. 3, pp. 545–54 (15 refs.), March 1958.

*1707. Shaphranov, V. D. "Propagation of an electromagnetic field in a medium with spatial dispersion" *J. Exp. Theor. Phys.*, Vol. 34, No. 6, pp. 1019–29, December 1958.

*1708. Shankaranarayana, Rao B. "A note on rotating configuration associated with toroidal magnetic field" *Proc. Nat. Inst. Sci. India* A, Vol. 24, No. 6, pp. 315–18, 1958.

1709. Shapiro, N. and Papas, C. H. "Electromagnetic scattering properties of a resonant plasma". ARDC, Conference on Ion and Plasma Research, University of Maryland, 30 Sept.–2 Oct. 1958.

*1710. Sharikadze, D. V. "Mouvements automodèles et l'explosion ponctuelle dans la magnétogaz-dynamique dans le cas de conductibilité infinie du gaz" C.N.R.S. Jan. 1960; *Dokl. Akad. Nauk.*, SSSR, Vol. 127, No. 6, pp. 1183–6, 1959 (in Russian).

1711. Schear, C., Mead, L. and Fitz, C. D. "The high intensity arc as a plasma propulsion source". ARDC, Conference on Ion and Plasma Research, University of Maryland, 30 Sept.–2 Oct. 1958.

1712. Shercliff, J. A. "Entry of conducting and non-conducting fluids in pipes" *Proc. Camb. Phil. Soc.*, Vol. 52, pp. 573–83, 1956.

*1713. Shercliff, J. A. "The flow of conducting fluids in circular pipes under transverse magnetic fields" *J. Fluid Mech.*, Vol. I, Pt. 6, Dec. 1956.

*1714. Shercliff, J. A. "Relation between the velocity profile and the sensitivity of electromagnetic flowmeters" *J. Appl. Phys.*, Vol. 25, pp. 817–18, 1954.

*1715. Shercliff, J. A. "Some engineering applications of magneto-hydrodynamics" *Proc. Roy. Soc.* A, Vol. 233, pp. 346–401, 1955.

1716. Shercliff, J. A. "Steady motion of conducting fluids in pipes under transverse magnetic fields" *Proc. Camb. Phil. Soc.*, Vol. 49, pp. 136–44, 1953.

1717. SHERCLIFF, J. A. "Axial current electromagnetic flow-meters reactor technology" *J. Nucl. Energy*, Vol. 1, pp. 3–9, 1959.

*1718. SHERCLIFF, J. A. "Experiments on the dependence of sensitivity on velocity profile in electromagnetic flowmeters" *J. Sci. Instrum.*, Vol. 32, pp. 441–2, 1955.

1719. SHERCLIFF, J. A. "Edge effects in electromagnetic flowmeters" *J. Nucl. Energy*, Vol. 3, p. 305, 1956.

*1720. SHERCLIFF, J. A. "Electromagnetic flowmeter without external magnet" *J. Appl. Phys.*, Vol. 28, p. 140, 1957.

*1721. SHERCLIFF, J. A. "Magnetogasdynamics and its possible aeronautical applications" *J. Roy. Soc.* To be published in 1959.

1722. SHIGULEV, V. N. "Analysis of a class of motions in magneto-hydrodynamics" *Prikl. Mat. Mekh.*, pp. 389–90, May–June 1958 (in Russian).

*1723. SHIROKOV, M. F. "Interaction between gravitational-capillary and magneto-hydrodynamic waves" *Zh. Eksp. Teoret. Fiz.*, pp. 50–4, July 1957.

1724. SHMOYS, J. and MISHKIN, E. "On the linear behavior of large-amplitude magneto hydrodynamic waves" *Phys. Fluids*, Vol. 3, No. 4, pp. 661–2, 1960.

*1725. SHMOYS, J. and MISHKIN, E. "Hydromagnetic waveguide with finite conductivity and arbitrary cross section" *Phys. Fluids*, Vol. 3, No. 3, pp. 473–65, 1960.

*1726. SHPIGEL, I. S. "Plasma acceleration" *J. Exp. Theor. Phys.*, No. 2, p. 285, August 1959.

1727. SIEGEL, K. M. "Basic concepts of plasma state, wave propagation and plasma motion". ARDC, Conference on Ion and Plasma Research, University of Maryland, 30 Sept.–2 Oct. 1958.

*1728. SIEGEL, R. "Effect of a magnetic field on forced convection heat transfer in a parallel plate channel" *J. Appl. Mech.*, Vol. 25, No. 3, pp. 415–16 (Notes), 1958.

1729. SIGRIST, W. "Resonance dispersion in ionized gases" *Helv. Phys. Acta*, Vol. 10, p. 73, 1937.

1730. SILIN, V. P. "On electromagnetic properties of relativistic plasma" *Ionization Phenomena in Gases*, Vol. 2, p. 697. Amsterdam, North-Holland, 1959.

*1731. SILIN, V. P. "The oscillations of a degenerate electron fluid" *J. Exp. Theor. Phys.*, No. 5, p. 870, May 1959.

1732. SILVERMAN, S. M. "A discussion of some recent work on electron collision cross sections". ARDC, Conference on Ion and Plasma Research, University of Maryland, 30 Sept.–2 Oct. 1958.

*1733. SIMON, A. "Ignition of a thermonuclear reaction in plasma by high-energy injection" *Phys. Fluids*, No. 1, pp. 495–500, Nov.–Dec. 1958.

1734. SIMON, A. "Diffusion of like particles across a magnetic field" *Phys. Rev.*, Vol. 100, pp. 1557–9, 1955.

1735. SIMON, A. "Ambipolar diffusion in a magnetic field" *Phys. Rev.*, Vol. 98, pp. 317–18, 1955.

1736. SIMON, A. *Introduction to Thermonuclear Research.* London, Pergamon Press, 1959.

1737. SIMON, A. "Alternative neutral burnout equation" *Phys. Fluids*, Vol. 2, p. 336, 1959.

*1738. SIMON, A. and HARRIS, G. E. "Kinetic equation for plasma and radiation" *Phys. Fluids*, Vol. 3, No. 2, pp. 245–54, 1960.

1739. SIMON, A. and NEIDIGH, R. V. "Diffusion of ions in a plasma across a magnetic field" *Phys. Rev.*, Vol. 98, p. 317, 1955.

*1740. SIMON, R. "On the reflection and refraction of hydromagnetic waves at the boundary of two compressible gaseous media" *Astrophys. J.*, Vol 128, No. 2, p. 392, 1958.

1741. SIMON, R. "The hydromagnetic oscillations of an incompressible cylinder" *Astrophys. J.*, Vol. 128, No. 2, p. 185, 1957.

1742. SIMONS, L. "Thin plasmas of variable densities" *Ionization Phenomena in Gases*, Vol. 2, p. 1181. Amsterdam, North-Holland, 1959.

1743. SIMONYI, K. and UZSOKY, M. "About a star-like fusion reactor" *Proc. Venice Conf. (1957)*, pp. 1036–49, 1959.

1744. SINELNIKOV, K. D., TOLOK, V. T., NAZAROV, N. I., BAKAYEV, I. I., BONDAREV, V. A. and BUGAY, U. P. "Investigation of ion cyclotron resonance in a dense plasma" *Ionization Phenomena in Gases*, Vol. 2, p. 1176. Amsterdam, North-Holland, 1959.

1745. SINGERS, S. F. "Trapped radiation in the earth's magnetic field" *Ionization Phenomena in Gases*, Vol. 2, p. 1187. Amsterdam, North-Holland, 1959.

1746. SINGH, B. N. "Effect of a longitudinal magnetic field on the conductivity and magnetic index of air" *Phil. Mag.*, (7), Vol. 26, p. 244, 1938.

*__1747.__ SISCO, W. and FISKIN, J. M. "Shock ionization changes EM propagation characteristics" *J. Aero/Space Sci.*, No. 3, pp. 66, 68 and 70 (1 fig.), March 1959.

1748. SITENKO, A. G. and STEPANOV, K. N. "Oscillations of an electron plasma in a magnetic field" *J. Exp. Theor. Phys.*, No. 1, pp. 82–5, Jan. 1959.

*__1749.__ SKABELUND, D. E. "Hydromagnetic waves of finite amplitude in a homogeneous magnetic field". Univ. Utah Dept. of Physics Tech. Rep. 14, 25 pp. Feb. 1955 (Ord. illus.) Ministry of Supply Report P51672.

*__1750.__ SKURIDIN, G. A. and STANIUKOVICH, K. M. "An approximate solution of a problem concerning the motion of a conducting plasma" *Dokl. Akad. Nauk.*, *SSSR*, Vol. 130, No. 6, pp. 1248–51, 1960.

*__1751.__ SKURIDIN, G. A. and STANIUKOVICH, K. M. "Motion of a conducting plasma under the action of a piston" *Dokl. Akad. Nauk.*, *SSSR*, Vol. 131, No. 1, p. 724, 1960.

1752. SLEPIAN, A. "Electron acceleration against an opposing field in a vacuum electromagnetic discharge" *Phys. Fluids*, Vol. 1, p. 547, 1958.

1753. SLEPIAN, J. "A fundamental error in thermonuclear research" *Phy. Fluids*, Vol. 3, No. 3, p. 490, 1960.

*__1754.__ SLEPIAN, J. "Hydromagnetic equations for two isotopes in a completely ionized gas" *Phys. Rev.*, Vol. 112, pp. 1441–4, 1958.

1755. SMETANA, F. O. "Some further results on heating a supersonic gas stream with a radio frequency discharge". AFORS TN-59-1127, Rep., Nov. 1959.

*__1756.__ SMIRNOV, A. G. "Free thermal convection of mercury in a closed circular tube in a transverse magnetic field, II" *Zh. Tekh. Fiz.*, p. 1549, July 1958.

*__1757.__ SMIRNOV, A. G. "Theory of certain magnetohydrodynamic phenomena occurring in the free laminar thermal convection of an electrically conducting fluid in a round vertical pipe located in a weak magnetic field" *Zh. Tekh. Fiz.*, Vol. 29, No. 10, pp. 1245–51, 1959; *Sov. Phys. Tech. Phys.* (New York), Vol. 4, No. 10, pp. 1141–7, 1960.

1758. SMITH, M. L. *Electromagnetically Controlled Isotopes and Mass Spectroscopy.* London, Butterworths, 1958.

1759. SMITH, C. G. "Motion of an arc in a magnetic field" *J. Atom. Phys.*, Vol. 28, pp. 1328–31, 1957.

1760. SNYDER, H. S. "Magneto-hydrodynamic equations of motion of a completely ionized plasma". Brookhaven National Lab. GNL 2222, 24 Feb., 1955.

1761. SOEHNGEN, E. "The effect of the environmental flow field on the convective and radiative heat transfer from gas-stabilized arc columns". ARDC, Conference on Ion and Plasma Research, University of Maryland, 30 Sept.–2 Oct. 1958.

1762. SOEHNGEN, E. "Heat transfer". ARDC, Conference on Ion and Plasma Research, University of Maryland, 30 Sept.–2 Oct. 1958.

1763. SOKOLOW, P. and SOSINSKI, S. "Movement of fluid in electrical fields" *Acta Physiochimica*, Vol. 5, p. 433, 1936.

1764. SOKOLOW, P. and SOSINSKI, S. "Movement of fluids in electrical fields: Part II" *Acta Physiochimica*, Vol. 5, p. 691, 1936.

1765. Son, H. K. "Structure of a magneto-hydrodynamic shock wave in a plasma of infinite conductivity" *Phys. Rev.*, Vol. 102, pp. 5–11, 1956.

*1766. Sorokin, V. S. and Sushkin, I. V. "Stability of equilibrium of a conducting liquid heated from below in a magnetic field" *Zh. Eksp. Teoret. Fiz.*, Vol. 38, No. 2, pp. 612–20, 1960.

1767. Spence, B. *Bibliography on Magnetohydrodynamics Plasma Physics and Controlled Thermonuclear Processes*, Oct. 1959.

1768. Speth, A. I. and Pai, S. I. "Wave motions of small amplitude in radiation electro-magneto-gas dynamics". TN 59–879, AD 225 691, July 1959, AF 49 (638-401) P. 9781 T. 37713.

1769. Spitzler, L. Jr. "Particle diffusion across a magnetic field" *Phys. Fluids*, Vol. 3, No. 4, pp. 659–61, 1960.

1770. Spitzer, L. "Equations of motion of a ideal plasma" *Astrophys. J.*, Vol. 116, p. 299, 1952.

1771. Spitzer, L. "Influence of fluid motions on the decay of an external magnetic field" *Astrophys. J.*, Vol. 125, p. 525, 1957.

*1772. Spitzer, L. Jr. "The stellarator concept" *Phys. Fluids*, Vol. 1, No. 4, pp. 253–64 1958.

1773. Spitzer, L. *Physics of Fully Ionized Gases*. Interscience 1956; Paris, Dunod, 1959.

1774. Spitzer, L. "Cooperative phenomena in hot plasmas" *Nature, Lond.*, Vol. 181, pp. 221–2, 1958.

1775. Spitzer, L. and Harm, R. "Transport phenomena in a completely ionized gas" *Phys. Rev.*, Vol. 89, pp. 977–81, 1953.

1776. Sporn, P. and Kantrowitz, A. "Large scale generation of electric power by application of the magnetohydrodynamic concept" *Power*, Nov. 1959.

*1777. Sporn, P. and Kantrowitz, A. "Magnetohydrodynamics future power process" *Power*, Vol. 103, No. 11, pp. 62–5, Nov. 1959.

*1778. Stambler, I. "Magneto-hydrodynamics" *J. Aero/Space Sci.*, No. 1, pp. 28–36 (7 figs., 4 photos), Jan. 1959.

*1779. Stanjukovich, K. P. "Ondes magnétohydrodynamiques cylindriques et planes" C.N.R.S. Jan. 1960; *J. Exp. Theor. Phys.*, No. 6, p. 1271, Dec. 1959.

1780. Stanjukovich, K. P. "Some results in relativistic magnetohydrodynamics" *Dokl. Akad. Nauk. SSSR*, Vol. 103, No. 1, pp. 73–6, 1955; Translation: U.S.A. E.C. TH Atom. OI: AEC-tr-2742.

*1781. Stanjukovich, K. P. "Quelques mouvements stationnaires relativistes d'un gaz dans un milieu conducteur" *J. Exp. Theor. Phys.*, pp. 529–31, March 1959.

1782. Stanjukovich, K. P. "Shock waves in a conducting ultrarelavistic gas" *J. Exp. Theor. Phys.*, No. 2, p. 359, Feb. 1959.

1783. Stanjukovich, K. P. "Cylindrical and plane magnetohydrodynamic waves" *J. Exp. Theor. Phys.*, No. 6, p. 1271, Dec. 1959.

*1784. Starr, W. L. "A propulsion device using an exploding-wire plasma accelerator". Lockheed Missiles and Space Division Report No. LMSD 418236, Dec. 1958.

*1785. Starr, W. L. "An exploding wire plasma accelerator" *J. Appl. Phys.*, Vol. 30, No. 4, pp. 594–5, 1959.

1786. Stefanov, V. G., Zakharenko, V. F. and Bezel, V. S. "On a rotating plasma" *Zh. Eksp. Teoret. Fiz.*, Vol. 34, No. 2, pp. 512–13, 1958 (in Russian); Translation by Morris D. Friedman Inc. 67 Reservoir St., Needham Heights 94, Mass. S-130 (2 pp.).

1787. Steginsky, B. "Magnetohydrodynamic cavities" *ARS J.*, Vol. 30, No. 7, p. 642, 1960.

1788. Stehle, P. "Particle transport, electric currents and pressure balance in a magnetically immobilized plasma" *Phys. Rev.*, Vol. 100, p. 443, 1955.

1789. Steinberg, M. "Magnetic properties of gas-discharge plasma" *Wiss Veroff a.d. Siemens-Werken*, Vol. 15, p. 1, 1936.

1790. STEINBERG, M. "Plasma oscillation and selective optical reflection of metals" *Z. Phys.*, Vol. 76, p. 260, 1932.

*1791. STEKETEE, J. A. "The oscillating plate in magnetohydrodynamics". Univ. Toronto Inst. Aerophys. Rep. 63, 36 pp., Aug. 1959.

*1792. STEKETEE, J. A. "An introduction to the equations of magnetogasdynamics". Univ. Toronto Inst. Aerophysics. UTIA Review n. 9 Apr. 1957.

1793. STEPANOV, K. N. "On the damping of electromagnetic waves in a plasma situated in a magnetic field" *J. Exp. Theor. Phys.*, No. 1, p. 195, Jan. 1959.

*1794. STEPANOV, K. N. "Low frequency oscillations of a plasma in a magnetic field" *J. Exp. Theor. Phys.*, No. 5, pp. 808–11, May 1959.

*1795. STEPANOV, K. N. "Penetration of an electromagnetic field into a plasma" *J. Exp. Theor. Phys.*, No. 5, p. 1035, Nov. 1959.

1796. STEPANOV, K. N. and TKALICH, V. S. "On electron plasma oscillations in external electric and magnetic field" *Zh. Eksp. Teoret. Fiz.*, No. 28, pp. 1789–800, 1958.

1797. STEPANOV, K. N. and TKALICH, V. S. "On the oscillations of an electron plasma in external electric and magnetic field" *J. Exp. Theor. Phys.*, No. 3, pp. 1649–59, 1959.

*1798. STEPANOV, V. G., ZAKHARENKO, V. F. and BEZEL, V. S. "Rotation of a plasma" *J. Exp. Theor. Phys.*, No. 2, Vol. 34, p. 353, 1958.

1799. STEWARTSON, K. "The dispersion of a current on the surface of a highly conducting fluid" *Proc. Camb. Phil. Soc.*, Vol. 53, p. 774, 1957.

1800. STEWARTSON, K. "Magneto-hydrodynamics of a finite rotating disk" *Quart. J. Mech. Appl. Math.*, pp. 137–47, May 1957.

1801. STEWARTSON, K. "Motion of a sphere through a conducting fluid in the presence of a strong magnetic field" *Proc. Camb. Phil. Soc.*, Vol. 52, pp. 301–316, 1956.

1802. STEWARTSON, R. "On the motion of a non-conducting body through a perfectly conducting fluid" *J. Fluid Mech.*, Vol. 8, p. 82, May 1960.

1803. STEWARTSON, K. "Magnetohydrodynamics of bodies in the presence of a strong field". Int. Symposium on M.F.D. Washington 1960.

*1804. STIX, T. H. "Generation and thermalization of plasma waves" *Phys. Fluids*, Vol. 1, p. 308, 1958.

*1805. STIX, T. H. "Absorption of plasma waves" *Phys. Fluids*, Vol. 3, No. 3, pp. 19–33, 1960.

*1806. STIX, T. H. "Oscillations of a cylindrical plasma" *Phys. Rev.*, Vol. 106, pp. 1146–50, 1957.

*1807. STIX, T. H. and PALLADINO, R. W. "Experiments on ion cyclotron resonance" *Phys. Fluids*, Vol. 1, No. 5, pp. 446–51, 1958.

*1808. STIX, T. H. and PALLADINO, R. W. "Observations of ion cyclotron waves" *Phys. Fluids*, Vol. 3, No. 4, pp. 641–8, 1960.

1809. STOLLENWERK, M. "Bibliography of plasma physics and related subjects". Tullahoma, Tenn. Arnold Engineering Development Center, Feb. 1959, 74 pp. (Rept. TR 59–5) Contract AF 40(600-700) (AD-211 155).

*1810. STONE, I. "Giannini Plasmadyne studies plasma jet applications" *Aviation Week*, No. 15, pp. 48–9, 51, 53, 55, 59, 61, 63 and 65 (4 figs., 9 photos, 1 table), Oct. 1958.

*1811. STUART, J. T. "On the stability of viscous flow between parallel planes in the presence of a co-planar magnetic field" *Proc. Roy. Soc.* A, Vol. 221, pp. 189–206, 1954.

1812. STURROCK, P. A. "A variational principle and an energy theorem for small amplitude disturbance of electron beams and of electron ion plasma" *Ann. Phys.*, Vol. 4, pp. 306–24, 1958.

*1813. STURROCK, P. A. "Excitation of plasma oscillations" *Phys. Rev.*, Vol. 117, No. 6, pp. 1426–9, 1960.

1814. SUMI, M. "On the excitation of oscillations in a thermal plasma" *J. Phys. Soc., Japan*, Vol. 9, p. 88, 1954.

1815. SUMI, M. "Excitation of oscillations in a plasma layer" *Phys. Rev. Letters*, Vol. 2, pp. 37–8, 1958.

1816. SUNDERLAND, R. D. "Positive ion emission from surfaces". ARDC, Conference on Ion and Plasma Research, University of Maryland, 30 Sept.–2 Oct. 1958.

1817. SUSSKIND, C. and WHINNERY, J. R. "Plasma work". ARDC, Conference on Ion and Plasma Research, University of Maryland, 30 Sept.–2 Oct. 1958.

*1818. SUTTON, G. W. "Electrical and pressure losses in a magnetohydrodynamic channel due to end current loops" *J. Aero/Space Sci.*, Jan. 60; G.E. MSVD AL TIS R59SD431, July 22, 1959, U.S.A.F.

1819. SUTTON, G. W. "Rocket propulsion system for interplanetary flight" *J. Aero/Space Sci.*, Vol. 26, No. 10, pp. 609–26, 1959.

*1820. SUTTON, G. W. "Design considerations of a steady DC magnetohydrodynamic electrical power generator" *J. Aero/Space Sci.*, Jan. 60; G-E MSVD AL TIS R59SD432, Sept. 15, 1959, 47 pp. U.S.A.F.

1821. SWEET, P. A. "The effect of turbulence on a magnetic field" *Mon. Not. Roy. Astr. Soc.*, Vol. 110, p. 69, 1950.

1822. SWEET, P. A. "The sun's general magnetic field" *Mon. Not. Roy. Astr. Soc.*, Vol. 109, p. 507, 1949.

1823. SYNGE, J. L. *The Relativistic Gas.* New York, Interscience, 1957.

*1824. SYKES, J. "The equilibrium of a self-gravitating rotating incompressible fluid spheroid with a magnetic field" *Astrophys. J.*, Vol. 125, pp. 615–21, 1957.

*1825. SYROVATSKII, S. I. "Sur la stabilité des ondes de choc en magnétohydrodynamique" *J. Exp. Theor. Phys.*, No. 6, pp. 1024–27, June 1959.

1826. SYROVATSKII, S. I. "Surface disturbances in magnetohydrodynamics". NASA-Tech. Trans. F. 23, May 1960.

*1827. SYROVATSKII, S. I. "Magneto hydrodynamics" *Fortsch. Phys.*, No. 9, pp. 437–503 (10 figs.), 1958.

1828. SYROVATSKII, S. I. "Analysis of theory of magnetohydrodynamics and review of previously obtained results" *Usp. Fiz. Nauk.*, pp. 247–303, 145 refs., July 1957.

1829. SYROVATSKII, S. I. "Magnitnaia gidrodinamika" (Analysis of theory of magnetohydrodynamics and review of previously obtained results) *Usp. Fiz. Nauk.*, pp. 247–303, 145 refs., July 1957.

1830. SZABO, J. "Schwache Unstetigkeiten in der Magnetohydrodynamick" *Z. Naturforsch.*, pp. 503–5, May/June 1960.

1831. SZÉKELY, A. "Investigation of an ionized gas by means of weak alternating magnetic fields" *Acta Phys. Austriaca*, Vol. 12, pp. 155–71, 1958.

1832. TAKEUCHI, H. and SHIMAZU, Y. "The instability of a rotating fluid sphere heated from within earth's magnetism and magnetohydrodynamics". Univ. of Utah, Physics Dept. TR No. 8, 25 pp., 1954.

*1833. TALWAR, S. P. and ABBI, S. S. "On the change in shape of a gravitating fluid sphere in a uniform external electric field" *Proc. Nat. Inst. Sci.*, Index A, Vol. 22, No. 1, pp. 7–12, 1956.

1834. TANBERG, R. "Motion of an electric arc in a magnetic field under low gas pressure" *Nature, Lond.*, Vol. 124, p. 370, 1929.

*1835. TANDON, J. N. "A note on the oscillations of an infinite cylinder subject to radial magnetic field" *Proc. Nat. Inst. Sci.*, Index A, Vol. 21, No. 6, pp. 394–403, 1955.

*1836. TANDON, J. N. and TALWAR, S. P. "Radial pulsations of an infinite cylinder in the presence of magnetic field" *Indian J. Phys.*, Vol. 32, No. 7, pp. 317–22, 1958.

*1837. TANIUTI, T. "Sur la propagation des ondes magnetiques dans un fluide compressible ionisé" *Progr. Theor. Phys.*, No. 1, pp. 69–76, Jan. 1958.

1838. TANIUTI, T. "An example of isentropic steady flow in magnetohydrodynamics" *Progr. Theor. Phys.*, Vol. 19, p. 749 (L), 1958.

1839. TANNELWALD, L. M. "Coulomb scattering in a very strong magnetic field" *Phys. Rev.*, 1960.

*1840. TAO, L. N. "Magnetohydrodynamic effects on the formation of Couette flow" *J. Aero/Space Sci.*, Vol. 27, No. 5, pp. 334–8, 1960.

1841. TARASOV, U. A. "On the stability of plane Poiseuille flow of a plasma of finite conductivity in a magnetic field" *Zh. Eksp. Theor. Fiz.*, Vol. 37, No. 6, pp. 1708–13 (2 figs.), 1959; *Soviet Physics JETP*, No. 6 (6/60), pp. 1209–1212.

1842. TATSUMI, T. "Energy spectra in magneto-fluid-dynamical turbulence". Int. Symposium on M.F.D. Washington, Jan. 1960.

1843. TAYLER, R. J. "Hydromagnetic instabilities of an ideally conducting fluid" *Proc. Phys. Soc. BTO*, pp. 31–48, 1957.

*1844. TAYLER, R. J. "Hydromagnetic instabilities of a cylindrical gas discharge". Parts 1, 2, 3, 4, 5. AERE T/R2262, June 1957.

1845. TAYLER, R. J. "The influence of an axial magnetic field on the stability of a constricted gas discharge" *Proc. Phys. Soc. B*, Vol. 70, pp. 1049–63, 1957.

*1846. TAYLER, R. J. "A note on hydromagnetic stability problems" *Phil. Mag.*, Vol. 2, pp. 33–6, 1957.

1847. TAYLER, R. J. "Stability of twisted magnetic fields in a fluid of finite conductivity". Int. Symposium on M.F.D., Washington, Jan. 1960.

1848. TCHEN, C. M. "Structure of correlation in plasma with an external field". Paper presented at the divisional meeting of the Division of Fluid Dynamics, American Physical Society, San Diego, Calif., 24–26 Nov. 1958.

1849. TCHEN, C. M. "Dispersion of surface waves between visco-elastic media under a magnetic field" *Proc. 9th Inter. Congr. Appl. Mech.*, Vol. 7, pp. 127–36, 1957.

1850. TCHEN, C. M. "Kinetic equation for a plasma with unsteady correlations" *Phys. Rev.*, Vol. 113, April 1959.

1851. TELLER, E. and DE HOFFMAN, F. "Rankine–Hugoniot equations for shock waves in an infinitely conducting fluid with superposed magnetic field" *Phys. Rev.*, Vol. 80, p. 692, 1950.

1852. TEMKO, S. "On the derivation of the Fokker–Planck equation for a plasma" *Zh. Eksp. Teoret. Fiz.*, Vol. 31, p. 1021, 1956.

1853. TEODWORAT, L. "Dispersion der Plasma frequenzen und abgeschirnite Austauschenergie im supraleitenden Zustand" *Z. Naturforsch.*, pp. 490–502, May–June 1960.

1854. TERLETSKII, Y. P. "Motion of an attenuated plasma in an attenuated magnetic field" *Zh. Eksp. Teoret. Fiz.*, Vol. 32, p. 927, 1957.

1855. TERLETSKII, Y. P. "Motion of rarefied plasma in alternating magnetic field" *Zh. Eksp. Teoret. Fiz.*, Vol. 32, p. 927–8, 1957.

1856. THIENE, P. G. "Flexure of a two-dimensional arc under forced convection". AFOSR TM 59–947, 80 pp., Aug. 1959.

1857. THOM, H. G. and PUPKE, H. "Die Relation von Plasmoiden in Magnetfeld" *Naturwissenshaften*, Vol. 43, p. 32, 1956.

1858. THOMPSON, W. B. "On the acceleration of cosmic ray particles by magneto-hydrodynamic waves" *Proc. Roy. Soc.*, A, Vol. 233, pp. 402–6, 1955.

*1859. THOMPSON, W. B. "The physical basis of magneto-hydrodynamics". Atomic Energy Research Est., Harwell, Preprint Congress A.S., Madrid, Pergamon Press, Sept. 1958.

1860. THOMPSON, W. B. "Linearized plasma dynamics. An introduction to the study of small oscillations and the growth of instabilities in a plasma" *Ionization Phenomena in Gases*, Vol. 2, p. 555. Amsterdam, North-Holland, 1959.

1861. THOMPSON, W. B. "Thermal convection in a magnetic field" *Phil. Mag.,* Vol. 42, pp. 1417–32, 1951.

1862. THOMPSON, W. B. "Long range forces and the diffusion coefficients of a plasma". Int. Symposium on M.F.D. Washington, Jan. 1960.

1863. THOMPSON, W. B. "Thermonuclear reaction rates" *Proc. Phys. Soc.* B, Vol. 70, pp. 1–5, 1957.

1864. THOMPSON, W. B. "Radiation from a plasma". AERE (Harwell) Memo T/M 73, 1957.

1865. THOMPSON, W. B. "Phenomenological theory of the constricted gas discharge at moderate currents". AERE (Harwell) Rept. T/R 997, 1955.

1866. THOMPSON, W. B. "Equations of motion for an ionized gas". Gt. Britain, Atomic Energy Research Establishment, AERE-T/M-71, 16 pp., Oct. 1952.

*1867. THOMSON, G. "The containment of plasma by pinch discharge" *Phil. Mag.,* Vol. 3, pp. 886–96, Aug. 1958.

1868. THOMSON, J. I. and THOMPSON, G. P. *Conduction of Waves in Ionized Gases.* pp. 353–8, Cambridge University Press, 1933.

1869. THOMSON, J. I. and THOMPSON, G. P. *Conduction of Electricity Through Gases.* Cambridge University Press, 1950.

1870. THONEMAN, P. C. *et al.* "Interaction of travelling magnetic fields with ionized gas" *Nature, Lond.,* Vol. 169, pp. 34–6, 1952.

1871. THONEMAN, P. C. "High temperature plasma" *Nuovo Cimento,* Suppl., Vol. 13, Ser. 10, No. 1, pp. 111–32, 1959.

1872. THONEMAN, P. C. *et al.* "Production of high temperatures and nuclear reactions in a gas discharge" *Nature, Lond.,* Vol. 181, pp. 217–20, 1958.

1873. THOURSON, T. L. "Pulsed plasma propulsion. An advance reaction space propulsion system". Summary of literature survey. Chicago III, Borg Warner Co., Apr. 1959, n.p. WADC TR 59-94 (con. AF 33(616)6036)(AD-212-838).

*1874. TIDMAN, D. A. "Structure of a shock wave in fully ionized hydrogen" *Phys. Rev.,* Vol. 111, pp. 1439–46, 1958.

1875. TIHONOV, A. N. and SVENISKOW I. "Slow motion of a conducting medium in a stationary magnetic field" *Izv. Akad. Nauk.,* SSSR, Ser. Geofiz., pp. 49–58, 1959.

1876. TOCHTE–HOLTGREVEN, W. "The thermally excited plasma in the column of an electric arc" *Appl. Sci. Res.* B, Vol. 5, p. 182, 1955.

*1877. TOLANSKY, S. "Dynamique du plasma et magnétohydrodynamique" *Discovery,* No. 8, p. 331, Aug. 1959.

1878. TONKS, L. "An exact analysis of a cylindrical plasma in a magnetic field" AEC Report UCRL 4439, 16 p., 1956.

1879. TONKS, L. "Theory of magnetic effects in the plasma of an arc" *Phys. Rev.,* Vol. 56, p. 360, 1939.

1880. TONKS, L. "Pressure of plasma electrons and the force on the cathode of an arc" *Phys. Rev.,* Vol. 46, p. 278, 1934.

1881. TONKS, L. "Theory and phenomena of high current densities in low pressure arcs" *Trans. Amer. Electrochem. Soc.,* Vol. 72, p. 167, 1937.

1882. TONKS, L. "Plasma-electron resonance, plasma resonance, and plasma shape" *Phys. Rev.,* Vol. 38, p. 1219, 1931.

1883. TONKS, L. "The high frequency behavior of a plasma" *Phys. Rev.,* Vol. 37, p. 1458, 1931.

1884. TONKS, L. "Particle transport, electric currents and pressure balance in a magnetically immobilized plasma" *Phys. Rev.,* Vol. 97, pp. 1443–5, 1955.

1885. TONKS, L. "Trajectory-wise analysis of cylindrical and plane plasmas in a magnetic field and without collisions" *Phys. Rev.,* Vol. 113, pp. 400–7, 1959.

1886. TONKS, L. and ALLIS, W. P. "Plasma electron drift in a magnetic field with a velocity distribution function" *Phys. Rev.,* Vol. 52, p. 710, 1937.

1887. TONKS, L. and LANGMUIR, I. "A general theory of the plasma of an arc" *Phys. Rev.*, Vol. 34, p. 876, 1929.

1888. TONKS, L. and LANGMUIR, I. "Oscillations in ionized gases" *Phys. Rev.*, Vol. 33, p. 195, 1929.

1889. TORWEGGE, H. "Influence of magnetic fields on thermal conductivity of NO and NO_2" *Ann. Phys.*, Vol. 33, p. 459, 1938.

1890. TOTARO, C. "On reflection and refraction in magnetohydrodynamics" *R. C. Acad. Naz. Lincei, Roma*, Vol. 24, pp. 310–16, 1958.

1891. TOWNSEND, J. "The conductivity produced in gases by the motion of negatively charged ions" *Phil. Mag.*, Ser. 6, No. 1, pp. 198–227, 1901.

1892. TRAUTZ, M. and FROSCHEL, E. "Die Anderung der inneren Reinbung von paramagnetischer Gasen in Magnetfeld" *Ann. Phys.*, Vol. 22, p. 223, 1935.

1893. TREAT, R. P. and WANIEK, R. W. "Relaxation heating of a plasma by surface interaction with a magnetic field". Plasmadyne Corp. T-3TN 109-335, 15, Oct. 1959, AFOSR TN 59-1151.

1894. TREHAN, S. K. "The hydromagnetic oscillations of twisted magnetic fields, II" *Astrophys. J.*, Vol. 127, p. 454, 1958.

1895. TREHAN, S. K. "The stability of an infinitely long cylinder with a prevalent force-free magnetic field" *Astrophys. J.*, Vol. 127, p. 436, 1958.

1896. TSERKOVNIKOV, Y. A. "Stability of plasma in a strong magnetic field" *Zh. Eksp. Teor. Fiz.*, Vol. 32, pp. 67–74, 1957; *J. Exp. Theor. Phys.*, No. 4, pp. 926–7, 1957.

1897. TSERKONIKOV, Y. A. "The question of convectional instability of a plasma" *Sov. Phys. Dokl.*, Vol. 5, No. 1, pp. 87–90, 1960.

1898. TSUNEJI RIKITAKE "Magneto-hydrodynamic oscillations of a perfectly conducting fluid sphere placed in a uniform magnetic field" *J. Phys. Soc., Japan*, pp. 1224–30, Oct. 1958.

1899. TUCK, J. L. "Los Alamos Research on controlled thermonuclear reactions" *Ionization Phenomena in Gases*, Vol. 2, p. 920. Amsterdam, North-Holland, 1959.

1900. TURKEVICH, J. "The physics of plasma" *Dokl. Akad. Nauk. SSSR* (Pergamon Press, 1959).

1901. TURNER, E. B. "Equilibrium hydrodynamic variables behind a normal shock wave in hydrogen". Space Res. Lab. GM-TR-0165-00460.

1902. TWISS, R. Q. "On oscillations in electron streams" *Proc. Phys. Soc.*, Vol. 64B, p. 654, 1951.

1903. TWISS, R. Q. and ROBERTS, J. A. "Electromagnetic radiation from electrons rotating in an ionized medium under the action of a uniform magnetic field". Appendix: Resolution of the radiated field into ordinary and extraordinary modes in the limit of vanishing electron density" *Aust. J. Phys.*, pp. 424–46 (2 refs.), Sept. 1958.

*1904. UDY, L. L. "Propagation characteristics of detonation general plasmas". AFOSR TN 58-754, Univ. Utah Explosion Res. Group, ASTIA AD 201-613, 32 pp., June 1958.

*1905. VALI, V. and GAUGER, J. "Plasma acceleration by means of a rotating magnetic field". Lockheed Missiles and Space Division Report No. LMSD-2489, 5 pp., 4 June 1958.

*1906. VANDAKUROV, Y. N. "Possible equilibrium configurations for a thin circular plasma conductor in a magnetic field" *Zh. Tekh. Fiz.*, Vol. 29, No. 11, pp. 1312–16, Nov. 1959; *Soviet Phys. Tech. Phys.*, New York, Vol. 4, No. 11, pp. 1207–11, 1960.

*1907. VANDAKUROV, Y. N. and PEREL, V. I. "The motion of positive ions in a natural gas under the effect of electric and magnetic fields" *Zh. Tekh. Fiz.*, Vol. 29, No. 8, pp. 958–61, 1959; *Soviet Phys. Tech. Phys.*, New York, Vol. 4, No. 8, pp. 871–4. 1960.

1908. VAN DE HULST, H. C. "Interstellar polarization and magnetohydrodynamic waves". Proc. Symposium Motion of Gaseous Masses; Paris, 1949, Central Air Documents Office No. 1103347, 1949.

1909. VAN DE HULST, H. C. *Problems of Cosmical Aerodynamics*, Chapter VI, p. 52, Central Air Documents Office, Dayton, Ohio, 1951.

*1910. VAN DE HULST, H. C. "The interstellar plasma" *Nuovo Cimento*, Suppl., Vol. 13, No. 1, pp. 205–232, 1959.

*1911. VAN DE HULST, H. C. "Density and velocity distribution of the interstellar gas" *Rev. Mod. Phys.*, Vol. 30, No. 3, pp. 913–21, 1958.

1912. VAN DE HULST, H. C. *The Solar Systems*, Chicago U.P., 1953.

1913. VAN DE HULST, H. C. and BURGERS, J. M. *Gas Dynamics of Cosmic Plasma*. Amsterdam, North-Holland Publ. Comp. 1955.

1914. VAN DER ZIEL, A. "Noise in gas discharges". ARDC, Conference on Ion and Plasma Research, University of Maryland, 30 Sept.–2 Oct. 1958.

1915. VAN KAMPEN, N. G. "On the theory of stationary waves in a plasma" *Physica*, Vol. 21, p. 949, 1955.

1916. VASSERMAN, I. I. "Resonance method for determining the electron density and the number of collisions in the plasma of a gaseous discharge" *Zh. Tekh. Fiz.*, Vol. 27, p. 516, 1957.

*1917. VEDENOV, A. A. "Certain solutions of the equations of plasma hydrodynamics" *J. Exp. Theor. Phys.*, Vol. 18/33 (6), pp. 1165–7, June 1958.

1918. VEDENOV, A. A. *et al.* "Thermal insulation and confinement of plasma with high frequency electromagnetic field" *Proc. 2nd Geneva Conf.*, Vol. 32, pp. 239–44, O.N.U., 1958.

*1919. VEDENOV, A. A. and LARKIN, A. I. "Equation of state of a plasma" *J. Exp. Theor. Phys.*, pp. 806–811, Oct. 1859; *Zh. Eksp. Teoret. Fiz.*, Vol. 36, pp. 1133–42, April 1959.

*1920. VEKSLER, V. I. and KOVRIZHNYKH, L. M. "Cyclic acceleration of particles in high-frequency fields" *J. Exp. Theor. Phys.*, No. 5, p. 781, May 1959.

*1921. VELIKHOV, E. P. "Stabilité de l'écoulement d'un liquide infiniment conducteur entre des cylindres tournant dans un champ magnétique". C.N.R.S. Jan. 1960; *Zh. Eksp. Teoret. Fiz. SSSR*, Vol. 36, No. 5, pp. 1398–404, 1959 (in Russian).

*1922. VELIKHOV, E. P. "Stability of an ideally conducting liquid flowing between cylinders rotating in a magnetic field" *J. Exp. Theor. Phys.*, No. 5, p. 995, Nov. 1959.

*1923. VELIKHOV, E. P. "Stability of a plane Poiseuille flow of an ideally conducting fluid in a longitudinal magnetic field" *J. Exp. Theor. Phys.*, No. 4, p. 848, Oct. 1959.

*1924. VERESS, G. "Design and operation of electromagnetic pumps, Pt. I, II" *Energ. Atomtechnika*, Vol. 11, No. 7/8, pp. 474–84, July/Aug. 1958 (in Hungarian); *ibid.*, Vol. 11, No. 9/10, pp. 633–9, Sept./Oct. 1958.

1925. VLASOV, A. "The oscillation properties of an electron gas" *Zh. Eksp. Teoret. Fiz.*, Vol. 8, pp. 291–318, 1938.

1926. VLASOV, A. *Many Body Theory*, State Techn. and Theor. Lit. Press, 1950.

1927. VLASOV, K. B. and ISHMUKHAMETOV, B. K. "Waves in a magnetically polarized medium" *J. Exp. Theor. Phys.*, No. 4, p. 921, Oct. 1959.

*1928. VOLKOV, T. F. "In oscillations in a plasma" *J. Exp. Theor. Phys.*, Vol. 37, (10), No. 2, pp. 302–4, 1960.

1929. VOLKOVISKY, V. "Transport des ions dans le fluide animé d'une vitesse supersonique" *C. R. Acad. Sci.*, Paris, Vol. 206, p. 1084, 1938.

1930. VON ROOS, O. "Boltzmann–Vlasov equation for a quantum plasma" *Phys. Rev.*, Vol. 119, No. 4, pp. 1174–9, 1960.

1931. WALEN, C. "On the theory of sun-spots" *Ark. Mat. Astr. Fys.*, Vol. 30A, No. 15, 1944.

1932. WALEN, C. "On the theory of sun-spots: Additional note" *Ark. Mat. Astr. Fys.*, Vol. 311B, No. 3, 1944.

*__1933.__ WANIEK, R. W. "Problems of magnetic propulsion of plasma" 10th Int. Astronautical Congress, London, Sept. 1959.

1934. WARE, A. A. "A study of a high-current toroidal ring discharge" *Phil. Trans.* A, Vol. 243, p. 197, 1950–51.

1935. WARE, A. A. "Galvanomagnetic and thermomagnetic effects in a plasma" *Proc. Phys. Soc.* A, Vol. 67, p. 869, 1954.

1936. WARE, A. A. "Constricted electrical discharge" *Phil. Trans. Roy. Soc.* A, Vol. 243, p. 197, 1951.

1937. WATKINS, R. L. "Theoretical and experimental study of plasmoids". ARDC Conference on Ion and Plasma Research, University of Maryland, 30 Sept.—2 Oct. 1958.

*__1938.__ WATSON, K. M. "Use of the Boltzmann equation for the study of ionized gases of low density" *Phys. Rev.*, Vol. 102; pp. 12–19, 1956, Amsterdam, North-Holland, 1960.

1939. WATT, D. A. "AC liquid metal pumps for laboratory use". AERE (Harwell) Rep. No. ED/R, 1856, 1956.

1940. WATT, D. A. "A study in design on travelling field electromagnetic pumps for liquid metals". AERE, ED/R 1696, June 1955, HMSO-7.

1941. WEBSTER, W. M., JOHNSON, E. O. and MALTER, L. "Studies of externally heated hot cathode arcs; Part II: The anode-glow mode" *RCA Review*, Vol. 13, p. 163, 1952.

1942. WEHNER, G. "Plasma oscillations". Overseas Research Report 235/51, Office of Technical Services, Washington, PB 110356.

1943. WEHNER, G. "Electron plasma oscillations" *J. Appl. Phys.*, Vol. 22, p. 761, 1951.

1944. WEIBEL, E. S. "Stabilization of a pinch by an alternating magnetic field". Space Res. Lab. GM-TR-0127-00399, 1958.

1945. WEIBEL, E. S. "Stable orbit of charged particles in an oscillating electromagnetic field". Space Res. Lab. GM-TR-0165-00481.

1946. WEIBEL, E. S. "On the confinement of a plasma column by radiation pressure" *The Plasma in a Magnetic Field*, Symposium, pp. 130, Stanford U.P., Stanford, 1958.

1947. WEIBEL, E. S. "Confinement of a plasma by magnetostatic fields" *Phys. Fluids*, Vol. 2, p. 52, 1959.

1948. WEIBEL, E. S. "A note on the confinement of a plasma by RF fields" *J. Electronics and control*, Vol. 5, p. 435, 1958.

1949. WEIBEL, E. S. "On the confinement of a plasma by standing electromagnetic waves". Space Res. Lab. ARL-57-1009.

*__1950.__ WEIBEL, E. S. "Oscillations of a non-uniform plasma" *Phys. Fluids*, Vol. 3, No. 3, pp. 399–408, 1960.

1951. WEIBEL, E. S. "Spontaneously growing transverse waves in a plasma due to an anisotropic velocity distribution" *Phys. Rev. Letters*, Vol. 2, No. 3; pp. 83–4, 1959.

1952. WEIBEL, E. S. "On the interpenetration of a plasma and its confining electromagnetic wave field". Space Res. Lab. ARL-57-1012.

1953. WEIBEL, E. S. "A resonant cavity with a uniform field section". Space Res. Lab. GM-TR-0127-00017.

1954. WEIBEL, E. S. "Confinement of a plasma column by radiation pressure and its applications to fusion power generation". Ramo–Wooldridge Corp. ARL-57-1026, 1957.

*__1955.__ WEIBEL, E. S. "On the confinement of a plasma by magnetostatic fields" *Phys. Fluids*, Vol. 2, No. 1, 1959.

1956. WEINER, F. D. and GEROMINE, R. L. "Applications of the corona discharge for measurements of density and velocity transients in air flow". WADC Techn. Rep. 53–142.

1957. WENK, F. "Motion and accumulation of ions and other suspended particles in turbulent flows" *Z. Angew. Math. Phys.*, Vol. 9B, p. 710, 1958.

*1958. WENTZEL, D. G. "Motion of charged particles in a force-free magnetic field" *Astrophys. J.*, Vol. 126, pp. 559–64, 1957.

*1959. WESTFOLD, K. C. "Magneto-hydrodynamic shock waves in the solar corona with applications to bursts of radio-frequency radiation" *Phil. Mag.*, Vol. 2, pp. 1287–302, 1957.

1960. WESTFOLD, K. C. "The wave equation for electromagnetic radiation in an ionised medium in a magnetic field" *Aust. J. Sci. Res.*, Vol. 2, p. 169, 1949.

*1961. WETSTONE, D. M., EHRLICH, M. P. and FINKELSTEIN, D. "Experiments of plasmoid motion along magnetic fields" *Phys. Fluids*, Vol. 3, No. 4, pp. 617–31, 1960.

1962. WEYMANN, H. D. "Properties of high temperature argon behind strong shock waves measured with a capacitive probe". Univ. of Maryland, Techn. Note BN-62.

1963. WEYMANN, R. and HOWARD, R. "Note on hydromagnetic waves passing through an atmosphere with a density gradient" *Astrophys. J.*, Vol. 128, p. 142, 1958.

1964. WHARTSON, C. B. "Microwave radiation measurements of very hot plasmas" *Ionization Phenomena in Gases*, Vol. 2, p. 737. Amsterdam, North-Holland, 1959.

1965. WHIPPLE, F. L. "Smithsonian contributions to astrophysics" *New Horizons in Astronomy*. Vol. I, No. 1, Smithsonian Institution, Astrophysical Observatory, 1956.

1966. WHITE, M. L. "Thermal and gravitational atmospheric-ionospheric dynamo effects included" *J. Atmos. and Terr. Phys.*, Vol. 17, No. 3, 1960.

1967. WHITE, M. L. "Atmospheric tides and ionospheric electrodynamics" *J. Geophys. Res.*, Jan. 1960.

1968. WHITE, M. L. "On the atmospheric dynamos theory" *J. Geophys. Res.*, Vol. 62, p. 329, 1957.

*1969. WHITHAM, G. B. "Converging cylindrical shocks in magnetohydrodynamics" New York Univ. Institute of Mathematical Science IMM-NYU 237, Ministry of Supply Report P64622, Jan. 1957.

*1970. WHITHAM, G. B. "Some comments on wave propagation and shock wave structure with application to magnetohydrodynamics" *Comm. Pure Appl. Math.*, No. 1, pp. 113–58 (7 figs.), Feb. 1959.

1971. WHITMER, R. F. "Investigations of microwave frequency harmonic generation in plasmas". Sylvania Microwave Physics Lab. Tech. Rep. MPL-14.

1972. WHITMER, R. F. "Investigation of non-linear phenomena associated with ionized plasma". ARDC, Conference on Ion and Plasma Research, University of Maryland, 30 Sept.–2 Oct. 1958.

1973. WHITMER, R. F. "Investigation of propagation phenomena in high temperature plasmas". ARDC, Conference on Ion and Plasma Research, University of Maryland, 30 Sept.–2 Oct. 1958.

1974. WIENECKE, R. "On an experiment and theoretical determination of the thermal conductivity of the plasmas high current carbon arcs" *Z. Phys.*, Vol. 146, p. 39, 1956.

*1975. WILCOX, J. M., BOLEY, F. I. and DE SILVA, A. W. "Experimental study of Alfvén-wave properties" *Phys. Fluids*, Vol. 3, No. 1, pp. 15–19, 1960.

*1976. WILCOX, J. M. and BOLEY, F. I. "Comments on experimental demonstration of hydromagnetic waves in an ionized gas" *Phys. Fluids*, Vol. 3, No. 1, pp. 141–2, 1960.

1977. WILD, J. P., MURRAY, J. D. and ROWE, W. C. "Harmonics in the spectra of solar radio disturbances" *Aust. J. Phys.*, Vol. 7, p. 437, 1954.

1978. WILHELM, A. "Zum Übergang Plasma-Raumladungsschicht" *Ann. Phys., Lpz.*, Vol. 13, p. 288, 1956.

1979. WILHELMOSSON, H. "Oscillatory properties of gyromagnetic electronic cold plasmas with drift motion" *Ionization Phenomena in Gases*, Vol. 2, p. 714. Amsterdam, North-Holland, 1959.

1980. WILHELMOSSON, H. "On the possibilities of oscillatory instabilities in time of a ring current" *Ionization Phenomena in Gases*, Vol. 2, p. 687. Amsterdam, North-Holland, 1959.

1981. WILLE, R. "Institut de recherches sur la turbolence". DVL-Nachrichten, No. 12, pp. 11–13, 4 photos, Jan. 1960.

*1982. WILLIAMS, J. C. *The Decaying Plasma as a Method of Heating a Supersonic Gas Stream*, pp. 222–35, Heat trans. Fluid. Mech. Inst. Univ. Calif. Los Angeles, Calif., June 1959.

*1983. WILLIAMS, W. E. "Exact solution of the magnetohydrodynamics equations" *J. Fluid Mech.*, Vol. 8, Pt. 3, pp. 452–65, 1960.

*1984. WILLIAMS, W. E. "Reflection and refraction of hydromagnetic waves at the boundary of two compressible media" *Astrophys. J.*, Vol. 131, No. 2, pp. 438–41, 1960.

*1985. WILLIAMS, W. E. "Propagation of small amplitude magnetohydrodynamic waves" *Quart. J. Mech. Appl. Math.*, Vol. XIII, Pt. 3, pp. 272–7, Aug. 1960.

*1986. WILSON, T. A. "Remarks on rocket and aerodynamic applications of magnetohydrodynamic channel flow". Dec. 58, 55 pp. inclu. illus. (Rept. No. AFOSR TN 58–1068) Contr. AF 18(600) 1523; Corbell U. Graduate School of Aeronautical Eng. Ithaca, N.Y.

1987. WINKLER, G. "Zur Theorie der Ausbreitung ebener Wellen in homogenen Plasmen" *Ann. Phys., Lpz.*, Vol. 16, p. 414, 1955.

1988. WOLFF, P. A. "Theory of plasma resonance" *Phys. Res.*, Vol. 103, pp. 845–50, 1956.

1989. WOLTJER, L. "On the theory of hydromagnetic equilibrium". Int. Symposium on M.F.D. Washington, Jan. 1960.

1990. WOOD, G. P. "Considerations in the design of a steady DC plasma accelerator", Preprint Third Biennial Gas Dynamic Symposium, ARS, Northwestern Univ. 24–26 Aug. 1959.

1991. WRIGHT, J. K. "An apparatus for the production of intense shock waves" *Ionization Phenomena in Gases*, Vol. 2, p. 1105. Amsterdam, North-Holland, 1959.

*1992. WRIGHT, J. P. "Diffusion of charged particles across a magnetic field due to neutral particles" *Phys. Fluids*, Vol. 3, No. 4, pp. 607–10, 1960.

*1993. WU, C. S. and HAYES, W. D. "Axisymmetric stagnant flow of a viscous and electrically conducting fluid near the blunt nose of a spinning body with presence of magnetic field, Pt. I: Exact solution of incompressible and constant-properties model". AFOSR TN 58-405; ASTIA AD 159208, April 1958.

*1994. WU, C. S. "Axisymmetric stagnant flow of a viscous and electrically conducting fluid near the blunt nose of a spinning body with presence of magnetic field; Part II: Consideration of realistic conditions: compressible viscous layer and small magnetic Reynolds number". Princeton University Report, No. 431, AD 162246, Sept. 1958.

*1995. WUERKER, R. F., SHELTON, H. and LANGMUIR, R. V. "Electrodynamic containment of charged particles" *J. Appl. Phys.*, Vol. 30, No. 3, pp. 342–9, 1959.

*1996. WYLD, H. W. Jr. "Dynamic stability of a self-pinched discharge" *J. Appl. Phys.*, pp. 1460–5, Oct. 1958.

1997. YANKOV, V. V. "On the ponderomotive force in localized plasma in the electromagnetic field of a plane wave" *J. Exp. Theor. Phys.*, Vol. 5, pp. 753–4, 1957.

*1998. Yankov, V. V. "Behavior of a conducting gaseous sphere in a quasi-stationary electromagnetic field" *J. Exp. Theor. Phys.*, No. 2, p. 388, Aug. 1959.

*1999. Yavorskaya, I. M. "The oscillations of an infinite gas cylinder with its own gravitation in magnetic fields" *Dokl. Akad. Nauk. SSSR.*, Vol. 114, No. 5, 1957, pp. 988–90.

2000. Yavorskaya, I. M. "Investigation of some irregular motions of a gravitating gas in the presence of shock waves of detonation, of the magnetic field". Autoref. Diss. Kand. Fiz. matem, Nauk MGU, Moscow, 1957 (in Russian); *Ref. Zh. Mekh.*, No. 3, 1958; Rev. 3044; *Appl. Mech. Rev.*, Vol. 12, No. 6322, p. 877, 1959.

2001. Yen, C. "Exact solution of impulse motion of a flat plate in MHD". Symposium high Temperature plasma, Amer. Phys. Soc. N.Y., Jan. paper No. 8, 1958.

2002. Yen, K. T. "Incompressible wedge flows of an electrically conducting viscous fluid in the presence of a magnetic field". Readers' Forum, *J. Aero/Space, Sci.*, Vol. 27, No. 1, p. 74, 1960.

*2003. Yih, C. S. "Ring vortices generated electromagnetically" *J. Fluid Mech.*, Vol. 5, No. 3, pp. 436–44, 1959.

*2004. Yih, C. S. "Effects of gravitational or electromagnetic fields on fluid motion" *Quart. Appl. Math.*, Vol. 16, pp. 409, 415, 1958.

*2005. Yih, C. S. "Inhibition of hydrodynamic instability by an electric current" *Phys. Fluids*, Vol. 2, No. 2, pp. 125–30, 1959.

2006. Yoler, Y. A. "On magnetohydrodynamic propulsion" *Proc. Amer. Astronaut. Soc.*, pp. 29–31, Jan. 1958.

2007. Yoler, Y. A. "A review of magneto-hydrodynamics". Boeing Flight Science Laboratory. Rep. No. 14, Oct. 1959. DI-82-0027.

*2008. Yosinobu, H. and Kakutani, T. "Two-dimensional Stokes flow of an electrically conducting fluid in a uniform magnetic field". C.N.R.S., Jan. 1960; *J. Phys. Soc. Japan*, pp. 1433–44, Oct. 1959.

2009. Young, T. H. and Sayers, J. "An RF probe technique for the measurement of plasma electron concentrations in the presence of negative ions" *Proc. Phys. Soc.*, Vol. 70B, p. 663, 1957.

2010. Young, G. and Evans, G. "On electrical disturbance due to tides and waves" *Phil. Mag.*, Vol. 140, No. 6, 1920.

*2011. Zababakhin, E. I. and Nechaev, M. N. "Electromagnetic field shock waves and their cumulation" *J. Exp. Theor. Phys.*, Vol. 33, No. 2, pp. 345–51, 1958.

*2012. Zabusky, N. J. "Hydromagnetic stability of a streaming cylindrical plasma". Paper presented at the divisional meeting of the Division of Fluid Dynamics, Nov. 14–26, 1958, American Physical Society, San Diego Calif.; *Phys. Fluids*, Vol. 3, No. 2, pp. 278–88, 1960.

*2013. Zagorodnov, O. G., Fainberg, Ya. B. and Egorov, A. M. "Reflection of electromagnetic waves from a plasma, moving in slow-wave guides" *J. Exp. Theor. Phys.*, Vol. 11, No. 1, pp. 4–5, July 1960.

2014. Zaitsev, A. A., Leonov, G. S. and Savchanko, I. A. "On electron oscillations in a plasma" *J. Exp. Theor. Phys.*, No. 4, p. 944, Oct. 1959.

2015. Zaitsev, A. A., Vasil'ev, M. Y. and Mnev, V. M. "Possibility of determining the potential distribution of a plasma from the characteristics of the noise generated in a gaseous discharge" *J. Exp. Theor. Phys.*, No. 5, p. 1130, Nov. 1959.

2016. Zavadskii, E. A. and Fadikov, I. G. "Producing very strong magnetic fields" *Fiz. Met. Metall.*, Vol. 6, p. 569, 1958.

2017. Zel'dovich, Y. B. "The magnetic field in a conducting turbulent liquid in two-dimensional motion" *Zh. Eksp. Teoret. Fiz.*, Vol. 31, pp. 154–5, 1956.

*2018. ZEL'DOVICH, Y. B. and RAIZER, Y. P. "Physical phenomena that occur when bodies compressed by strong shock waves expand *in vacuo*" *J. Exp. Theor. Phys.*, No. 6, p. 980, June 1959.

2019. ZEULI, T. "On circular cylindrical vortices in magneto-hydrodynamics" *Atti Accad. Sci.*, *Torino*, I, Vol. 92, p. 105, 1957–58.

2020. ZEULI, T. "Magneto-hydrodynamic oscillations in a rotating electrically conducting, ellipsoidal liquid mass" *Atti Accad. Sci. Torino*, I, Vol. 89, pp. 270–85, 1954–55.

2021. ZHETKOV, V. "Flow of anisotropic liquids in rotating magnetic fields" *Zh. Eksp. Teoret. Fiz.* Vol. 9, p. 602, 1939.

2022. ZHARINOV, A. "Investigation of transverse motion of ions in a discharge in a strong longitudinal magnetic field" (IRE No. 2696, Oct. 1958) *ARS J.*, No. 9, pp. 642–7, Sept. 1959; *Zh. Eksp. Teoret. Fiz.*, Vol. 27, pp. 1803–1810, Aug. 1957.

*2023. ZHARINOV, A. "Study of the transverse motion of ions in discharge in a strong longitudinal magnetic field" *Sov. Phys. Tech. Phys.*, pp. 1675–82, Aug. 1958.

2024. ZHIGOULEV, V. N. "Theorie de la couche limite magnetique" *Dokl. Akad. Nauk. SSSR*, Vol. 124, No. 5, pp. 1001–4 (2 figs.), 1959.

*2025. ZHIGOULEV, V. N. "On a class of motion in magnetohydrodynamics" *Prikl. Mat. Mech.*, Vol. 22, pp. 389–90; *ibid.*, pp. 537–9, 1958.

2026. ZHIGOULEV, V. N. "Theory of magnetic boundary layer" *Sov. Phys. Dokl.*, Vol. 4, No. 1, pp. 57–60, 1959.

2027. ZHIGOULEV, V. N. "Analysis of weak discontinuities in magnetohydrodynamics" *Prikl. Mat. Mekh.*, Vol. 23, No. 1, pp. 81–5, 1959.

2028. ZHIGOULEV, V. N. "Theory of electrical discharge in a moving conducting fluid" *Sov. Phys. Dokl.*, Vol. 4, No. 1, pp. 61–4, 1959.

*2029. ZHIGOULEV, V. N. "Sur le Phénomène de striction magnétique du courant en Milieu electroconducteur". C.N.R.S., Jan 60 (in Russian); *Dokl. Akad. Nauk. SSSR*, Vol. 126, No. 3, pp. 521–3, 1959.

*2030. ZIEMER, R. W. "Experimental magneto-aerodynamics". American Rocket Soc. Paper No. 707–58, Nov. 1958 (presented at the 13th Annual Meeting, New York, N.Y.).

2031. ZIEMER, R. W. "An electromagnetic shock tube for aerodynamic research". Space Res. Lab. GM-TR-0127-00419.

2032. ZIEMER, R. W. "Experimental investigation in magneto-aero-dynamics" *IAS Journal*, Vol. 29, No. 9, pp. 642–7, 10 refs., 1959.

2033. ZIEMER, R. W. and BUSH, W. B. "Magnetic field effects on bow shock Stanoff distance". Space Res. Lab. GM-TR-0127-00396.

2034. ZUMINO, B. "Some questions in relativistic hydromagnetics" *Phys. Rev.*, Vol. 108, pp. 1116–21, 1957.

2035. ZWETKOFF, V. "Action of the magnetic field and of the electric field on anisotropic liquid mixtures" *Acta Physiochim.*, Vol. 6, p. 865, 1937.

2036. ZWETKOFF, V. "Cause of the motion of Anisotropic liquid in the electric fields" *Acta Physiochim.*, Vol. 6, p. 885, 1937.

2037. ZWETKOFF, V. "Action of magnetic field on viscosity of p-Azoxyanisole" *Acta Physiochim.*, Vol. 8, p. 77, 1938.

*2038. ZYRYANOV, P. S. and TALUTS, G. G. "Electroacoustic phenomena in a degenerate electron-ion plasma" *J. Exp. Theor. Phys.*, No. 1, p. 100, July 1959.

ABSTRACTS

1. (6) ADLAM, J. H. and ALLEN, J. E.
   The Structure of Strong Collision-Free Hydromagnetic Waves.
   A theoretical study has been made of the structure of strong "hydromagnetic" waves which are propagated, across a magnetic field, in a low density plasma where collisions can be neglected. Under these conditions the ions are accelerated in the direction of propagation and then brought to rest again. The thickness of the wave is determinated by the characteristic distance ($mc^2/4\ ne^2$) and the wave velocity lies between the Alfvén speed and twice the Alfvén speed.

2. (8) ADLAM, J. D. and TAYLER, R. J.
   The Diffusion of Magnetic Fields in a Cylindrical Conductor.
   The conventional stabilized pinched discharge requires axial and aximuthal magnetic fields which are to a high degree separated. The finite electrical conductivity of the discharge causes these fields to diffuse into one another. A complete discussion of this process would be very complicated requiring consideration of anisotropic transport processes and dynamic behaviour of the plasma. The simplest discussion states that significant field mixing occurs in an electromagnetic penetration time τ determined by the relevant electrical conductivity. The further result of this memorandum is to show, on very simple assumptions, what fraction of τ is important in stability problems. It is shown that regarding the discharge as an incompressible fluid of uniform conductivity, sufficient field diffusion to lead to loss of stability can occur in times of the order of $10^{-3}\ \tau$.

   (TIL/MOS)

3. (9) AGOSTINELLI, C.
   Figure di equilibrio ellissoidali per una massa fluida elettricamente conduttrice uniformemente rotante, con campi magnetici variabili col tempo.
   Si dimostra come per una massa fluida incompressibile, elettricamente conduttrice, uniformemente rotante e soggetta alla propria gravitazione, si possano avere figure ellissoidali a tre assi in cui si generano campi magnetici periodici rispetto al tempo, con un periodo uguale a quello di rotazione della massa fluida.

4. (11) AGOSTINELLI, C.
   Oscillazioni magnetoidrodinamiche in una massa fluida cosmica uniformemente rotante dotata di un campo magnetico assiale e di un campo magnetico equatoriale rotante.
   Si studiano le oscillazioni magnetoidrodinamiche in una massa fluida nelle stesse condizioni considerate nella nota precedente, supponendo inoltre che essa sia soggetta a un campo magnetico rotante normale all'asse di rotazione, il quale caso interessa particolarmente il sole, che'oltre al campo magnetico assiale'è dotato di campi magnetici molto intensi dovuti alle machie solari, localizzate in prossimità dell'equatore solare.

5. (12) AGOSTINELLI, C.
   Oscillazioni magneto idrodinamiche in una massa fluida rotante di dimensioni cosmiche di forma ellisoidale rotonda.
   Si studiano le oscillazioni magnetoidrodinamiche in una massa fluida omogenea, incompressibile, ellissoidale rotonda, di dimensioni cosmiche, elettricamente conduttrice, uniformemente rotante interno al proprio asse, soggetta alla propria

gravitazione e a un campo magnetico assiale che si suppone uniforme, nella quale viene inoltre indotto un campo magnetico trasversale parallelo alla velocità delle particelle fluide.

6. (**13**) AGOSTINELLI, C.
   Moti magnetoidrodinamici simmetrici rispetto a un asse. Caso delle piccole oscillazioni in una massa fluida sferoidale.
   Si studiano i moti magnetoidrodinamici, simmetrici rispetto a un asse, in una massa fluida rotante uniformemente intorno a quell' asse e soggetta a un campo magnetico, pure uniforme, secondo lo stesso asse. Si considerano in particolare le oscillazioni magnetoidrodinamiche in una massa fluida sferoidale, lentamente rotante, che interessano la fisica stellare, e si dimostra la possibilità di propagazione di queste oscillazioni da un polo all'altro, con una frequenza arbitraria, ma con velocità di propagazione corrispondenti a una successione di autovalori.

7. (**15**) AGOSTINELLI, C.
   Onde magnetoidrodinamiche in una massa fluida incompressibile cilindrico circolare indefinita.
   Si studia la propagazione di onde magnetoidrodinamiche di assegnata frequenza, in direzione assiale, in una massa fluida viscosa, incompressibile ed elettricamente conduttrice, contenuta in un tubo cilindrico circolare indefinito e immersa in un campo magnetico uniforme avente la direzione dell'asse del tubo. Si determinano soluzioni in cui le componenti della velocità e del campo magnetico dipendono dalla coordinata assiale e dal tempo per mezzo di un fattore di propagazione e sono inoltre variabili col raggio e coll'anomalia.

8. (**18**) AGOSTINELLI, C.
   Su alcuni moti magneto idrodinamici ai quali è applicabile la teoria di Helmholtz sui vortici.
   Vengono caratterizzati esplicitamente alcuni moti magneto idrodinamici notevoli ai quali è applicabile la teoria di Helmholtz sui moti vorticosi.

9. (**19**) AGOSTINELLI, C.
   Sui vortici sferici in magnetoidrodinamica.
   Si dimostra come in un fluido indefinito, incompressibile, di conduttività elettrica infinita e soggetto a un campo magnetico uniforme, sia possibile la formazione di un vortice sferico magnetoidrodinamico, analogo a quello di Hill, il cui centro si muove di moto rettilineo uniforme nella direzione del campo magnetico uniforme esterno.

10. (**21**) AGOSTINELLI, C.
    Sull'equilibrio relativo magnetoidrodinamico di masse fluide elettricamente conduttrici uniformemente rotanti e gravitanti.
    Si considerano le figure di equilibrio magneto idrodinamico di una massa fluida incompressibile, di conduttività elettrica infinita e si distinguono i casi più notevoli che si possono presentare, mettendo in rilievo quelli che danno luogo a figure di equilibrio ellissoidali rotonde. Questi casi sono stati analizzati in altri lavori in corso di stampa.

11. (**22**) AGOSTINELLI, C.
    The Equations of Adiabatic Magnetodynamic equilibrium of a uniformly rotating and gravitating gaseous fluid mass.
    It is shown that the field is necessarily axially symmetrical, and that the magneto-hydrodynamic equations reduce to two partial differential equations in which the dependent variables are essentially the density and $H\phi$.   (O. Penrose)

12. (**23**) AGOSTINELLI, C.
Su alcuni moti magneto idrodinamici in una massa fluida cilindrica rotante interessanti la Cosmogonia.

Si considerano alcuni moti magnetoidrodinamici in una massa fluida cilindrica indefinita, incompressibile ed elettricamente conduttrice, che sono independenti dalla coordinata assiale e che possono essere utilizzati nello studio del movimento di masse fluide nelle nebulose spirali.

13. (**24**) AGOSTINELLI, C.
Soluzioni stazionarie delle equazioni della magnetoidrodinamica interessanti la Cosmogonia.

Si considerano delle soluzioni stazionarie delle equazioni della magnetoidrodinamica applicabili al caso di una massa fluida sferica ed ellissoidale rotonda elettricamente conduttrice e soggetta alla propria gravitazione. In particolare si dimostra la possibilità di un moto rotatorio uniforme della massa gravitante immersa in un campo magnetico uniforme diretto secondo l'asse di rotazione, con la generazione di un campo magnetico indotto, diretto trasversalmente e proporzionale alla velocità.

14. (**26**) AGRANOVICH, V. M. and RUKHADZE, A. A.
On the Propagation of Electromagnetic Wave in a Medium with Appreciable Spatial Dispersion.

A method for dealing with electromagnetic waves in a medium with spatial dispersion is presented which is more detailed than that given by Ginzburg. Expansions are obtained for the "direct" and the "inverse" spatial dispersions.

15. (**27**) AGRANOVICH, V. M., PAFONOF, V. E. and RUKHADZE, A. A.
Cerenkov Radiation of an Electron Moving in a Medium with Spatial Dispersion.

An analysis is given of Cerenkov radiation in an isotropic gyrotropic medium, with spatial dispersion taken into account. The angular distribution of the Cerenkov radiation and the emergence of the radiation at the boundary of the medium are considered.

16. (**39**) AKHIEZER, A. I., POLOVIN, R. V. and TSINTSADZE, N. L.
Simple Waves in the Chew–Goldberger–Low Approximation.

Simple waves in a plasma with a sintropic pressure are treated. It is shown that there exist three types of simple wave. The direction of the variations of the magnetohydrodynamic quantities in these waves is investigated.

17. (**40**) AKHIEZER, A. I. and POLOVIN, R. V.
Motion of a Conducting Piston in a Magneto-hydrodynamical Medium.

The types of waves excited in a hydromagnetic medium by a uniformly moving conducting plane (piston) are investigated. Decay of an initial discontinuity is discussed.

18. (**41**) AKHIEZER, A. I., LYBARSKII, G. Y. et POLOVIN, R. V.
Stabilité des Ondes de Choc en Magnétohydrodynamique.

Détermination des zones d'instabilité d'une onde de choc stationnaire magnétohydrodynamique par rapport aux perturbations unidimensionnelles. Étude de 2 types d'ondes de choc stables. Recherches sur les ondes de choc pouvant se succéder les unes aux autres. 2 références bibliographiques.   (SDIT)

19. (**45**) AKHIEZER, A. I. and POLOVIN, R. V.
Sur la Théorie des Ondes Magnétohydrodynamiques Relativistes.

Etude théorique des ondes monodimensionnelles simples dans l'hydro-mécanique magnétique relativiste et aussi des discontinuités magnétohydrodynamiques relativistes. Démonstration du théorème de Cemplen pour les ondes de choc d'*i* arbitraire. (En russe.)   (CNRS)

20. (**46**) AKHIEZER, A. I., PROKHODA, I. G. and SITENKO, A. G.
  Scattering of Electromagnetic Waves in a Plasma.
Combination scattering by plasma density oscillations may occur when electromagnetic waves are propagated in a plasma. The intensity of combination scattering of electromagnetic waves in a plasma is determined in the absence and in the presence of acoustant uniform magnetic field.

21. (**47**) AKHIEZER, A. I., LYBARSKII, G. Y. and POLOVIN, R. V.
  Simple Waves in Magnetohydrodynamics.
The relation between simple waves and ordinary plane waves is established. All the simple one-dimensional waves are considered. It is shown that, in the absence of shock waves, a region of constant flow can be bounded only by a single wave.

22. (**48**) AKHIEZER, A. I. et SITENKO, A. G.
  Théorie de l'excitation des Ondes Hydromagnétiques.
Etude de l'excitation des ondes hydromagnétiques et magnéto-acoustiques à l'aide de courants électriques extérieurs. Calcul de l'amortissement des ondes, compte tenu de la conductivité et de la viscosité du milieu. Comparaison entre les excitations provoquées par un courant électrique et par un procédé mécanique.
2 références bibliographiques.   (SDIT)

23. (**52**) ALFVÉN, H.
  Cosmical Electrodynamics.
Cosmic physics is still in the stage where the most important task is to find out what are the dominating factors. Hence in this book the stress is always laid more on the physical than on the mathematical side. It is clearly understood that definite tests of any theory can be made only by rigorous mathematics, but the scope of this book is more to put the problems than to solve them.
                                                                (Oxford U.P.)

24. (**65**) ALFVÉN, H.
  Magneto-hydrodynamic Waves in the Atomic Nucleus.
Hydrodynamic models are important for the understanding of some properties of the atomic nucleus. Since the nucleus has a magnetic moment, hydrodynamic phenomena should be affected by a magnetic field. The order of magnitude of possible magnetohydrodynamic resonance frequencies is calculated.

25. (**66**) ALFVÉN, H.
  Magneto-hydrodynamic Waves in the Sun.
In the presence of a magnetic field, a fluid having a sufficiently high electric conductivity is able to transmit magneto-hydrodynamic waves. In the sun, the general magnetic field and the high degree of ionization found there provide conditions favourable for the existence of such waves. Magneto-hydrodynamic effects have been investigated in the laboratory, using mercury and a magnetic field of 10,000 to 15,000 gauss. The mercury, in the presence of the magnetic field, behaves as though it possessed a highly anisotropic "electromagnetic viscosity." Since all motions of the conducting liquid cause electric currents, the properties of the mercury change remarkably. Magneto-hydrodynamic waves may be of great importance in connection with the origin of sunspots. The magnitude of the Zeeman effect in emission from sunspots indicates the presence of a magnetic field of several thousand gauss. By assuming the magnetic field to be the primary mechanism, it seems likely that the other observed properties of sunspots may be explained adequately. The magnetic field in sunspots might reasonably be thought to originate deep in the solar interior, in the region of energy production by nuclear fusion. The concept of magneto-hydrodynamic waves could then explain the propagation of the sunspot magnetic field outward to the solar surface. Magneto-hydrodynamic waves could also clarify the phenomena of magnetically variable stars and granulation in the solar photosphere.

26. (**85**) ALLEN, J. E. and SEGRÉ, S. E.
Experiments on the Orthogonal Pinch Effect.
Some orthogonal pinch effect experiments are reported, which were carried out using a condenser bank of 11.25 μF at 20 kV, the period of oscillation being 35 μsec. Magnetic probe measurements have been made of the spatial and temporal variations of magnetic field strength within the plasma.
The design of a larger condenser bank is then discussed, which includes a multi-sector coil enabling a large voltage per turn to be developed.

27. (**92**) ALLIS, W. P. and BUCHSBAUM, S. J.
The Conductivity of an Ionized Gas in a Magnetic Field.
Presented at the ARS-Northwestern Gas Dynamics Symposium at Northwestern University, Evanston, Illinois, 24–26 August, 1959.

28. (**103**) ANDERSON, O. A., BAKER, W. R., BZATENAHL, A., FURTH, H. P. and KUNKEL, W. B.
Hydromagnetic Capacitor.
Very high dielectric constant can easily be achieved by means of an ionized gas in a strong magnetic field. When an orthogonal electric field is applied, the resultant particle drift stores electrical energy. In a coaxial capacitor, which makes use of a rotating plasma disc, dielectric constants in the range 10^6 to 10^8 have been measured. The potential usefulness of hydromagnetic capacitors in fast-discharge work is considered.

29. (**104**) ANDERSON, O. A., FURTH, H. P., STONE, J. M., and WRIGHT, R. E.
Inverse Pinch Effect.
An electric current passing along a conducting rod and returning through ionized gas surrounding the rod forms a magnetic field pushing the plasma outward, leaving behind a cylindrical vacuum region. This effect appears to be more amenable to experimental studies than is the pinch effect. Displacement and thickness of the plasma front were measured optically and magnetically. At low mass densities, the observed front thickness justifies use of the "snow-plough" model, and the front velocity is described to good approximation by analytical results based on this model. At higher densities, it appears that the magnetic field is diffused significantly into the cold plasma. Authors' suggestion that these studies of the inverse dynamic pinch be followed by studies of the inverse stabilized pinch seems to merit consideration. (F. Knuth)

30. (**112**) ARKHIPOV, V. N.
The Influence of a Magnetic Field on the Stability of a Boundary Layer.
Rosjow (*Z. Angew. Math. Phys.*, Vol. 96, No. 5–6, p. 519, 1958) has calculated the velocity profile of the boundary layer of a viscous electrically conducting fluid flowing parallel to a flat plate. Here the stability of this profile is investigated, assuming perturbations which vary sinusoidally in the direction of flow and applying Galerkin's method to compute a curve of neutral stability. The results, presented graphically, indicate that a small magnetic field (Hartmann number of the order of 0.04) nearly doubles the critical Reynolds number. (O. Penrose)

31. (**117**) ARTSIMOVICH, L. A., LUK'YANOV, S. Y., PODGORNYI, I. M. and CHUVATIN, S. A.
Electrodynamical Acceleration of Plasma Bunches.
An electrodynamic method of accelerating plasma bunches is proposed. The results of preliminary experiments are described. The data obtained are in qualitative agreement with the elementary theory of the phenomena.

32. (**124**) ATKINSON, W. R., FOWLER, R. G. and HOLDEN, W. R.
Magneto-Hydrodynamic Flows in Hydrogen and Helium.
An electrically energized shock tube was used to produce a stream of luminous
conductive gas. Two aspects of the interaction between this flow and a stationary
magnetic field were observed.

33. (**126**) ATKINSON, W. R., HOLDEN, W. R. and FOWLER, R. G.
Shock Waves Reflected by Magnetic Fields.
Fast-moving plasmas encountering transverse magnetic fields of order 10^4 gauss
are decelerated so rapidly as to produce reflected shock waves. Observations in
hydrogen at gas pressures of 1 to about 10 mm Hg are analysed. There are critical
conditions of magnetic field for the onset of the reflection. The velocities of the
advancing and reflected waves are recorded as a function of pressure and field.

34. (**127**) AUER, P. L., HURWITZ, H., Jr. and MILLER, R. D.
Collective Oscillations in a Cold Plasma.
The waves considered here are linearized displacements in a plasma in which
there exists a strong magnetic field, assumed as homogeneous in the special
applications. Only one kind of positive ions is admitted. The temperature motions
of the particles as well as any collisions are neglected, so that the medium is non-
dissipative. Starting from a characteristic equation (dispersion relation) given for
this case by Aström in 1950, authors discuss extensively the nature of the various
modes that can arise. This discussion is first carried on in terms of potentials and
the field quantities derived from them, and then in terms of particle orbits. It is
found that when the Alfvén dielectric constant, $4\pi n(M + m)c^2 B_0^2$ becomes
comparable in magnitude to the ion-to-electron mass ratio, plasma space charges
may become important in the oscillations. (W. M. Elsasser)

35. (**132**) BABSUKOV, K. A. and KOLOMENSKII, A. R.
Doppler Effect in an Electron Plasma in a Magnetic Field.
The complex Doppler effect produced in the motion of an oscillator in an anisotropic plasma is analysed. The ionospheric Doppler effect is given as a numerical
example.

36. (**138**) BADE, W. L.
Hydromagnetic Effects of Upwelling Near a Boundary.
Since the geomagnetic secular variations may be attributed to the distortion of
pre-existing magnetic fields in the earth's core by upwelling motions of the fluid
toward the core-mantle boundary, the object of this work has been to compute the
hydromagnetic effects of such an upwelling. The main problem is to determine the
effects at the surface of the core. This is solved approximately in two steps:
(1) the magnetic viscosity is set equal to zero and the fluid motion is permitted to
operate on the field for a time "t", and (2) the fluid motion is stopped and the
diffusion is permitted to act for an equal time "t" on the field which was produced
by the fluid motion in step (1). (TIL/MOS)

37. (**139**) BADER, M. and CARLSON, W. C. A.
*Measurement of the Effect of an Axial Magnetic Field on the Reynolds Number of
Transition in Mercury Flowing Through a Glass Tube*
Experiments were conducted to determine the effect of a 15,000 gauss axial mag-
netic field on the flow of mercury through a glass tube of 0.027 in. inside diameter.
It was found that when only slight instabilities were present at Reynolds numbers
from 5,000 to 8,000, the Reynolds number of transition could be increased by as
much as 10 per cent. (NACA)

38. (**146**) BALESCU, R.
   Irreversible Processes in Ionized Gases.

The general theory of irreversible processes, developed by Prigogine and Balescu, is applied to the case of long range interactions in ionized gases. A similar diagram technique permits the systematic selection of all the contributions to the evolution of the distribution function, to an order of approximation equivalent to Debye's equilibrium theory. The infinite series which appear in this way can be summed exactly. The resulting evolution equations have a clear physical significance: they describe intersections of "quasi particles", which are electrons or ions "dressed" by their polarization clouds. These clouds are not a permanent feature, as in equilibrium theory, but have a nonequilibrium, changing shape, distorted by the motions of the particles from the mathematical point of view, these equations exhibit a new type of nonlinearity, which is very directly related to the collective nature of the interactions.

39. (**147**) BANISTER, J. R.
   Separation of Magnetic Driving and Ohmic Heating.

In this experiment, brief uni-directional current discharges were passed through nitrogen in the presence of a transverse uniform magnetic field. The gas between the electrodes was heated and given a directed velocity. Since flow is limited to the direction of this directed velocity, the usual shock-tube theory modified for this velocity may be used to describe shock development. This theoretical method, which provides separation of the order of magnetic driving and ohmic heating, was found to be precisely applicable until the material transverses more than half the electrode dimension during the discharge. The technique seems potentially useful for studying plasma conductivity and equation state.

40. (**151**) BAÑOS, A.
   Theoretical Study of Magneto-Hydrodynamic, Magneto-Acoustic, and Magneto-Elastic Phenomena.

The theoretical investigation of the soluble unbounded media and boundary value problems involved in these phenomena is restricted (1) to a purely macroscopic approach to serve as a guide in the solution of the more complicated problems of plasma dynamics and (2) to a class of soluble linearized wave propagation problems. The macroscopic medium (homogeneous and isotropic) is characterized by the constant parameters μ, ε, and σ, where $\mu\varepsilon = c^{-2}$ and σ is the (ohmic) conductivity. The modes of propagation are examined for 5 cases: (1) an ideal incompressible fluid, (2) an ideal compressible fluid subject to adiabatic processes, (3) an ideal elastic solid, (4) an incompressible fluid with finite viscosity, and (5) a compressible fluid with finite viscosity and heat conductivity. A study of the energy and momentum balance in a magneto-hydrodynamic field resulted in the derivation of a heat diffusion equation in a compressible fluid with finite viscosity and heat conductivity. (ASTIA)

41. (**153**) BARABANENKOV, U. N.
   Solution of the Kinetic Equation for a Plasma in a Variable Magnetic Field.

The motion of a completely ionized plasma (collision being neglected) along a narrow magnetic tube of an axially symmetrical magnetic field is considered by means of the kinetic equation. The equation is solved under the assumption of sufficiently slow variation of the magnetic field. Canonical variables are chosen as the independent variable of the distribution function.

42. (**156**) BARNES, A. H.
   Direct Current Electromagnetic Pumps.

Principles of operation and the design of pumps are described, including the one used in the primary coolant circuit of the Experimental Breeder Reactor.

43. **(157)** BARROS, D., Jr.
   Fundamental Wave Functions in an Unbounded Magneto-Hydrodynamic Field.
   V. General Theory.
   This is the first of two papers dealing with a systematic study of the linearized, unbounded medium problems in magneto-hydrodynamics of incompressible and compressible fluids. Part I deals with the fundamental equations which are set up quite generally for an ideal, homogeneous and isotropic, conducting fluid derived of viscosity and expansive friction, subject only to the initial assumption that the externally applied field of magnetic induction be constant and uniform.

44. **(163)** BARTHEL, J. R. and LYKOUDIS, P. S.
   The Slow Motion of a Magnetized Sphere in a Conducting Medium.
   This paper considers the slow motion of a sphere, permanently and uniformly magnetized in one direction, in a viscous electrically conducting medium. The line of the magnetic poles is assumed to be parallel to the direction of the motion of the sphere. The velocity and pressure fields are calculated by two iterations. The distortion of the magnetic field is also calculated. An expression is obtained for total drag due to the viscous pressure and magnetic forces.

45. **(168)** BAY, W.
   Theoretical Treatments in Magneto-Hydrodynamics.
   Abstracts of 40 papers published in various scientific periodicals are given which are concerned with the following subjects: (1) the equilibrium of magnetic stars, (2) oscillations of magnetic stars and related problems on hydromagnetic stability, (3) problems in wave propagation, (4) propagation of hydromagnetic disturbances, (5) the stability of superposed fluids, (6) viscous flow between rotating cylinders, (7) the Bènard problem, (8) the dynamo problem, (9) axisymmetric magnetic fluids and fluid motions, and (10) theory of hydrodynamic and hydromagnetic turbulence.   (ASTIA)

46. **(178)** BAZER, J. and ERICSON, W. B.
   Hydromagnetic Shocks.
   Les auteurs résolvent et discutent, dans le cas le plus général, les équations des chocs magnétoaérodynamiques pour un gaz polytropique. La vitesse du choc et les grandeurs qui caractérisent l'état du fluide après le choc sont exprimées en function de la discontinuité du champ magnétique; ces fonctions sont algébriques. Les chocs sont classés en fonction de cette représentation.   (M. Cabannes)

47. **(179)** BAZER, J. et FLEISCHMAN, O.
   La Propagation des Discontinuités Aéromagnétiques Faibles.
   Calcul théorique de la propagation de ces discontinuités. 19 références bibliographiques.   (SDIT)

48. **(180)** BEARD, D. B.
   Cyclotron Radiation from Magnetically Confined Plasmas.
   The cyclotron emission from a hot, completely ionized, magnetically confined plasma has been estimated by computing the absorption of an incident plane wave. The harmonics of the fundamental cyclotron frequency, which are emitted perpendicular to the magnetic field direction, were summed over and also treated individually. Because of the Doppler effect and the relativistic variation in mass the behaviour of the electrons and the electromagnetic properties of the medium are

functions of electron velocity. Assuming a Maxwell-Boltzmann distribution in electron velocity, the polarization of the plasma was computed by integrating over electron velocity. Solution of Maxwell's equations yielded the absorption of an incident wave, and thus, from Kirchhoff's relation, the emission of the plasma was determined. The entire calculation was carried out nonrelativistically to first order in v^2/c^2 and at temperatures too low for fluctuations to play a dominant role.

49. (**182**) BEARD, D. B.
Incoherent Microwave Radiation from an Ionized Gas Confined by a Magnetic Field.
The cyclotron emission from a hot, completely ionized magnetically-confined plasma was estimated by computing the absorption of an incident plane wave. The harmonics of the fundamental cyclotron frequency, which are emitted perpendicular to the magnetic field direction, were summed over and also treated individually. Because of the Doppler effect and the relativistic variation in mass, the behaviour of the electrons and the electromagnetic properties of the medium are functions of electron velocity. Assuming a Maxwell-Boltzmann distribution in electron velocity, the polarization of the plasma was computed by integrating over electron velocity. Solution of Maxwell's equations yielded the absorption of an incident wave, and thus, from Kirchhoff's relation, the emission of the plasma was determined. As a result, the emission was found to depend inversely on the temperature. The emission perpendicular to the confining magnetic field is much less than the collision bremsstrahlung for sufficiently high temperature of several tens of kilovolts, depending on the plasma dimensions, density and magnetic field shape. (ASTIA)

50. (**185**) BEGIASHVILI, G. A. and GEDALIN, E. V.
Motion of a Charged Particle in an Anisotropic Medium.
Expressions are derived for the electromagnetic field components and the total energy losses are determined for a charged particle moving in anisotropic gyroelectric and gyromagnetic medium.

51. (**188**) BELOKON, V. A.
The Permanent Structure of Shock Waves with Joule Dissipation.
If the dominating dissipating mechanism in a magnetohydrodynamic shock is that due to electrical conductivity, and if the shock strength is such that with respect to a co-ordinate frame fixed to the shock the flow is supersonic upstream and subsonic downstream with respect to the local acoustic speeds of sound, the paper shows that the shock consists of a relatively thick zone through which all flow parameters and the magnetic field strength change continuously and is followed by a discontinuity surface through which no change in entropy and the magnetic field strength occur, but the rest of the flow parameters change abruptly. Following the analogous case discussed by Landau and Lifshitz for an isothermal discontinuity in an ordinary shock (*Fluid Mechanics*, Pergamon Press, 1959), such a discontinuity is called an isentropic discontinuity by the author, or preferably, an isentropic-isomagnetic discontinuity. (C. Chang)

52. (**192**) BERGER, J. M., NEWCOMB, W. A., DAWSON, J. M., FRIEMAN, E. A., KULSRUD, R. M. and LENARD, A.
Heating of a Confined Plasma by Oscillating Electromagnetic Fields.
There are two ways of heating a plasma confined by a strong axial magnetic field. In the first of these the electric field is parallel to the magnetic field, the situation that obtains in ohmic heating. In the second of these, the electric field is perpendicular to the main axial magnetic field. In this paper we consider the second case only and consider the electric field to be produced by an externally imposed oscillation of the axial field. This method of heating is often called magnetic

pumping. It is found that as far as the heating of the plasma is concerned, there are four characteristic times which play a fundamental role. These four times are: (1) the collision time, (2) the period of the oscillating field, (3) the time of transit of a typical ion through the heating region, and (4) the cyclotron period of an ion. If these four characteristic times are all of comparable order, the theoretical analysis is exceedingly complex. Therefore, four cases were considered in which these were taken to be of different orders. The heating mechanism differs in each of these four cases since the period of the externally produced electric field is chosen to be comparable to one of the characteristic times in the analysis. In each of the four cases configurations were found which led theoretically, at least, to efficient heating of the plasma. In those cases where the energy imparted to the plasma appears in the form of wave motion, the subsequent damping of these waves is discussed.

53. (**195**) BERNSTEIN, I. B.
    Waves in a Plasma in a Magnetic Field.
The small oscillations of a fully ionized plasma in a constant external magnetic field is treated by the Laplace transform method; collision effects were considered to be negligible. The full set of Maxwell equations is employed, and the ion dynamics are included. Various limiting cases are considered. Self-excitation of waves around thermal equilibrium is impossible. For longitudinal electron oscillations propagating perpendicular to the constant magnetic field, there are gaps in the spectrum of allowed frequencies at multiples of the electron gyration frequency, but zero Landau damping (*J. Phys. U.S.S.R.*, 10 : 25, 1946). The particular waves are also associated with a non-uniformity of convergence in the limit of vanishing magnetic field. When the ion dynamics are included, 2 classes of low-frequency oscillations are found (longitudinal ion waves and transverse hydro-magnetic waves). Calculations indicated that in many cases the transport equations are capable of yielding correct results for a wide class of waves in a collision-free plasma.

54. (**196**) BERNSTEIN, I. B., *et al.*
    An Energy Principle for Hydromagnetic Stability Problems.
The problem of the stability of static, highly conducting, fully ionized plasmas is investigated by means of an energy principle developed from one introduced by Lundquist. The derivation of the principle and the conditions under which it applies are given. The method is applied to find complete stability criteria for two types of equilibrium situations. The first concerns plasmas which are completely separated from the magnetic field by an interface. The second is the general axisymmetric system.

55. (**198**) BERNSTEIN, I. B. and RABINOWITZ, I. N.
    Theory of Electrostatic Probes in a Low-Density Plasma.
Authors present computational method for electrostatic probes in low-density plasmas where collisions are negligible. Particular application is made to collection of positive ions by spherical and cylindrical probes. Boltzmann equation gives particle density and flux as functionals of electrostatic potential and absorptive characteristics of probe. Potential is determined by Poisson's equation. Numerical computations are given for collection of monoenergetic ions, assuming negligible electron current. Results show influence of ion temperature on potential, and possibility of trapped ions for sufficiently small probe radii, which could affect local potential.   (F. Wattendorf)

56. (**201**) BERNSTEIN, I. B., FRIEMAN, E. A., KULSRUD, R. M., and ROSENBULTH, M. M.
    Ion Wave Instabilities.
The limited confinement time of plasma in the B-3 stellarator is explained in terms

of the enhanced diffusion of ions across the magnetic field due to low frequency ion wave instabilities. It is shown that a minimum value of current is required for their onset. (A. Gabriel)

57. (**202**) BERNSTEIN, W. and KRANZ, A. Z.
Ohmic Heating in the B-1 Stellarator.
This paper presents a detailed comparison between ohmic heating theory and the experiments made on the B-1 stellarator over a wide range of axial magnetic confining field, electric heating field and helium pressure. It is found that, in the early stage of the discharge, agreement between theory and experiment is good, and the predicted scaling laws are valid. However, experimentally it is found that it takes about 5 times longer to complete first ionization than predicted. Also, the current is seen to level off at a plateau at a time when theory predicts a continuous heating. These discrepancies are attributed to three energy sinks: cold neutral particles entering the discharge, runaway electrons leaving the discharge and radiation from impurities. In addition, the electron density is observed to decrease during the discharge (pump-out). For the early current plateau observed at low ratios of heating field to pressure, it appears that the plasma density is about 15 per cent less at 18,000 gauss than at 27,000 gauss as a result of this pump-out. Further, it is suggested that Kruskal's hydromagnetic instability results physically in an increased rate of diffusion. (F. Tamaki)

58. (**204**) BERNSTEIN, W., CHEN, F. F., HEALD, M. A. and KRANZ, A. Z.
"Runaway" Electrons and Cooperative Phenomena in B-1 Stellarator Discharges.
An experimental and detailed investigation of X-ray radiation from a B-1 stellarator during pulsed discharge. The results cannot be explained by single-particle models or macroscopic plasma physics. The evidence suggests that "collective phenomena" do occur. The runaway electrons indicate the existence of instabilities at currents well below the Kruskal limiting current. Intense microwave radiation is also observed. (R. Betchov)

59. (**205**) BERSHADER, D.
Magnetodynamics of Conducting Fluids.
The third volume in the series on magnetohydrodynamics resulting from the Lockheed Missiles and Space Division sponsored symposia. The essays in this volume are devoted to conducting fluids, particularly gases. (Lockheed)

60. (**207**) BERSHADER, D. AND LANDSHOFF, R.
Magnetohydrodynamics—A Symposium Report.
Compte rendu des mémoires présentés au congrès tenu en décembre 1957 par la Lockheed Missile Systems Division. (SDIT)

61. (**208**) BERTOTTI, B.
Uniform Electromagnetic Field in the Theory of General Relativity.
A cosmological solution of the Einstein-Maxwell field equations, corresponding to the case of a uniform (that is covariant constant) electromagnetic field, is derived by means of simple geometrical arguments; the Riemannian manifold it corresponds to is the product of two ordinary surfaces of constant curvature, whose type and radius depend on the electromagnetic field. The world-line of charged test particles has also a very simple geometrical meaning.

62. (**209**) BEZBATCHENKO, A. L. and GOLOVIN, I. N.
The Influence of a Longitudinal Magnetic Field on an Impulsive Gaseous Discharge at High Current Intensity.
The influence of a longitudinal magnetic field on the stability of the plasma column obtained with impulsive current flow through deuterium, has been investigated.

101

Observations made and conclusions drawn are given. The conductivity of the plasma was calculated by measuring the rate of escape of the longitudinal field from the column discharge. (TIL/MOS)

63. (210) BEZBATCHENKO, A. L., GOLOVIN, I. N., IVANOV, D. P., KIRILLOV, V. D. and YAVLINSKY, N. A.
   An Investigation of a High-Current Gas Discharge in a Longitudinal Magnetic Field.
A gas discharge in deuterium has been investigated at current up to 700 kA in a longitudinal magnetic field of up to 12,000 e. The influence of the field on the development of the discharge column was detected. Estimates are given of the plasma conductivity and the ionization coefficient.

64. (212) BHATNAGAR, P. L.
   The Equilibrium of a Self-Gravitating Incompressible Fluid Sphere with Magnetic Field.
Equations of equilibrium of a self-gravitating incompressible fluid and electromagnetic Maxwell's equations, in the steady case, are used to study the problem of magnetic fields that can prevail in an axisymmetric configuration. A new class of axisymmetric magnetic fields is characterized and the following special types are studied: force-free, poloidal, toroidal, and combination of toroidal and poloidal fields. The paper relates to the problem of magnetic stars. (G. Sestini)

65. (219) BIERMANN, L.
   Stellar Atmospheres as a Plasma.
The basic equations for a two-fluid plasma are given, and these are considered in relation to the transport of radiation through the opaque and the transparent layers of the sun. A survey is given of current theories on the subjects of sunspots, ionization in the solar corona, and the rotation of interplanetary gases. A number of models for comet tails are described.

66. (223) BIERMANN, L. and PFIRSCH, D.
   Cooperative Phenomena and Diffusion of a Plasma in a Transverse Magnetic Field. I.
The possibility is discussed that, under certain conditions, local fluctuations of charge density may be excited in an inhomogeneous plasma. Their maximal amplitudes are estimated and the influence of these instabilities on the confinement of a plasma by a magnetic field is investigated.

67. (225) BIRZVALK, Y. and VEZE, A.
   Velocity Distribution in Electromagnetic Pump Channels, with a Rectangular Cross-section.
Sherdiff's methods of solution of the Navier-Stokes equation (Abstr. 4220 of 1953) is used, while replacing the magnetic field intensity by a scalar electric potential. Approximate (least square) solutions are obtained.

68. (226) BISHOP, A.
   Project Sherwood.
This book is a useful survey on plasma application to controlled fusion devices. Some up-to-date engineering applications (Stellarators, mirror machines, etc.) are presented in a quite elementary form, together with many interesting news and comments dealing with U.S. controlled fusion programs. (G. Contursi)

69. (234) BLANK, A. A. and GRAD, H.
   Notes on Magneto-Hydrodynamics, Fluid Magnetic Equations—General Properties.
In this note we describe and collect some general properties of the equations of fluid magnetics. In this supplement to MH-I we describe the fluid magnetic

systems to which we shall have most frequent reference. Here, we shall adopt a set of standard non-dissipative fluid equations coupled with Maxwell's equations by a Lorentz force term and some form of Ohm's law. Within this frame, there is a considerable amount of flexibility; e.g. in the choice of an equation of state and of a form of Ohm's law, and in the decision to include or omit displacement current, electrostatic forces, and electro-magnetic momentum. An important criterion in making these decisions is the mathematical tractability of the resultant equations; this desideratum should on occasion even override in importance the criterion of the precise physical validity of a given assumption.

70. (**236**) BLANK, A. A., FRIEDRICHS, K. O. and GRAD, H.
Notes on Magneto-Hydrodynamics. Theory of Maxwell's Equations without Displacement Current.
We use the term *pre-Maxwell equations* to signify a formalization of the electromagnetic theory which existed prior to Maxwell's introduction of the concept of displacement current. The purpose of this report is to give a general descriptive survey of the theory of these equations which is aimed primarily at applications. In formulations of fluid magnetics which use non-relativistic fluid dynamic equations, the pre-Maxwell equations, being Galilean invariant, are in some respects even more appropriate than Maxwell's equations. The system of pre-Maxwell equations has its own intrinsic mathematical interest because of properties which are entirely different from those of Maxwell's equations. It is possible to give a rather complete existence theory for the system of pre-Maxwell equations.

71. (**238**) VAN BLERKOM, R.
Magnetohydrodynamic Flow of a Viscous Fluid Past a Sphere.
The flow of a viscous incompressible electrically conducting fluid past a sphere is studied; the uniform ambient flow field is colinear with the ambient uniform magnetic field. The force exerted on the sphere is computed for various conductivities and Reynold numbers; of particular interest is the distinction in behaviour between the flow with the ambient particle speed greater than ambient Alfvén speed and that with particle speed less than Alfvén speed.

72. (**239**) BLEVISS, Z. O.
Magneto-Gasdynamics of Hypersonic Couette Flow.
In the present report, the Couette flow problem is extended to include a uniform externally imposed magnetic field normal to the walls. Assuming thermodynamic equilibrium and reasonable variations of electrical conductivity, viscosity, and Prandtl number with temperature, numerical solutions are presented for air for the case of the insulated wall (no heat transfer to the wall) for Mach numbers from 10 to 30 and for the case of heat transfer for Mach numbers of 20 and 30. The effects of the magnetic field upon the velocity, temperature, electrical current density, and induced magnetic field distributions and upon the skin friction, heat transfer, and total drag (i.e. skin friction plus the magnetic stress due to the interaction of the electrically conducting fluid with the magnetic field) are shown. Comparing results with magnetic field to results without magnetic field for a given high-speed laminar boundary layer, the present investigation shows that relatively weak magnetic fields produce large increases in the total drag, large reductions in the skin friction, and at the same time have relatively little effect on the heat transfer. Whereas the total drag without magnetic field is skin friction drag, the total drag with magnetic field is primarily magnetic drag. This implies that if the comparison is made on the basis of the same total drag the heat transfer for the magnetic case will be much less than that for the non-magnetic case. The expected qualitative and quantitative applicability of the Couette flow results to the boundary layer is discussed.   (ASTIA)

73. (**240**) BLEVISS, Z. O.

The Effects of Combined Electric and Magnetic Fields on Hypersonic Couette Flow.
At hypersonic speeds the air in a high-speed boundary layer becomes an electrical conductor as a result of thermal ionization and it can then be made to interact with electric and magnetic fields to alter the skin friction, heat transfer, and total drag. A very simple, pure shear, laminar flow (Couette flow) problem is investigated because it contains many important features of boundary layer flow and because it can be solved with a minimum of assumptions about the gas. The effects of radial magnetic fields on this Couette flow were studied by Bleviss (*J. Aero/Space Sci.*, Vol. 25, No. 10, pp. 601–615, Oct., 1958). The present study extends the Couette flow problem to include both radial magnetic circumferential electric fields. The conclusions are concerned with the effects and possible usefulness of the presently considered configuration of electromagnetic fields applied to the boundary layer of a body of revolution that is flying at hypersonic speeds and is slender enough so that its drag is primarily caused by skin friction. For a given magnetic field strength, the increase of the ratio of the total drag to the heat transfer rate is maximum for zero electrical field. The reduction in the heat transferred to a vehicle is accomplished by a reduction in the speed of a vehicle through the atmosphere. Therefore, this configuration cannot be used to decrease heat transferred to a slender re-entry vehicle. The maximum reduction is obtained for zero electric field for a fixed magnetic field strength. (ASTIA)

74. (**241**) BLEVISS, Z. O.

A Study of the Structure of the Magneto-hydrodynamic Switch-on Wave.
The structure of the steady magnetohydrodynamic switch-on shock wave is investigated for several order-of-magnitude orderings of the 4 diffusivities involved in the problem. The various orderings are approximated by allowing one or more of the appropriate diffusivities to approach zero, and approximate solutions that are uniformly valid to order unity are sought. In general, singular perturbation problems are encountered, the number of them (from 0 to a maximum of 3) depending upon the ordering of the diffusivities and the magnitude of the downstream velocity normal to the shock relative to certain critical velocities downstream of the shock. Where necessary, the approximate solutions are rendered uniformly valid to first order by the insertion of boundary layers, for which the approximate equations are determined to first order. For most of the cases considered, the limiting forms of the integral curves are determined and they are sketched in appropriate 3-dimensional phase spaces.

75. (**242**) BLEVISS, Z. O.

Transmission of Electromagnetic Waves through Ionized Air Surrounding Hypersonic Aircraft.
Transmission through two different regions on a hypersonic aircraft are studied, the blunt nose region and the high speed laminar or turbulent boundary layer on a slender afterbody. Conclusions that may be drawn from this study for speeds up to about 25,000 ft/sec and altitudes up to 250,000 ft are that vacuum wave lengths less than about one millimetre are necessary for transmission through the blunt nose region. Vacuum wave lengths less than about one metre are necessary for transmission through the high-speed boundary layer. (TIL/MOS)

76. (**243**) BLOKHINTSEV, D. I.

On a Possible Limit on the Applicability of Quantum Electrodynamics.
Processes that can compete with electromagnetic processes at high energies are considered. It is shown that these can be processes associated with four-fermion interactions.

77. (**249**) BODIN, H. A. B., GREEN, T. S., NIBLETT, C. B. F. and PEACOCK, N. J.
   An Experimental Investigation of the Rapid Compression of a Plasma using Azimuthal Currents (Thetatron).
An experimental study of phenomena accompanying the compression of a plasma by a rapidly-rising axial magnetic field is described. The field is produced by the discharge of a low inductance condenser bank (30 kV, 100 μF, 5 mμH) through a single turn coil, and peak currents of 1.8×10^6 amperes and fields of 1.1×10^5 gauss are recorded. High speed photography and electrical measurements are used to study the characteristics of discharges in air and deuterium.

78. (**250**) BOGDANKEVICH, L. S.
   Radiation from a Current-carrying Ring Moving Uniformly in a Plasma Situated in a Magnetic Field.
Energy losses due to Cherenkov-Vavilov radiation are computed for a current-carrying ring moving uniformly in a plasma perpendicular to its plane and parallel to the external magnetic field.

79. (**257**) BOLOTOVSKII, B. M. and RUKHADZE, A. A.
   Field of a Charged Particle in a Moving Medium.
The field produced by a charge passing through a moving medium is considered. Energy losses due to emission of Cherenkov-Vavilov radiation and excitation of plasma waves are determined.

80. (**259**) BOND, J. W.
   Plasma Physics and Hypersonic Flight.
A clear review of the problems encountered at Mach numbers greater than 12 to 15. Dissociation and ionization are evaluated. Shock-front structure and boundary-layer structure are discussed as well as the conditions in which the different components of an ionized gas may be found. (R. Betchov)

81. (**264**) BONNEVIER, B. and LEHNERT, B.
   The Motion of Charged Particles in a Rotating Plasma.
The confinement of charged particles by magnetic mirror in a rotating plasma is considered. The forbidden regions of a charged particle in crossed electric and magnetic fields are discussed with special attention to the centrifugal and Coriolis forces. It is found that, under certain conditions, particles will move almost along the magnetic field lines and will be completely reflected at the mirrors by means of the centrifugal force. A high reflection power is obtained by fields with large radial extensions such as that generated by a circular current loop.

82. (**266**) BOON, M. H., LAING, E. W. *et al.*
   Hydromagnetic Instabilities of a Cylindrical Gas Discharge, Part 6. Energy Principle Calculations for Axisymmetric Perturbations.
Stable gas discharge configurations have been shown to exist, in which the discharge current flows entirely on its surface. The finite electrical conductivity of the discharge causes the thickness of the current layer to increase and eventually the discharge becomes unstable. Stability against axisymmetric perturbations has been studied using a variational procedure developed at Princeton. For one simple evolutionary sequence of discharge configurations, stability is lost when the current layer has a thickness of about 15 per cent of the discharge radius. Approximate stability criteria are found for more general discharge configurations which are not linked in an evolutionary sequence. (TIL/MOS)

83. (**268**) BOPP, F.
   Remarks on the Conformal Invariance of Electrodynamics and the Basic Equation of Dynamics.
Isolating the source of the lack of general covariance of the equations of electrodynamics, a new proof is given for their covariance under the group of conformal

co-ordinate transformations (Cunningham and Bateman, 1910). Moreover, it is shown that the equations of motion too, are conformal covariant if the mass is transformed like a reciprocal length. Similar parameter transformations in conjunction with transformations of the conformal group (dilatations corresponding to scale transformations of the field) have also been considered by Heisenberg *et al.* in recent work on the symmetries of the non-linear equation of Heisenberg and Pauli.

84. (**273**) BORRUNOV, N. A., ORLINSKII, D. V. and OSOVETS, S. M.
Investigation of High Current Pulse Discharges in Conical Chambers.
Some general considerations are presented concerning the possibility of formation of a cumulative jet in the course of contraction of a conical plasma envelope. Preliminary results of some experiments performed with so-called single and double conical systems are presented. Photographs of discharges in conical chambers are presented, and also results of some other measurements.

85. (**276**) BOSTICK, W. H. and LEVINE, M. A.
Experiments on the Behaviour of an Ionized Gas in a Magnetic Field.
Measurements with probes in a plasma of helium ions and electrons in the afterglow of an induction excited discharge in a toroidal tube with a toroidal magnetic field reveals an oscillatory probe current which is presumably indicative of fluctuations in the ion density. Measurements of electron density in another toroidal tube show that in this tube the degree of diffusion control in helium at low pressures is apparently orders of magnitude less than one would calculate from the classical theory of ambipolar diffusion of ions and electrons in a magnetic field. An attempt is made to explain this minimum and the lack of diffusion control in terms of plasma waves.

86. (**277**) BOSTICK, W. H. and LEVINE, M. A.
Relationships Involved in the H_z-E_ϕ Pinch Effect.
The transient H_z-E_ϕ type of pinch effect was treated in the same manner as was the E_z-H_ϕ type discussed in AD–25 257. A simple theory is presented involving the assumption of an adiabatic magnetic compression of the gas. The diameter of the pinch and the temperature can be calculated in terms of the current and other discharge parameters. (ASTIA)

87. (**279**) BOSTICK, W. H., LEVINE, M. A. and MORTON, A.
Magneto-Hydrodynamic Waves Generated in an Ionized Gas in a Toroidal Tube Having an Annular D.C. Magnetic Field.
The behaviour of ionized gases at low pressures in the afterglow period following a discharge was studied by using a pulsed, induction-excited toroidal discharge tube with an annular d.c. magnetic field to retard ion diffusion to the walls. Oscillations attributed to magnetohydrodynamic waves were observed in the current to the probe which was inserted into a region of high ion-density gradient in a plasma in a d.c. magnetic field. (ASTIA)

88. (**281**) BOSTICK, W. H., WEINTRAUB, H., and LEVINE, M. A.
Diffusion of a Plasma Across an Inhomogeneous Magnetic Field.
An attempt is made to solve the magnetohydrodynamic equations (AD–25 255 and AD–25 256) in the presence of a d.c. magnetic field. The solution appeared to agree with the qualitative conclusion that for a given z-position and time t, the wave amplitude of h_y and v_y increase toward lower values of the magnetic field; h_y is a component of the wave field superimposed upon the d.c. field and v_y is the velocity of the medium in the y direction. (ASTIA)

89. (**282**) BOULLOD, A.
  The Effect of Temperature on Pre-breakdown Currents in Compressed Gases.
  A brief note describing measurements of pre-breakdown current between, e.g. stainless steel electrodes. Temperature varied from about 25 to 50°C, and the corresponding current from $\sim 5 \times 10^{-10}$ to 4×10^{-8} A. The currents increase with temperature. Results are shown graphically and the effect is briefly discussed.

  (J. Craggs)

90. (**283**) BOURDEAU, R. E., WHIPPLE, E. C., Jr. and CLARK, J. F.
  Analytic and Experimental Electrical Conductivity between the Stratosphere and the Ionosphere.
  Data on atmosphere conductivity obtained experimentally in the altitude region between 35 and 80 km by use of rocket-borne Gerdien condensers are presented. Analytic expressions based on ion equilibrium and ionization by cosmic rays only are derived for comparison. The experimental technique is described, and several factors that might influence the measurements are evaluated. There is good agreement between the measured and predicted values of negative conductivity at altitudes up to 50 km. Low conductivity values observed between 50 and 80 km are attributed to ionic diffusion to particulate matter, the reduction agreeing quantitatively with that calculated from present estimates of the radius and concentration of noctilucent cloud particles. It is suggested that meteoritic dust may be an important agent for electron destruction in the ionosphere.

91. (**287**) BOYD, R. L. F. and TWIDDY, N. D.
  Electron Energy Distribution in Plasmas, I.
  The theory of the positive column is commonly based on the assumption of a Maxwellian energy distribution for the electron, though in many cases it is far from clear how such a condition may be brought about. Moreover, past work has shown that the distribution is by no means always Maxwellian. Indeed, in any detailed consideration of the rates of inelastic collision processes occurring in the plasma it is desirable to be able to determine the distribution experimentally. A method of carrying out a Druyvesteyn analysis electronically is reported, and a critical account of its performance given. A high-frequency voltage of small amplitude chopped with a certain lower frequency is applied to a spherical probe, and the second derivative of the current-voltage characteristic is found from the amplitude of the sine wave the chopping frequency present in the probe current. An adequate signal-to-noise ratio is obtained by using narrow bend amplification with phase-sensitive detection. A large amount of data have now been obtained with this method in a variety of striated discharges. It is found that in every case studied so far the energy distribution takes the form of two well-separated groups of electrons with sometimes a very small third group. The high-energy group is generated by the potential difference across the striation head and becomes progressively attenuated towards its tail. An effect of the varying distribution is a sudden increase in the net rate of loss of electrons from the low-energy group resulting from the fall in number of electrons capable of ionizing and the change in potential difference between wall and discharge at the end of the striation. This loss of electrons causes a fall in the local discharge conductivity and so gives rise to another potential step and striation head.

92. (**289**) BRAGINSKII, S. I.
  The Behaviour of a Completely Ionized Plasma in a Strong Magnetic Field.
  In the first part of this certain paradoxes are considered which arise when transfer equations are applied to a quasi-stationary, completely ionized plasma in the case in which the frequency of collisions between particles is much smaller than their frequency of rotation in the magnetic field. In the second part a cylindrical pinched plasma is considered in which the plasma pressure is balanced by the

electrodynamic forces produced by the current which flows through the pinched plasma. Several solutions of the plasma equations are found for stationary and non-stationary cases.

93. (**291**) BRAGINSKII, S. I.
Magnetohydrodynamics of Weakly Conducting Liquids.
The approximate form of magnetohydrodynamic equations was derived for a liquid possessing a low electrical conductivity (small magnetic Reynolds numbers) and located in an external magnetic field. Some characteristic problems are considered which describe the physical nature of the behaviour of such liquids in a strong magnetic field.

94. (**294**) BRIN, A., DELCROIX, J. and OZIAS, Y .
Action d'un champ électrique continu sur im plasma: établissment de l'équation donnant la fonction de distribution.
On montre que l'équation obtenue par Spitzer pour la fonction de distribution des électrons dans un plasma soumis à un dramp électrique continu peut se retrouver par la méthode plus générale de Rosenbluth.

95. (**296**) BRINKMAN, H. C.
The Vortex Equations of Magneto-hydrodynamics
Introduction dans les équations de l'aéromagnétodynamique d'un tourbillon électrique et d'un tourbillon magnétique s'ajoutant au tourbillon matériel. Application à un plasma tournant dans an appareil thermo-nucléaire.

96. (**301**) BROGAN, T. R.
The Conduction of Electric Current to Cold Electrodes in Shock Tubes.
In the experimental investigation, the interaction between the moving gas and a magnetic field is used to generate the applied voltage. At 1 cm Hg initial pressure in argon the experimental results are found to agree with the above predictions, if the applied voltage is less than about thirty volts. Above thirty volts, electrical breakdown of the gas results in large currents. (Cornell Aer. Lab.)

97. (**308**) BUCHSBAUM, S. J.
Resonance in a Plasma with Two Ion Species.
When a high-density plasma column in an axial magnetic field possesses two (or more) ion species of different charge-to-mass ratios, there exists a plasma resonance condition which involves only the ion cyclotron frequencies. At resonance the two ion clouds oscillate transversely to the static magnetic field and 180 degrees out of phase with each other, while the electrons remain relatively motionless. The ratio of the ion oscillatory energy to that of the electrons is of the order of the ratio of the ion-to-electron masses. Collision between the two ion clouds randomize the large order velocities of the ions with great efficiency. Thus, by exciting this resonance, considerable ion heating may be realized. The effect of varying the relative concentration of the two ions is discussed.

98. (**313**) BULLARD, E. C.
A Discussion on Magneto-Hydrodynamics.
Results of theoretical and experimental investigations to develop and apply principles of fluid mechanics. Partial contents: An Instability of Laminar Flow of Mercury Caused by an External Magnetic Field, B. Lehnert. Magneto-Hydrodynamic Oscillations of a Rotating Fluid Globe, T. G. Cowling. Hydromagnetic Turbulence. I—A Deductive Theory; II—An Elementary Theory, S. Chandrasekhar. Magneto-Hydrodynamic Waves in Incompressible and

Compressible Fluids, A. Baños, Jr. The Structure of Magneto-Hydrodynamic Shock Waves, W. Marshall. Waves in a Heavy, Viscous, Incompressible, Electrically Conducting Fluid of Variable Density, in the Presence of a Magnetic Field, R. Hide. Some Engineering Applications of Magneto-Hydrodynamics, J. H. Shercliff. (Aero/Space)

99. (**317**) BUNEMAN, O.
   Instability, Turbulence and Conductivity in Current-Carrying Plasma.
Author investigates the effects of collective Coulomb interactions in fully ionized plasma. He concludes that small angle collisions cause instabilities which grow so rapidly that relative motions of ions and electrons are continually damped down by conversion of directed energy into random fluctuation energy. The implications of this effect on gas conductivity and plasma radiation are suggested. Speculations relative to explanation of Langmuir's paradox and deleterious effects in devices in which electrons are channelled through ions, or vice versa, are stated.
(C. Crain)

100. (**318**) BUNEMAN, O.
   Transverse Plasma Waves and Plasma Vortices.
Plasmas at high-electron temperatures can carry transverse waves in which self-magnetic fields and relativistic effects become important. In this paper the relativistic perturbation equations for an isotropic uniform plasma are solved as an initial-value problem, i.e. by Laplace transformation, and the propagation or dispersal of both longitudinal and transverse perturbations is calculated. In both cases transients occur which have a continuous frequency spectrum. While transverse perturbations also yield pure persistent waves (with phase velocity exceeding that of light) of all wavelengths, longitudinal perturbations of very short wavelength will not be propagated as pure waves but will die out eventually with only longer wavelengths persisting. The transverse plasma perturbations discussed in the analysis are nonvortical and the dispersal of vortices is covered by a separate discussion. The vortices do not give rise to a new mode of propagation of perturbations.

101. (**319**) BURGERS, J. M.
   The Penetration of a Shock Wave into a Magnetic Field.
Consideration is given to a number of problems which present themselves when a plane shock wave moving in a gas of high electric conductivity approaches a magnetic dipole field. The subject is treated in a number of steps: first the conductivity is considered to be infinite and the reaction of the magnetic field upon the motion of the gas is neglected; in this way a provisional picture of the distortion of the magnetic field by the shock wave can be obtained. In the next part of the paper the conductivity is treated as finite, although large; in the third part the effect of the magnetic field upon the motion of the gas in the immediate neighbourhood of the shock front is investigated. In part IV some considerations are developed concerning the reaction of the magnetic field upon the propagation of the wave; while part V brings a tentative discussion of the possibility of a steady field of flow. (ASTIA)

102. (**321**) BURGERS, J. M.
   The Application of Transfer Equations to the Calculation of Diffusion, Heat Conduction, Viscosity and Electric Conductivity.
The equations of transfer are deduced from the Maxwell-Boltzmann equation, in the form in which this is known for binary collisions. The results have been given in a form with all terms complete, including those depending upon electric and magnetic forces. Part I (sections 1–15) brings the deduction of the transfer equations. Part II (sections 16–26) gives applications to the calculation of the coefficients of diffusion in first and second approximation, including thermal

diffusion, of heat conduction, of viscosity, of electric conductivity, and of temperature exchange between the constituents of a gas mixture. Although attention mainly has been directed to binary mixtures, the expressions are presented in such a way that extension to multi-component mixtures is possible. Particular attention is given to the influence of a homogeneous magnetic field upon electric conductivity and upon viscosity.

103. (327) BURNETT, C. R., GROVE, D. J., PALLADINO, R. W., STIX, T. H. and WAKEFIELD, K. E.
The Divertor, a Device for Reducing the Impurity Level in a Stellarator.
The heavy ions released from the walls of the stellarator can be side tracked by a special magnetic device. This article contains a detailed discussion of the divertor, the various design problems, experimental procedures and some results. The impurity concentrations have been reduced by factors 2 to 3, perhaps even more in the core of the discharge. With the divertor the ion temperature has been increased from 40 eV to 60 eV for He, ionized once, and to 130 eV for O, ionized four times. (R. Betchov)

104. (329) BUSH, W. B.
Magneto-Hydrodynamic-Hypersonic Flow Past a Blunt Body.
Analysis of the flow field near the stagnation point of an axisymmetric blunt body in hypersonic flow having a spherical detached shock. A magnetic field is applied to the fluid in the shock layer which is assumed to be incompressible, inviscid, and of constant electrical conductivity. A family of solutions is found for which the body shape is a sphere concentric with the detached shock. For this family of solutions, the standoff distance and pressure relief increase with increasing magnetic field strength. Moreover, with increasing magnetic field strength, the gradient of the tangential velocity at the body decreases. (Aero/Space)

105. (330) BUSH, W. B.
Compressible Flat-Plate Boundary-Layer Flow with an Applied Magnetic Field.
USAF-supported development of the boundary-layer equations and solutions for a flat-plate in high-speed compressible air flow where equilibrium dissociation and ionization are assumed and where there is an applied magnetic field having its component normal to the plate proportional to $1/\sqrt{x}$. The results show that the skin friction and heat transfer at a given free-stream velocity decrease with increasing magnetic field strength, and the percentage reduction is constant along the length of the plate. They also exhibit the same hysteresis behaviour as was first found in the case of magnetoaerodynamic Couette flow; however, for the flat plate the hysteresis effect disappears at a higher Mach Number. Furthermore, it was found that the reduction in heat transfer with increasing field strength is opposite in behaviour from that for Couette flow. (Aero/Space)

106. (331) BUSH, W. B.
On One-Dimensional Channel Flow in the Presence of a Magnetic Field.
USAF-supported study covering the formulation of differential equations for the one-dimensional channel flow of a perfect gas. The simplifying assumptions introduced into the calculation are stated. The integration of the equations is performed for two cases, and the solutions are presented in analytical and graphical form. The results show that with increasing magnetic field the sonic point moves downstream from the channel's throat and that, in general, a larger exit area is needed to obtain a given supersonic flow Mach Number. (Aero/Space)

107. (334) BUTZ, J. S., Jr.
Basic Factors Complicate Plasma Work.
Some of the fundamental phenomena and elementary theory of magnetohydrodynamics are outlined. Problems of control and production of effects are discussed. (TIL/MOS)

108. **(335)** BUTZ, J. S., Jr.
Magnetohydrodynamics. I.—Hope for Space.
Discussion on the physical bases of magnetohydrodynamic sciences, and their possible application to space vehicles. (IAS)

109. **(336)** BUTZ, J. S., Jr.
Magnetohydrodynamics. II.—Controlled Fusion Studies Open Space Engine Field.
Discussion on fusion-powered rocket engines. (IAS)

110. **(338)** CABANNES, H.
Calcul de la conductivité thermique d'un courant ionique.
On calcule, par les méthodes de la théorie cinétique, le tenseur de conductivité thermique de la partie ionique d'un plasma. Les résultas sont explicités dans le cas d'une interaction du tipe de Maxwell.

111. **(339)** CABANNES, H.
Dynamique des gaz ionisés: determination des chocs stationnaires attachés a la pointe d'un diedre.
Derivation of equations describing the shock phenomena in an infinitely conducting compressible fluid, and calculation of the stationary shock wave attached to the apex of a dihedral. The shock angle, the pressure, and the temperature over the dihedral are calculated for the zero electric field. Results show that the presence of a magnetic field increases the wake and reduces the temperature.
(Aero/Space)

112. **(341)** CABANNES, H.
Sur l'Attachement des Ondes de Choc dans les Ecoulements à Deuse Dimensions.
The conditions of attachment of a shock-front to the point of a wedge are discussed as functions of wedge angle, fluid velocity, magnetic field and ratio of specific heats.

113. **(342)** CABANNES, H.
Sur la propagation des discontinuités du premier ordre dans un fluide compressible doué de conductivité électrique.
Etablissement des équations qui gouvernent la dynamique des gaz ionisés. Recherche des problèmes posés par la propagation des ondes sonores. Etude de quelques applications. 43 références bibliographiques. (SDIT)

114. **(348)** CAMAC, M. and JANES, G. S.
Applied Magnetohydrodynamics at AVCO-Everett Research Laboratory.
This report is a survey of theoretical and experimental basic research conducted by the AVCO-Everett Research Laboratory in the following four specific fields of application of MHD: Flight MHD—(1) Space flight propulsion; (2) Re-entry "drag" devices. Electric Power Generation—(3) "Low" temperature process; (4) Fusion methods.

115. **(355)** CARINI, G.
Energy Considerations in Magnetohydrodynamics.
An energy conservation theorem is obtained, based on the expression

$$(8\pi)^{-1}[\varepsilon E^2 + \mu H^2 - (r/c)(\varepsilon\mu - 1)v.E \times H]$$

for the electromagnetic energy in a medium whose velocity is v. The theorem is then applied to the special case of adiabatic processes in an inviscid perfectly conducting fluid.

116. **(357)** CARRIER, G. F. and GREENSPAN, H. P.
The Time-Dependent Magnetohydrodynamic Flow Past a Flat Plate.
Two time-dependent magnetohydrodynamic flow problems are discussed. In part I we consider the situation in which a semi-infinite flat-plate is moved impulsively in its own plane into an electrically conductive viscous fluid. The ambient

magnetic field has the same direction as the motion of the plate; it is found that when $\mu H_0^2/\rho V_0^2 < 1$, the flow pattern approaches asymptotically the steady flow found earlier (Greenspan & Carrier, 1959). When $\mu H_0^2/\rho V_0^2 > 1$, the asymptotic state is one in which the fluid accompanies the plate in a rigid body motion as was anticipated in the earlier work. In part II an infinite plate is moved impulsively in its plane in the presence of an ambient magnetic field which is perpendicular to the plane of the plate. It is shown that the problem is not uniquely set until one specifies what three-dimensional problem reduces in the limit to the two-dimensional problem so defined. The answers in the conceptually acceptable limit case investigated here (the plate being a pipe of very large radius) have an asymmetry which at first sight is unexpected.

117. (**359**) CARSTOIU, J.
    Sur le mouvement lent d'un fluide visqueux conducteur entre deux plans paralleles.
Calcul de la vitesse du mouvement pris par un fluide visqueux conducteur entre deux plans parallèles lorsqu'on lui applique une force constante et un champ magnétique uniforme. Discussion du probleme et, notamment, des conditions aux limites. 5 références bibliographiques. (SDIT)

118. (**360**) CARSTOIU, J.
    Hydromagnetic Waves in a Compressible Fluid Conductor.
An attempt is made to generalize Alfvén wave propagation for medium in which density varies with position or time. Using the quantities, vorticity ($w = \frac{1}{2}$ curl velocity) and current density, a set of equations is derived. It is shown that the components of these quantities in the direction of the magnetic field are propagated in the Alfvén manner along the field lines. Expressions for the variation of density are given. (A. Gabriel)

119. (**363**) CESS, R. D.
    Magnetohydrodynamic Effects upon Heat Transfer for Laminar Flow Across a Flat Plate.
Extension au cas des liquides conducteurs (eau salée, métaux liquides) d'un problème déjà étudié par Rossow pour les gaz, en vue de la détermination de l'échauffement cinétique. 13 références bibliographiques. (SDIT)

120. (**366**) CHAKRABORTY, B. B. and RAMAMORTY, P.
    On the Pulsations of an Infinite Cylinder with a Force-Free Magnetic Field.
Discusses the problem of radial pulsations of an infinitely conducting infinite fluid cylinder under its own gravity and a force-free magnetic field whose components in cylindrical co-ordinates are

$$H_0 = [O, A, S, (\alpha\bar{\omega}), A_1 J_0(\alpha\bar{\omega})]$$

For different magnitudes of the fields strength the displacement function and the change in the magnetic field inside the cylinder are calculated for the fundamental modes of the vibrations. The ratios of the periodic times with a magnetic field present to those without the magnetic field are also determined.

121. (**373**) CHANDRASEKHAR, S.
    The Stability of Non-Dissipative Couette Flow in Hydromagnetics.
Non-viscous purely azimuthal flow of a perfectly conducting fluid between coaxial cylinders in a uniform axial magnetic field is studied. It is shown that monoteric increase of angular speed with distance from the axis is sufficient for stability. The minimum field necessary to stabilize the flow is obtained for the case of nearly equal cylinders with the velocity distribution permissible under viscous flow.

(O. Penrose)

122. (**376**) CHANDRASEKHAR, S.

The Stability of Viscous Flow Between Rotating Cylinders in the Presence of a Magnetic Field.

The theory of the stability of viscous flow between two rotating coaxial cylinders is extended to the case when the fluid is an electrical conductor and there is a magnetic field along the axis of the cylinders. An eighth-order differential equation governing the system in marginal stability is derived and boundary conditions for the problem formulated. The case when two cylinders are rotating in the same direction and the difference in their radii is small compared with their mean radius is considered in detail. A variational procedure for solving the underlying characteristics value problem and determining the critical Tayler numbers for the onset of instability is described. The effect of the magnetic field is to inhibit the onset of instability, the inhibiting effect being the greater, the greater the strength of the field and the value of the electrical conductivity. (TIL/MOS)

123. (**378**) CHANDRASEKHAR, S.

The Partition of Energy in Hydromagnetic Turbulence.

The partition of energy between the velocity and the magnetic fields in hydromagnetic turbulence is discussed. It is pointed out that in the framework of a universal theory the discussion must be restricted to the inertial range of eddy sizes which does include the largest energy containing eddies. On a particular theory of stationary, homogeneous, and isotropic turbulence it is shown that in this inertial sub-range the spectra of the magnetic and kinetic energies are both kolmogororian with a constant ratio of amplitudes; further, that in this range, the energy in the magnetic field is 1·6265 times the energy in the velocity field.

124. (**381**) CHANDRASEKHAR, S.

The Gravitational Instability of an Infinite Homogeneous Medium when Coriolis Force is Acting and a Magnetic Field is Present.

It is shown that Jean's criterion for the gravitational instability of an infinite homogeneous medium is unaffected by the presence of a magnetic field, even if the system is partaking in rotation and Coriolis force is operative.

125. (**385**) CHANDRASEKHAR, S., *et al.*

Properties of an Ionized Gas of Low Density in a Magnetic Field. IV.

Description of a systematic method for solving the Boltzmann equation for the steady states of an ionized gas of low density in a strong magnetic field. The solution is developed as a series in inverse powers of the gyration frequency ω, assuming that the term representing the Lorentz force in the Boltzmann equation dominates all others. The solution is explicitly carried out to the first order in ω^{-1}. Expressions for the drifts which arise in the first order are also obtained.

(Appl. Mech. Rev.)

126. (**387**) CHANDRASEKHAR, S. and LIMBER, D. N.

On the Pulsation of a Star in which there is a Prevalent Magnetic Field.

In this paper a simple approximate formula is obtained for the frequency of radial pulsation of a gaseous star in which there is a prevalent magnetic field.

127. (**390**) CHANDRASEKHAR, S., KAUFMAN, A. N. and WATSON, K. M.

The Stability of the Pinch. Appendix—The Propagation of Plane Hydromagnetic Waves in an Infinite Medium.

Investigation on the stability of a cylindrical plasma with an axial magnetic field and confined between conducting walls by solving, for small oscillations about equilibrium, the linearized Boltzmann and Maxwell equations. A criterion for marginal stability is derived; this differs slightly from the one derived by Rosenbluth from an analysis of the particle orbits. However, Rosenbluth's principal results on the possibility of stabilizing the pinch under suitable external conditions are confirmed. In addition a dispersion relation is derived which discloses under the simplest conditions certain types of instabilities which may occur in plasma physics.   (Aero/Space)

128. (**391**) CHANG, C. C. and LUNDGREN, T. S.
       The Flow of an Electrically Conducting Fluid through a Duct with Transverse Magnetic Field.
This paper extends earlier work by Hartman and by Shercliff [AMR **12** (1959), Rev. 476] on the steady flow of an electrically-conducting fluid through a straight duct in a transverse uniform magnetic field. The flow equations are derived with emphasis placed on boundary conditions on velocity at the rigid walls of the duct and on the pertinent components of the electric field intensity and magnetic flux density at electrical interfaces and at infinity. If the walls of the duct have finite conductivity, the solution of the problem does not parallel the solution of an ordinary boundary-value problem except in special cases: Perfectly insulating or conducting walls, thin duct walls, and so forth. The flow through a rectangular duct with walls parallel to the external field displaced to infinity and the other walls of arbitrary wall conductivity is solved exactly. The flow through a finite rectangular duct with perfectly conducting walls is also solved exactly; and a different exact solution in series form is given for the perfectly isolating walls, complementing the different solutions obtained earlier by Shercliff. These solutions reveal that when the wall conductivity is increased, the pressure gradient must be increased to maintain the same mass flow.   (T. Higgins)

129. (**395**) CHANG, C. C. and YEN, J. T.
       On Rayleigh's Problem in Magnetohydrodynamics.
USAF-supported extension of Rayleigh's problem to magnetohydrodynamics for the case of a perfectly conducting plate with a transversely applied magnetic field. Induced electric and magnetic fields are both included in the analysis. Results obtained show that along the plate an electromagnetic body force will act in the direction of fluid motion. The results are found to be the same whether the applied magnetic field is fixed in space or attached to the moving plate. A comparison of these results with those of Rossow (magnetic field fixed with fluid) shows opposite trends in the velocity profile. Such discrepancies are discussed.   (Aero/Space)

130. (**396**) CHAO-KAI-HUA.
       Surface Oscillations of a Charged Column in a Longitudinal Magnetic Field.
An analysis is given of the surface oscillations and stability of a hydrodynamic charged column in an external magnetic field. This analysis represents an extension of the well-known work of Kruskal and Schwarzchild and Tayler on the stability of an uncharged hydrodynamic column. The surface-wave dispersion equation is derived and the features of the oscillation spectrum are investigated. From the experimental point of view these results are of value for investigating the nature of the radiation from a plasma in a magnetic field, an effect which is, as yet, not fully understood.

131. (**402**) CHARIKADZE, D. V.
       Mouvements analogiques et explosion ponctuelle en magnéto-aérodynamique dans le le cas d'une conductibilité de gaz infinie.
Etude des mouvements d'un milieu magnétique gazeux, le potentiel du champ magnétique étant fonction des puissances de l'entropie.   (SDIT)

132. (**404**) CHAU-CHIN WEI.
       Relativistic Hydrodynamics for a Charged Non-Viscous Fluid.
The classical vorticity theorem for a non-viscous fluid is generalized to the case of a relativistic electrically-charged fluid in an electromagnetic field.

133. (**406**) CHESTER, W.
The Effect of a Magnetic Field on Stokes Flow in a Conducting Fluid.
Motion of a fluid in a magnetic field produces an associated electrical field which sets up electrical currents in the fluid if it is a conductor. Interaction of these currents with the magnetic field produces a body force which must be included in the Navier-Stokes equation for the motion of the fluid. The ultimate result of this body force is an increase in drag and a formula for this drag is developed. (Experimental investigations are to be made in the future at the Guggenheim Aeronautical Laboratory on the motion of small spheres in a column of mercury the magnetic field being provided by a surrounding coil.) (TIL/MOS)

134. (**409**) CHIA-SHUN YIH.
Effects of Gravitational or Electromagnetic Fields on Fluid Motion.
Analysis indicating that the effect of gravity on a stratified fluid is to inhibit steady motion in the direction of gravity; that, for small values of the magnetic viscosity, the effect of a main magnetic field is to make steady weak motions of a fluid independent of the distance along the lines of force; and that, again for small values of the magnetic viscosity, the effect of a uniform electric field is to make steady weak motions of a fluid rotationally symmetric with respect to an axis in the direction of the fluid field. These results, together with those of Proudman for a rotating fluid, show that the effects of rotation, gravity, and electromagnetic fields are to endow the fluid with anisotropic rigidity by "stiffening" it along the vorticity lines, the isopycnic surfaces or lines, or the lines of force, as the case may be.
(Aero/Space)

135. (**410**) CHIA-SHUN YIH.
Inhibition of Hydrodynamic Instability by an Electric Current.
OOR-sponsored investigation of the instability inhibition of a viscous fluid showing that unsymmetric convections can be delayed or completely inhibited by an electric current, whereas symmetric convection is not affected. This indicates a very interesting physical situation at the critical Rayleigh Number 452.1, for an electric current just strong enough to inhibit unsymmetric convection. If the current is slightly increased, only symmetric motion will occur; if it is slightly decreased, unsymmetric convection, being less stable, prevails. Thus, the physically significant solution of a differential system can change abruptly at certain critical values of its parameters. (Aero/Space)

136. (**411**) CHIA-SHUN YIH.
Ring Vortices Generated Electromagnetically.
If an electric current of uniform density j_0 is passed axially through a stationary fluid between concentric cylinders of radii r_2 ($> r_1$), the fluid is stable to axisymmetric disturbances only if the damping provided by viscosity and electrical resistivity is sufficiently large. It is shown herein that the fluid may also be stabilized by passing a line current $\mathcal{J}$ along the axis, sufficient condition for stability being

$$\mathcal{J} \leqslant - \pi j_0 (r_2{}^2 - r_1{}^2), \text{ or } \geqslant \mathcal{J} \pi j_0 r_1{}^2.$$

The values of $\mathcal{J}$ needed to stabilize the fluid when the fluid has non-zero viscosity and finite conductivity are calculated for the case $r_2 - r_1 \ll r_1$. In this latter case, the ring vortices which exist under conditions of neutral stability are exactly the same as those for flow between rotating cylinders if $\mathcal{J}$ and j_0 have the same sign, and if $\mathcal{J}$ is not very small compared with $\pi j_0 r^2$.

137. (**414**) (CHING-SHENG) WU.
A Class of Exact Solutions of the Magnetohydrodynamic Navier-Stokes Equations.
A class of similarity solutions of the magnetohydrodynamic Navier-Stokes equations have been found in this paper so that the original differential system may reduce to two ordinary differential equations. The equation governing the velocity

field appears to be of first order but with a non-linear interaction term of the magnetic field. On the other hand, the magnetic induction equation is of second order. Solutions similar to that obtained by Landau and Squire for non-magnetic case are found by using a perturbation expansion of small α (α is the ratio of kinematic viscosity and magnetic viscosity). Throughout the analysis, the fluid is assumed to be incompressible, viscous and electrically conducting. The physical properties are also postulated to be constant. (ASTIA)

138. (**415**) (CHING-SHENG) WU.
  Simple Vorticity Laws in Magnetohydrodynamics.
Derivation of simple vorticity laws in magnetohydrodynamics. The analysis includes the generalized Crocco's vorticity law and Lighthill's expression for vorticity behind a three-dimensional shock wave. No consideration is given to microscopic phenomena of an ionized gas. A generalization of Hayes derivation of vorticity jump across a gas dynamic discontinuity is also obtained. (Aero/Space)

139. (**416**) (CHING-SHENG) WU.
  Hypersonic Viscous Flow Past a Blunt Body with an Applied Magnetic Field.
Analysis showing that local similarity solutions of flow field and temperature distribution are obtainable if both hydromagnetic interaction and viscous effect are taken into account. Various simplifying assumptions are made. The similarity solutions for the two-dimensional problem are presented, and the boundary conditions associated with different physical problems discussed. Boundary conditions and similarity solutions for the stagnation point flow behind a detached shock wave with spherical shape are investigated. The temperature distribution and the pressure variation in the shock layer near the stagnation. (IAS)

140. (**417**) (CHING-SHENG) WU and HAYES, W. D.
  Axisymmetric Stagnant Flow of a Viscous and Electrically Conducting Fluid near the Blunt Nose of a Spinning Body with Presence of Magnetic Field. Part I: Exact Solution of Incompressible and Constant-Properties Model.
This is the first part of a series of studies of the stagnation point flow of a viscous and conducting fluid near the blunt nose of a moving and spinning body in the presence of magnetic field. The body under consideration is axisymmetric and the fluid is assumed to be incompressible and has constant properties. Exact similar solution is verified in existence. The final differential systems contain one principal system and two systems. Only general discussions are given in this report. The results of numerical computation will be presented some time later.

141. (**417**) (CHING-SHENG) WU.
  Axisymmetric Stagnant Flow of a Viscous and Electrically Conducting Fluid near the Blunt Nose of a Spinning Body with Presence of Magnetic Field. Part II: Consideration of Realistic Conditions. Compressible Viscous Layer and Small Magnetic Reynolds Number.
The second part of the present study of the axisymmetric stagnation point flow of a viscous and conducting fluid near a spinning body is presented. A more realistic physical model is adopted in the present case. The compressibility and variable physical properties are taken into consideration. In the viscous layer, boundary layer approximation is employed since magnetic Reynolds number is postulated too small, mathematical simplification of the induction equation is, therefore, obtained.

142. (**418**) CHING-SHILIU.
  Magnetogasdynamic Flow Regimes.
The prediction of plasma flow subject to a magnetic field is of a considerable interest to the engineer designing magnetogasdynamics devices. In this note the

author evaluates some dimensionless parameters for certain simple cases and delineates the associated flow regimes.

143. (**419**) CHINITZ, W., EISEN, C. L. and GROSS, R. A.
Aerothermodynamic and Electrical Properties of Some Gas Mixtures to Mach 20.
Pressure, temperature, chemical composition and electrical conductivity data are presented for gas mixtures behind strong air shocks and detonations of hydrogen-air and acetylene-air mixtures up to Mach 20. A digital computer programme was developed which solves the simultaneous aerodynamic and chemical equilibrium equations. The latest thermodynamic and collision cross section data are used. Data are also presented wherein the initial gas composition was varied to obtain the maximum electrical conductivity for a given shock or detonation strength.

144. (**421**) CHOPRA, K. P.
Some Problems in Hydromagnetics.
Induction drag of a sphere moving in a conducting fluid in the presence of a magnetic field. Hydromagnetic flow in a circular pipe. Magnetic fields in a conducting fluid sphere and infinite cylinder with electric currents flowing in them. Change in energy of a magnetic sphere under a P_1-deformation (equilibrium configurations of the sphere). Radial adiabatic pulsations of an infinite cylinder in the presence of a magnetic field. Tunnel effect in hydromagnetics. Compressible hydromagnetics. Thermodynamics of compressible hydromagnetic flow. Hydromagnetic shock waves. Diffusion and plane hydromagnetic shock waves. Drag of a sphere in an ionized gas. Transmission properties of Alfvén waves. (ASTIA)

145. (**423**) CHOPRA, K. P.
Induction Drag.
The problem is considered of the induction drag of a sphere of finite and constant electrical conductivity moving in an incompressible and non-viscous conducting fluid in a uniform magnetic field.

146. (**424**) CHOPRA, K. P.
On the Radial Adiabatic Pulsation of an Infinite Cylinder in the Presence of Magnetic Field Parallel to its Axis.
The higher approximations to the characteristic functions and the contributions of other modes are dealt with.

147. (**425**) CHOPRA, K. P. and TALWAR, S. P.
On the Radial Pulsations of an Infinite Cylinder with a Magnetic Field Parallel to its Axis.
The expression for the amplitude of the radial adiabatic pulsations and consequent magnetic variations of an infinitely conducting infinite cylinder, subject to a variable axial field, are obtained. The numerical calculations of the characteristic amplitudes are carried out for six different models of the particular case in which the magnetic field is assumed to be proportional to the square root of pressure. Further, the period of pulsation is found to decrease with the magnetic field.

148. (**426**) CHOPRA, K. P. et SINGER, S. F.
La traînée s'exerçant sur une sphère se déplaçant dans un fluide conducteur en présence d'un champ magnétique.
Exposé des trois types de traînée, fonction des conditions du mouvement, des propriétés du solide et des propriétés du milieu fluide, qui peuvent s'exercer, suivant le cas, sur un solide se déplaçant dans un liquide conducteur tel qu'un plasma. 4 références bibliographiques.   (SDIT)

149. (**427**) Chopra, K. P. and Singer, S. F.

Drag of a Sphere Moving in a Conducting Fluid in the Presence of a Magnetic Field.
Three types of drag associated with magnetohydrodynamic flow are treated
theoretically. First, induction drag is considered where the drag is basically due
to joule dissipation of energy caused by induced currents in either the medium or
the body. The magnetic field may originate within the sphere or in the external
medium. The second drag is called Coulomb drag and is associated with momentum transfer between a charged body and electrons and ions moving in the medium.
The third type of drag is wave drag associated with energy transfer between highly
charged particles moving in a plasma in the presence of an external magnetic field
and plasma waves excited by the motion of the body. The plasma waves can
propagate through the medium with a frequency below the critical and with phase
velocity less than the material velocity of the body. This paper is recommended to
all interested in learning more of the fundamentals of plasma flow in magnetic
fields. An understanding of vector notation is required however. (R. Minolak)

150. (**431**) Chu, B. T.

La thermodynamique des fluides conducteurs de l'électricité.
Etude par la théorie non relativiste de Minkowski des propriétes thermodynamiques
du milieu fluide sous l'action commune des variations électromagnétiques et
mécaniques. Déduction de formules susceptibles d'étre utilisées pour le calcul de
l'effet électrocalorique, de l'effet magnétocalorique et des effets d'électrostriction et
de magnétostriction. 12 références bibliographiques. (SDIT)

151. (**432**) Chu, B. T.

*Thermodynamics of Electrically Conducting Fluids and its Application to Magneto-
Hydromechanics.*
Professor Chu has studied the thermodynamics of electrically conducting fluids
from a consideration of the Helmholtz free energy per unit mass. The principal
assumptions are that the fluid is isotropic and hence the free energy is independent
of the orientation of the co-ordinate system, and that the dielectric constant and
magnetic permeability are known functions of density and temperature. A consequence of these assumptions is that the free energy, and hence thermodynamic
properties, all consist of the standard mechanical and thermal terms plus an
electromagnetic term. The electromagnetic contribution to the entropy depends
only on the derivative of the dielectric constant and the magnetic permeability
with respect to the temperature. Hence if these properties are either independent
of temperature (i.e. a Lorentz polarization and a perfect diamagnetic substance)
or follow Langevin's assumption (a perfect dielectric and a paramagnetic substance),
the familiar formula for isentropic changes holds, but the ratio of specific heat may
include electromagnetic contributions. The conservation equations are derived
on the basis of the thermodynamics. Finally, Professor Chu critically discusses the
energy equation of magneto-fluid-dynamics in terms of his development of the
thermodynamics and the general assumptions about the dielectric constant and
the magnetic permeability. This discussion should be recommended reading for
all students of magneto-fluid-dynamics. In the application of the results presented
in this report to a situation in which the external electric and magnetic fields are
strong, it should be remembered that the fields might not be isotropic since the
effect of these fields is to introduce anisotropic effects. The Hall current and the
propagation of acoustic waves are two well-known examples of the anisotropic
processes. The effects of these anisotropies occur, for the most part, in the material
properties, i.e. the viscosity electrical and thermal conductivity, etc. Consequently
if these effects are allowed for, it is expected that Chu's conservation equations are
still valid. (E. Covert)

152. (**433**) CHU, E. L.

The Lagrangian and the Energy Momentum Tensors in the Perturbation Theory of Classical Electrodynamics.

The theory of infinitesimal transformations is incorporated in the variational principle for the solution of perturbation problems in classical electrodynamics. Every variable quantity is transformed to the unperturbed co-ordinate system and expanded into a power series of a small perturbation parameter. The Lagrangian of any given order of magnitude in the unperturbed co-ordinate system characterizes a closed physical system. This is proved by showing that the total energy-momentum tensors of the first and second orders are symmetric. The proof for the higher orders is obtained by deduction. Sturrock's asymmetric tensor is recognized as being the result of using an incomplete Lagrangian. Small-amplitude solutions can also be obtained by first applying variation to the total Lagrangian function and then transforming and expanding the results in different orders of magnitude. This method, as exemplified by the proof of the symmetry of the second-order energy-momentum tensor, is in many cases more convenient.

153. (**435**) CHUAN, R. L.

Plasma Heating of Hypersonic Gas Flow.

For the production of condensation-free hypersonic flow in a wind tunnel it is proposed to add energy to the electrons in the air downstream of the throat by high frequency electrodeless discharge, and allow electron energy to go into random kinetic energy of the molecules in the decay process. Previous work in this respect has dealt only with the discharge process, measuring the energy that can be added to the plasma by various types of discharges. The present work examines the decay processes in an attempt to channel as much of the electron energy as possible into raising the temperature of the gas, by preventing losses by ambipolar loss mechanism. Inhibition of ambipolar diffusion by means of an axial, constant magnetic field is examined, as well as the attendant possibility of having such an inhibiting effect nullified by drain diffusion resulting from hydromagnetic instability. An experimental investigation is being initiated.

154. (**437**) CHUAN, R. L.

Preliminary Results of Plasma Heating of High-Speed Air Flow.

Presentation of preliminary experimental results from a simple model in which supersonic flow of nominal Mach Number 3·5 and Reynolds Number 2,000 (per cm) is heated by the decay of a plasma. The process of plasma heating and the experimental apparatus used are described. The maximum stagnation temperature attained is 934°C at a mass flow of 0·15 g/sec, which represents at net heat input rate of about 100 watts. Inputs up to 300 watts have been achieved at higher mass flows and higher static pressures.   (Aero/Space)

155. (**438**) CHUAN, R. L. and SMETANA, F. O.

Experiments on a Radio Frequency Discharge Plasma in Supersonic Flow.

Experiments have been conducted with the view toward developing a radio frequency discharge for use as a heat source in low density, supersonic flows. Early studies had indicated that this heating technique is attended by several little-studied problems, and it was the purpose of these experiments to provide additional data on these phenomena. Among the problems studied was that of providing a suitable electrode configuration which permits matching of the generator to the load and which provides for minimum stray radiation and high density power input. Also studied was the problem of determining an optimum length of time or distance during which the recombination processes would be sufficiently near completion and for which the physical length would not be unreasonable or the heat transfer to the walls self-defeating. As a means for permitting the decay processes to reach equilibrium, control of diffusion of free electrons with its subsequent heat transfer to the wall was also studied. The results of these studies to date and some preliminary interpretations of their significance are given.

156. (**441**) CLARKE, J. F.
The Linearized Flow of a Dissociating Gas.
The equations for planar two-dimensional steady flow of an ideal dissociating gas are linearized, assuming small disturbances to a free stream in chemical equilibrium. As an example of their solution, the flow past a sharp corner in a supersonic stream is evaluated and the variations of flow properties in the relaxation zone are found. Numerical illustrations are provided using an "oxygen-like" ideal gas and comparison made with a characteristic solution. The flow past a sharp corner can be studied in a conventional shock tube and it may be possible to verify the present theory experimentally. In particular it may prove feasible to use the results to obtain a measure of the reaction rates in the gas mixture.

157. (**443**) CLAUSER, M. U.
State of the Art, 1959: Magnetohydrodynamics
Revue succincte de l'état actuel des recherches. 9 références bibliographiques.
(SDIT)

158. (**448**) CLINTON, A. C.
Magnétohydrodynamique.
Définition, principes fondamentaux, applications aéronautiques: moteurs à plasma, souffleries hypersoniques, etc. 5 références bibliographiques. (SDIT)

159. (**451**) COENSGEN, F. H., CUMMINS, W. F. and SHERMAN, A. E.
Multistage Magnetic Compression of Highly Ionized Plasma.
The mean energy of the charged particles of a plasma which is confined in a magnetic field may be increased by increasing the magnitude of the magnetic field in a time which is short with respect to the ion relaxation time (magnetic compression). It is shown that the necessary stored energy can be reduced and the efficiency greatly increased if the magnetic compression is performed in several stages, such that the plasma is compressed and transferred to successively smaller volumes. The predicted transfer behaviour has been confirmed by studying the plasma movement in a three-stage system. In the course of the investigation a plasma source has been developed which provides bursts of plasma of 10^{16} to 10^{18} ions with an average velocity of the order of 10^7 cm/sec.

160. (**453**) COLE, G. H. A.
Some Aspects of Magnetohydrodynamics.
The first part of the paper is devoted to small disturbances. The equations of magnetohydrodynamics are first set down and discussed. The conditions necessary for the magnetic force to control the fluid motion are then considered. The second part of the paper is devoted to high velocity (shock) disturbances. Some features of the theory are considered, and this is followed by a discussion of the propagation of shocks. (ASTIA)

161. (**455**) COLE, J. D.
Magnetohydrodynamic Waves.
Special magnetohydrodynamic waves and the boundary conditions under which they are produced are studied. Possible wave motions of a fluid form the underlying structure of the mathematical description. The magnetohydrodynamic approximation used is the conventional one in that displacement currents are neglected. Shock waves in an infinitely conducting fluid are studied by means of an idealized piston problem. Switch-on waves are shown to be associated with the discharge of

a current sheet. The effect of finite conductivity is studied for both ordinary and switch-on waves. Diffusal of current sheets about the wave front are shown. The effects of nonlinearity are discussed qualitatively.

162. (**459**) COLGATE, S. A.
  A Description of a Shock Wave in Free Particle Hydrodynamics with Internal Magnetic Fields.

The structure of an extremely strong magnetohydrodynamic shock is discussed in the limit of no particle collisions. It is tentatively concluded that the shock transition takes place through the mechanism of a strong electric field produced by charge separation. The pressure in the shocked plasma is due primarily to a very high electron temperature. The ions, on the other hand, undergo an irreversible temperature change of only 3.

163. (**467**) COLOMBO, S.
  Effet dynamo en théorie magnétohydrodynamique.

S. Colombo envisage l'aspect général des phénomènes magnétohydrodynamiques et établit le système d'équations aux dérivées partielles qui les régit. La linéarisation de celles-ci conduit à envisager les ondes transversales d'Alfvén. L'effet dynamo, dont il est question au cours de cette étude, consiste en la création d'un champ magnétique stable à partir de champs de vitesses présentant une asymétrie suffisante; les conditions nécessaires à la production d'un tel effet sont envisagées. Une interprétation géométrique et une méthode de calcul sont brièvement exposées; elles montrent la possibilité de production d'un effet dynamo dans certaines conditions.

164. (**468**) COLOMBO, S.
  La théorie hydromagnétique.

Aspect analytique des problèmes hydromagnetiques. Système d'équations résultant de l'approximation hydromagnétique. Nombre de Reynolds magnétique. Ondes d'Alfvén. 28 références bibliographiques. (SDIT)

165. (**474**) COOR, T., CUNNINGHAM, S. P., ELLIS, R. A., HEALD, M. A. and KRANZ, A. Z.
  Experiments on the Ohmic Heating and Confinement of Plasma in a Stellarator.

The basic concepts of confinement of a plasma in a figure-eight stellarator are outlined and an experimental apparatus is described. Single particles can be confined by magnetic fields up to 30 Kilogauss for several milliseconds. The temperature reaches 10^6 degrees at the beginning of a run in helium, when ohmic heating is used. This condition does not last more than 100 microseconds before unstable processes occur. In particular the hydromagnetic kink instability predicted by Kruskal has been clearly observed. (R. Betchov)

166. (**476**) COVERT, E. E.
  On Some Fundamentals in Magneto-Fluid-Mechanics.

The basic equations of magneto-fluid-mechanics are derived from classical kinetic theory for a gas consisting of neutral particles, positive particles (ions) and electrons. The equations of conservation of mass and momentum for each type of particle, an energy equation, the Maxwell equations of electrodynamics, and suitable state equations are included. The basic equations are normalized and the resulting dimensionless parameters are discussed briefly. Formulae for the fluid properties are presented, and a summary of the values of these properties is given. Some elementary solutions are given to illustrate the nature of magneto-fluid interactions. The problem of adding energy to a gas by magneto-fluid mechanical means is discussed. Results indicate that these means are practical only at high power densities (700 kW/sq ft $\sim 5 \times 10^6$ Btu/sec-sq ft). A device which absorbs such power densities and generates a plasma is discussed theoretically and some preliminary experimental results are given.

167. (**477**) COVERT, E. E.
A Microscopic Analysis of Magneto-Gas-Dynamics.

Discussion of the kinetic theory approach to magneto-gas-dynamics. Several methods for considering interactions, in which the long range forces are of importance, are compared critically. The effects of the magnetic field on the particle interactions and their trajectories are shown to introduce anisotropies in magneto-gas-dynamics. The effects of these anisotropies are briefly discussed.

(Aero/Space)

168. (**483**) COWLING, T. G.
Magnetohydrodynamics (Magnétohydrodynamique).

Principes généraux, applications simples; magnétohydrostatique; mouvement ondulatoire; champ magnétique et instabilité; théories de la dynamo; gaz ionisés. Nombreuses références bibliographiques. (SDIT)

169. (**492**) COWLING, T. G. and HARE, A.
Two-Dimensional Problems of the Decay of Magnetic Fields in Magnetohydro-dynamics.

The normal modes of decay of a magnetic field in the presence of steady motions in a fluid conductor are studied in the two-dimensional case. Slow motions are considered by perturbation methods, which show that to a first approximation the motion always increases the rate of decay in the lowest mode. For fast motion, there exists a limited class of modes little affected by the motion, in which the lines of force and streamlines nearly coincide. In the general class of modes the motion profoundly affects the decay; these are studied in two special cases, those of streaming in a fluid slab between parallel walls and of non-uniform rotation in a circular cylinder. The motion is found to transport and distort the field, and to increase the rate of decay in the lower modes, roughly proportional to the two-thirds power of the velocity. For the slab problem, velocities of intermediate magnitude are studied by numerical methods. The extension of the results to more general classes of two-dimensional motion is briefly considered.

170. (**496**) CRUPI, G.
Sulla velocitá di gruppo nella magnetoidrodinamica.

This paper considers the relationship between group velocity and phase velocity of magneto-hydrodynamic waves, propagating in an incompressible fluid, which is electrically conductive and moves in an external magnetic field of flux density Bo. Starting from a previously deduced [same *Boll.* 12 (1957), pp. 604–609] formula for the phase velocity W_f, the calculation of group W_g is straightforward and leads to the result:

$$W_g = \frac{W_f}{1 - a}$$

where a is a positive number inferior to unity. Some special cases are considered.

(M. Strutt)

171. (**499**) CURLE, N.
On the Stability, in the Presence of a Coplanar Magnetic Field, of a Laminar Mixing Region in a Viscous Electrically Conducting Fluid.

The solution for the stability of the free laminar boundary layer between parallel streams is extended to include the effects of coplanar magnetic field. It is shown that, to a first approximation, the mean velocity profile is unaffected by the magnetic field, which influences the problem only by the addition of one term to the fourth order Orr-Sommerfeld equation of hydrodynamic stability. The modified equation is solved by a technique similar to that used in the absence of a magnetic field, in which the fourth-order term "v" is assumed to be important only near to the singular layer. It is found that as q increases the critical Reynolds number rises. There is an indication that when q is large enough the flow may be completely stabilized. (TIL/MOS)

172. (**500**) CUSHING, V. and SODHA, M. S.
    Confinement of Plasma by Standing Electromagnetic Waves.
In this paper the authors have discussed the confinement of plasma by a one-dimensional stationary electromagnetic wave. Their analysis is similar to that carried out by former workers for a TM mode but they have examined the assumptions limiting the applicability of present theories in detail. One of the conditions for the applicability of the present theory is that the frequency of the electromagnetic wave should be of the same order or greater than the plasma frequency at the nodes where particle density is maximum. This condition makes the present theories nonapplicable in cases of thermo-nuclear interest.

173. (**502**) DAMBURG, R. Y.
    Flow of a Viscous Conducting Liquid Round an Infinite Cylinder in the Presence of a Magnetic Field.
The velocity and magnetic field at infinity are taken parallel to each other and perpendicular to the cylinder. Both the Reynolds number and the magnetic Reynolds number are taken to be negligibly small. The resulting simplified equations of motion are solved in terms of Bessel Functions with the Hartmann number as a parameter. For the case of very small cylinder radius, the drag force is also obtained.

174. (**503**) DAMBURG, R. Y. et KRAVTCHENKO, V. Y.
    Excitation des ondes hydromagnétiques dans le plasma par une charge en mouvement.
Etude du plasma quasi neutre situé dans un champ magnétique extérieur. 4 références bibliographiques. (SDIT)

175. (**508**) DAVIES, T. V.
    On Steady Axially Symmetric Solutions of the Idealized Hydromagnetic Equations and for a Compressible Gas in which there is no Diffusion of Vorticity, Heat or Current.
An investigation is made of the steady compressible magneto hydrodynamic equations of motion in which certain idealizations are made, namely, that the kinematic viscosity is zero, the thermal conductivity is zero, and the magnetic diffusivity is zero. These assumptions imply that there is no diffusion of vorticity, heat, or magnetic intensity. Under these circumstances it is shown that a Bernoulli equation exists containing terms which depend upon the magnetic field in addition to the well-known terms are present in the non-magnetic case. An extended vorticity equation is also derived which shows that there exist in general certain stream surfaces within a gas at which the magnetic field and the vorticity field have infinities. As these singular surfaces are approached, the velocity and magnetic intensity vectors tend to become parallel. A particular example of a helical flow field is discussed which shows that there may be non-uniqueness in certain cases if the cylindrical boundaries are not chosen appropriately.

176. (**510**) DAVIS, L., LÜST, R. and SCHLÜTER, A.
    The Structure of Hydromagnetic Shock Waves. Part I: Nonlinear Hydromagnetic Waves in a Cold Plasma.
The waves in a cold (no thermal motions) quasi-neutral gas consisting of ions and electrons are treated neglecting collisions but not neglecting the inertial effects associated with the electric current. Provided the particle trajectories do not

123

make loops, the nonlinear equations for infinite plane compressional waves travelling perpendicular to a uniform magnetic field with unchanging form and speed are reduced to a single second-order ordinary differential equation in the field strength and solved exactly. The solutions can be expressed in terms of elliptic functions. Graphs give the properties of the waves. Both wave trains and solitary waves are found, all solutions being symmetrical about maxima and minima in the field strength. The wavelengths are of the order of the gyro-radius. The velocities range from zero to twice the Alfvén velocity, higher velocities leading to looped trajectories. The relation of these waves to hydromagnetic shock waves in low density plasmas is considered and it is concluded that the entire shock will have a thickness determined by the product of mean time between collisions and the gas velocity with respect to the shock front. Two analogues of the Rankine-Hugoniot conditions are given. (G. Sestini)

177. (512) DAWSON, J. M.

Plasma Oscillations of Large Number of Electron Beams.

Longitudinal oscillations of a large number of electron beams are investigated. The normal modes for the beams are found. An orthogonality relation between the modes is obtained and is used to solve the initial value problem and the problem of forced oscillations. It is demonstrated that no signal propagates faster than the fastest beam. The problem of passing to the limit of a continuous velocity distribution is considered in detail. It is shown that in the limit the results of Landau, Von Kampen, and others are recovered. The problem of Landau damping is discussed from the point of view of the beams.

178. (514) DAWSON, J. M. and OBERMAN, C.

Oscillations of a Finite Cold Plasma in a Strong Magnetic Field.

Analysis stressing the coupling of a bounded plasma with external electromagnetic fields in plasma investigations. The properties of the normal modes of a cold plasma slab and cylinder, situated in a strong magnetic field, are derived and then used to discuss the transmission and reflection of radiation, the scattering by a plasma cylinder, the response to driving sources in the vicinity of the plasma, and the radiation due to plasma oscillations. (Aero/Space)

179. (515) DAWSON, J. M., FRIEMAN, E. A., KULSRUD, R. M., LENARD, A., BERGER J. and BERNSTEIN, I.

Heating of a Confined Plasma by Oscillating Electromagnetic Fields.

There are two ways of heating a plasma confined by a strong axial magnetic field. In the first of these the electric field is parallel to the magnetic field, the situation that obtains in ohmic heating. In the second of these, the electric field is perpendicular to the main axial magnetic field. In this paper we consider the second case only and consider the electric field to be produced by an externally imposed oscillation of the axial field. This method of heating is often called magnetic pumping. It is found that as far as the heating of the plasma is concerned, there are four characteristic times which play a fundamental role. These four times are: (1) the collision time, (2) the period of the oscillating field, (3) the time of transit of a typical ion through the heating region and (4) the cyclotron period of an ion. If these four characteristic times are all of comparable order, the theoretical analysis is exceedingly complex. Therefore, four cases were considered in which these were taken to be of different orders. The heating mechanism differs in each of these four cases since the period of the externally produced electric field is chosen to be comparable to one of the characteristic times in the analysis. In each of the four cases configurations were found which led theoretically, at least, to efficient heating of the plasma. In those cases where the energy imparted to the plasma appears in the form of wave motion, the subsequent damping of these waves is discussed.

180. (**520**) DEMETRIADES, S. T.
Magnetogasdynamic Acceleration of Flowing Gases and Applications.
Descriptors: Magnetogasdynamics; Gas flow; Magnetic fields; Electric fields; Conductivity; Acceleration; Plasma physics. The theory of steady, inviscid, one-dimensional flow of a perfect conducting gas in magnetic and electric fields is developed with special emphasis on the basic assumptions and the physical foundations of such flows. It is concluded that external electric and magnetic fields (acting along the z and y axes of a Cartesian co-ordinate system respectively) can accelerate a gas of high conductivity (0·1 to 100 mhos/cm) flowing along the x-axis to several times its initial velocity with moderate field strengths (ca. 1000 gauss and 10 volts/cm). The properties of gases of interest in magnetogasdynamic flows are discussed with the emphasis on conductivity. Several successful methods are described for increasing the conductivity of air flows to the range where useful acceleration can be accomplished. Some speculative remarks are made on the feasibility of a magnetogasdynamic orbital ramjet and a magnetogasdynamic low-density hypersonic wind tunnel.

181. (**522**) DEMKOV, Y. N. and ERMOLAEV, A. M.
Fock Expansion for the Wave Functions of a System of Charged Particles.
The method with which Fock investigated the wave function of the ^1S state of helium is generalized to an arbitrary system of charged particles and to states of any symmetry.

182. (**524**) DENISOV, N. G.
Resonance Absorption of Electromagnetic Waves by an Inhomogeneous Plasma.
A calculation of absorption of electromagnetic waves in the "resonance region" (one of the refraction indices becomes infinite) was carried out by Budden using a simplified model of an inhomogeneous layer. The author shows that the complete solution of the problem can be obtained in the case in which the plasma is not highly inhomogeneous.

183. (**531**) DESSLER, A. J.
Ionospheric Heating by Hydromagnetic Waves.
The rate of energy dissipation per unit volume is investigated for hydromagnetic waves travelling downward through the ionosphere. A calculation of the heating rate is made, based on assumptions as to the amplitude and Fourier spectrum of the hydromagnetic waves. It is argued in a general way that the peak heating rate due to hydromagnetic waves occurs near 175 kilometers. The results, which are strongly dependent on the assumed values for the amplitude and Fourier spectrum of the hydromagnetic waves, indicate that hydromagnetic heating is normally not important in determining the temperature of the F region. However, during a magnetic storm, the hydromagnetic heating may become the dominant source of heat in the F region. The suggestion is made that the observed lifting of the F region during a magnetic storm is due to an increased heating rate caused by the storm-generated hydromagnetic activity. It is shown that it is not possible to account for the main phase of a magnetic storm by ionospheric heating.

184. (**532**) DIAMOND, F., GOZZINI, A. and KAHAN, T.
Interaction des Ondes Centimétriques avec un Plasma en présence d'un Champ Magnétique.
On décrit et on discute de divers résultats d'expériences sur l'interaction d'ondes centimétriques avec un plasma en présence d'un champ magnétique.

185. (**534**) DICKERMAN, P. J. and PRICE, C. F.
  Flow of a Partially Ionized Gas in an Axial Magnetic Field.
An experiment is described to study this configuration, by directing a stream of plasma from an air-stabilized arc along the axis of a solenoid magnet. The rate of transfer of energy to the walls is measured. (A. H. Gabriel)

186. (**539**) DOLDER, K.
  The Transmission of Strong Shock Waves Through Magnetic Fields.
Existing theoretical and experimental investigations of the passage of shock waves through fields are reviewed. Two procedures by which the strength of hydromagnetic interaction can be estimated are then described. In the first method equations governing hydromagnetic flow are set down and dimensionless parameters, which determine the strength of this interaction, are obtained. Values of these parameters are calculated for conditions likely to be encountered in our shock tubes. The second method is based upon more detailed calculations given by Lin and affords not only a rough quantitative guide but also a useful qualitative account of the flow pattern produced by the passage of a shock through an impressed field.

187. (**544**) DOMBROWSKI, G. E.
  A Small-signal Theory of Electron-wave Interaction in Crossed Electric and Magnetic Fields.
Stream perturbations produced by the fields. Differential equations for perturbations in the interaction space. Solutions of the potential differential equations. The transverse boundary-value problem. Induction theory. Effect of the stream on the circuit; the circuit equation. Guided-wave solutions. The self-consistent combination of the ballistic equation and the induction equation; the dispersion equations. The dispersion equation for quasi-synchronous waves. Solutions of the quasi-synchronous dispersion equation. Cyclotron waves. Non-interacting electromagnetic waves. Trivial solutions of the dispersion equations; a phantom solution. The longitudinal boundary-value problem. An approximate solution to the input problem. Forward-wave interaction. Backward-wave interaction.
(ASTIA)

188. (**545**) DONALDSON, C.
  The Magnetohydrodynamics of a Layer of Fluid Having a Free Surface.
I. Application de l'analogie du niveau hydrostatique (analogie entre le niveau d'une mince couche se déplaçant dans un plan et un écoulement bidimensionnel de fluide compressible) à certains phénomènes aéromagnétodynamiques en vue de reproduire les phénomènes qui doivent se produire dans certains écoulements des plasmas. 3 références bibliographiques.
II. The analysis treats an essentially one-dimensional open channel flow of an electrically conductive liquid in the presence of a vertical external magnetic field. The electric current crosses the channel horizontally perpendicular to the flow direction and it returns through a special conductor placed under the channel. The imposed external magnetic field is vertical in direction and its intensity may vary slowly along the flow direction. In addition there will be an induced magnetic field in the flow direction attaining maximum intensity between the liquid and the shorting plate. In the analysis, viscosity is neglected but electrical conductivity is assumed to be finite. The first finding is that the hydrostatic pressure at the bottom of the channel may be cancelled out if the magnetic field is of sufficient strength. The unsteady small perturbation (linearized) analysis shows that the gravity waves now suffer a magnetic damping. When the steady flow is presented in a non-dimensional form (by using analogous compressible flow parameters such as Mach number) the findings are similar to the treatment of the one-dimensional compressible flow case given by Resler and Sears [*J. Aero. Sci.* **25**, 4, 235–245, 1958; AMR **12** (1959), Rev. 1032]. (L. Kovasznay)

189. (**547**) Dow, D. G. and KNECHTLI, R. C.
Plasma Containment by R.F. and D.C. Field Combinations.
An investigation has been made concerning the use of radio frequency fields for the containment of hot, dense plasmas, such as those needed for controlled thermonuclear fusion. Because high losses due to skin effect are associated with r.f. fields, they will be used at the lowest possible frequency, and only where they constitute a useful supplement to the cheaper d.c. fields. Such r.f. fields are to be useful for reducing the plasma leakage present in most d.c. confinement systems, and to prevent some of the instabilities inherent to d.c. systems. One particular combination of d.c. and r.f. fields has been analysed in detail. It consists of a homogeneous axial d.c. magnetic field (or a d.c. mirror field) containing a plasma column against radial diffusion; the ends of the column are "sealed" by means of r.f. fields. By using the proper polarization of the r.f. fields, it is shown that appreciable plasma pressures may be contained, using r.f. fields of frequencies as low as a few megacycles. By using r.f. powers of the order of a few kilowatts, it is expected to be feasible to contain plasmas of a density exceeding 10^{14} charges/cm^3 at temperatures exceeding 10 eV.

190. (**548**) DOYLE, P. H. and NEUFELD, J.
Behavior of Plasma at Ionic Resonance.
An electromagnetic wave having its wave vector parallel to the direction of the steady magnetic field E is attenuated in plasma very effectively when the frequency ω is equal to the ionic resonance frequency Ω_g of the plasma. A small localized periodic disturbance initiated in a plasma in thermodynamic equilibrium at $t = -\infty$ and having frequency $\omega = \Omega_g$ produces along the direction of the magnetic field a wave motion characterized by a complex wave vector $k \sim (\Omega_0 \Omega_g / c^2 u_{0i})^{\frac{1}{3}} (\sqrt{3} + i)$ where Ω_0 is the Langmuir frequency and u_{0i} is the mean thermal velocity of the ions in the plasma. The attenuation per wavelength at the resonance frequency is substantial since $\mathrm{Im}k/\mathrm{Re}k = 1/\sqrt{3}$. However, the attenuation per unit of length is not at maximum at ionic resonance since it increases for increasing frequencies when ω passes through the resonance. This is shown by the fact that for $\omega = \Omega_g$ we have $\mathrm{Im}(dk/d\omega) > 0$ since at resonance $\mathrm{Im}(dk/d\omega) = K_1/u_{0i} + (K_2/u_0{}^2 u_{i0})^{\frac{1}{2}}$ where K_1 and K_2 are appropriate positive constants and u_0 is the velocity of the magnetohydrodynamic wave.

191. (**549**) DRAGANU, M.
On the Fokker-Plank Equation of a Plasma.
Given the form taken by the Fokker-Plank equation when spherical polar co-ordinates are used in velocity space and azimuthal symmetry is absent. The work is based on formulae due to Rosenbluth, MacDonald and Judd.

192. (**556**) DRUMMOND, W. E. and ROSENBLUTH, M. N.
Cyclotron Radiation from a Hot Plasma.
In their Geneva paper, Trubnikov and Kudrgavtsev calculated the cyclotron radiation from a hot plasma. In doing this, the assumption was made that the individual particles radiated as though they were in a vacuum. We have investigated this approximation by calculating the absorption length directly from the Boltzmann equation, and we find that indeed this assumption is correct whenever $(\omega_p/\omega_e)^2 \ll m^2$, where m is a harmonic number of the radiation in question, ω_p is the plasma frequency, and ω_e is the cyclotron frequency. For a contained plasma, the left-hand side of this inequality is of the order of magnitude of one, and thus the inequality is well satisfied for the dominant radiation from a plasma at high temperature. The angular independence of the absorption coefficient has been calculated, and this together with a more careful examination of the mechanism of thermonuclear energy transfer to the electrons, leads to a modification

127

of the results presented by Trubnikov and Kudrgavysev at Geneva. In addition, it is shown that by the use of reflectors the critical size can be reduced by two orders at magnitude.

193. (580) EDMONDS, F. N., Jr.
    Hydromagnetic Stability of a Conducting Fluid in a Circular Magnetic Field.
USAF-supported extension of the theory for viscous flow between two rotating coaxial cylinders as developed by Taylor and Chandrasekhar to the case when the fluid is an electrical conductor and a circular magnetic field is present. The equations governing marginal stability are derived, and boundary conditions for perfectly conducting cylinders (Fermi boundary conditions) are formulated for two cases when the difference in cylinder radii is small compared to their mean.

(Aero/Space)

194. (582) EIDMAN, V. Y.
    The Radiation From an Electron Moving in a Magnetoactive Plasma.
The author considers the spectral and angular distribution of the energy radiated by an electron moving in a magnetoactive plasma, and finds the polaritation of the radiation.

195. (586) ELSASSER, W. M.
    Dimensional Relations in Magnetohydrodynamics.
An analysis was made of the dimensional relations characteristic of electromagnetic phenomena in fluids of large dimensions. Most dimensionless quantities were exceedingly small, or large, compared to unity, with resultant simplifications of the theory. In the absence of instabilities, the conditions for the acceleration of particles to the higher cosmic-ray energies are favourable only when the linear dimensions of the fluids involved are very large. (Contractor's abstract) (See also AD-23 027.)   (ASTIA)

196. (589) ELSASSER, W. M.
    Hydromagnetism. A Review.
This paper gives a survey of the theories (Part I) and phenomena (Part II) of cosmic magnetism, extending from geomagnetism over solar and sunspot magnetism to stellar and interstellar magnetic fields. The theoretical treatment is purely classical and Maxwellian. The fundamental equations of hydromagnetism are the electromagnetic field equations together with the hydromagnetic equation, both containing coupling terms between magnetic field and motion. Among other theoretical developments, the "dynamo" theory which describes the cosmic magnetic fields to amplifying processes in the moving fluid is described and it is well suited to represent the observed phenomena of the generation and maintenance of cosmic magnetic fields.

197. (590) ELSASSER, W. M.
    Hydromagnetic Dynamo Theory.
The problem of which it is reported is that of using the hydromagnetic equations (combination of the electromagnetic field equations with the Euler (or Stokes) equations of fluid motion with suitable coupling terms between motion and field) to study the mechanism whereby the most conspicuous cosmic magnetic fields, those of the earth, of sunspots and the sun, and of magnetic stars are generated and maintained. A system which can maintain magnetic fields (either stationary field or at least average fields) owing to motions in electrically conducting fluids, will be designated as a "hydromagnetic dynamo". The most important of these problems is that of the magnetic field of the earth.

198. (596) ELSASSER, W. M.
    Magneto-hydro-dynamics.
In Russian. Study of magnetohydrodynamics covering the basic magnetic concepts, magnetohydrodynamic waves, turbulence and instability, formation of cosmic

magnetic fields, secular variation of the Earth's magnetic field, paleomagnetism, solar and astral magnetism, and fields in the rarefied cosmic gas. (Aero/Space)

199. (605) ENGELKE, B. A.
   The Pressure Variation of the Electron Temperature in the Plasma of a Positive Column in Molecular Gas Glow Discharges.
An analytical paper dealing with, for example, the influence of dissociation processes on the electron temperature in molecular gases.

200. (606) ERICSON, W. B. and BAZER, J.
   On Certain Properties of Hydromagnetic Shock.
Proofs of four basic properties of stationary, planar, non-relativistic hydromagnetic shocks are presented. These properties are: (P_1) the specific entropy behind a hydromagnetic shock exceeds that ahead, if and only if, the shock is compressive; (P_2) the specific entropy behind a compressive shock varies in the same sense as the mass flux; (P_3) in the region behind (compressive) fast shocks, the fast disturbance speed is greater than the normally directed fluid velocity relative to the shock; (P_4) in the region behind (compressive) slow shocks, the slow disturbance speed may be less than, equal to, or greater than the normally directed fluid velocity relative to the shock. The equality holds when the specific entropy and the mass flux assume their maximum values. In these statements the state in front is assumed fixed and attention is focused on the variation of the state behind with an appropriate shock strength parameter. The proof of P_1 is designed especially to cover the case of the slow shock where the dependence of the state behind on the "natural" shock-strength parameters in non-monotonic. Our proofs of P_3 and P_4 require the medium to be a polytropic ideal gas; however, a less stringent assumption suffices for P_1 and P_2.

201. (607) ERICSON, W. B. and BAZER, J.
   Hydromagnetic Shocks.
The problem is to determine and to classify by analytic means all planar shock wave solutions of the hydromagnetic discontinuity relations. The state ahead of the shock (i.e., on the low density side) is assumed to be known; no restriction is placed on the direction of the magnetic field in front. It is shown, apart from certain "limit" shocks (e.g., pure gas shocks), that the shock velocity and the quantities characterizing the state behind hydromagnetic shocks may be expressed as simple algebraic functions of the discontinuity in the magnetic field across the shock. A natural classification of all hydromagnetic shocks, based on this representation of the state behind the shock, is given. Several useful analytical properties of the various types of hydromagnetic shocks are derived. The results are illustrated graphically for the case of an ideal monatomic gas. The relation between earlier schemes of classification and the present scheme is discussed.

202. (610) FAINBERG, Y. B. and TKALICH, U. S.
   The Reflection of an Electromagnetic Wave from a Plasma Moving Through a Dielectric in a Constant Magnetic Field.
Deduces expressions for the reflection coefficient and frequency change of steady plane waves by an electron plasma moving through a non-dispersive dielectric medium, in the presence of a magnetic field. A significant part of the energy can be reflected from very small plasma densities in certain cases.

203. (611) FAINBERG, Y. B. and GORBATENKO, M. F.
   Electromagnetic Waves in a Plasma Situated in a Magnetic Field.
Investigates the propagation of slow electromagnetic waves in a plasma rod which is situated in an external unvarying, homogeneous magnetic field, and is isolated from the continuing metallic walls. The scattering equation is obtained

which determines the form of the electromagnetic fields, and numerical results are given.

204. (**613**) FALK, D. S.

Magnetohydrodynamic Distortion of a Magnetic Field due to a Uniform Flow.

Presentation of an exact solution for the distortion of the magnetic field of a straight wire of vanishing diameter, due to the uniform flow of a fluid with constant scalar conductivity, in the limit where the effect of the field on the flow is neglected.

(Aero/Space)

205. (**616**) FARLEY, D. J., Jr.

A Theory of Electrostatic Fields in a Horizontally Stratified Ionosphere Subject to a Vertical Magnetic Field.

A theory is developed to describe quantitatively the idea that in an ionized gas subject to an imposed magnetic field such as the ionosphere, the lines of magnetic flux are approximately equipotential lines. The ionosphere is assumed to be horizontally stratified, and the case in which the earth's magnetic field is vertical is considered. Small-scale electrostatic fields are studied with a view towards elucidating the phenomena of spread F and radio star scintillation. The analysis indicates that in the ionosphere the results are strongly affected by the variation of conductivity with height, as well as by the anisotropy. For a reasonable model of the ionosphere it is shown that it is possible, under certain conditions, for a horizontal field three kilometers or larger in extent, at a height of about 120 or more kilometers, to produce a similar, localized electric field in the F region, not appreciably reduced in strength. The height of the source is the most important factor, but the temperature and ionization-density profiles are also significant. The fact that the strength of the small-scale fields in the F region could vary by one or two powers of 10 for plausible diurnal variations of the ionospheric parameters suggests that these fields could perhaps be responsible for the puzzling diurnal behaviour of spread F and radio star scintillation.

206. (**619**) FEDORCHENKO, V. D., RUKTEVICH, B. N. and CHERNYI, B. M.

Motion of an Electron in a Spatially Periodic Magnetic Field.

An analysis is made of the motion of electrons in a magnetic field which is constant in time but which is modulated weakly in the longitudinal direction. Under certain conditions, a "resonance" relation obtains between the velocity of the electron, the fixed component of the magnetic field, and the period of the spatial modulation; in this case, the magnetic moment of electron is no longer conserved and the energy is divided between the longitudinal and transverse components of the motion.

207. (**622**) FELDMAN, S.

On the Hydrodynamic Stability of two Viscous Incompressible Fluids in Parallel Uniform Shearing Motion.

A new problem in hydrodynamic stability is investigated. Given two contiguous viscous incompressible fluids the fluid on one side of the plane interface being bounded by a solid wall and that on the other side being unbounded by a solid wall, the problem is to determine the hydrodynamic stability when the fluids are in steady unidirectional motion, parallel to the interface, with uniform rate of shear in each fluid. The mathematical analysis, based on small disturbance theory, leads to a characteristic value problem, in a system of two linear ordinary differential equations. The essential dimensionless parameters that appear in the present problem are the viscosity ratio m, the density ratio μ, the Froude number F, and the Weber number W, as well as the parameters α, R (which is proportional here to the flow rate of the inner fluid) and c, that occur in the study of hydrodynamic stability of a single fluid. The results obtained are presented graphically for most fluid combinations of possible interest. The neutral stability curve in the (α, R)-plane is single-looped, as in the boundary layer case. The calculated critical Reynolds numbers are higher than the values observed in liquid film cooling experiments. (In these experiments the outer fluid is usually a turbulent gas, in which the thickness of the laminar sublayer is of the same order of magnitude as the liquid film thickness.) General agreement between the theoretical and experimental values exist for all critical quantities except the Reynolds numbers. Gravity and surface tension are found here to have a destabilizing effect on the flow in agreement with experimental evidence. Semi infinite plane Couette flow is a special case of the present problem and the known stability of this flow is recovered. The linear velocity profile of two adjacent fluids with the same viscosity but different densities, is shown to be unstable for high enough Reynolds numbers.

208. (**634**) FERRARO, V. C. A.
On the Reflection and Refraction of Alfvén Waves.
It is shown that plane harmonic hydromagnetic waves polarized at right angles to the plane of incidence can be reflected and refracted from a plane surface of separation of two infinitely conducting liquids. The general laws of reflection and refraction are derived, and it is shown that these depend on the orientation of the permanent uniform magnetic field with respect to the surface of separation and the plane of incidence. The propagation of hydromagnetic waves in a horizontally stratified isothermal atmosphere lying over an infinitely conducting liquid is briefly discussed. It is shown that eventually the magnetic field associated with waves decreases with height proportionately to the density of the atmosphere.

209. (**638**) FETISOV, I. K.
Wall Probe in a Magnetic Field.
The current flowing to a wall probe in a strong magnetic field is computed in the case when the motion of the electrons can be considered free along the magnetic field and diffuse across the field.

210. (**644**) FINKELSTEIN, D., SAWYER, G. A. and STRATTON, T. F.
Supersonic Motion of Vacuum Spark Plasmas along Magnetic Fields.
Studies of plasmas produced by sparks in vacuum are reported. The observations of principal interest concern the speed with which such plasmas leave the spark. The conclusions about plasma speeds are that they are approximately ten times greater than the thermal speeds associated with spark temperature, varying between 2×10^6 and 2×10^7 cm/sec, and in the range observed the velocities are approximately independent of the spark parameters. It is suggested that the pinch effect may be the mechanism of plasma acceleration.

211. (**648**) FISHMAN, F.
End Effects in Magnetohydrodynamic Channel Flow.
Some effects associated with the termination of electrodes and magnetic field in an otherwise uniform magnetohydrodynamic channel flow are investigated theoretically. Because of the end effects, the electrodes may carry more, or less, current than the same length of electrode in the middle of a long channel; this leads to the definition of a length representing the end correction for current. Similarly a difference in the total force on the working fluid leads to a length representing the end correction for force. These lengths are calculated for various geometries. The electrical efficiency of a channel acting as a generator is computed for these same conditions. It is shown that the end effects decrease generator efficiency least if the magnetic field extends at least one-half a channel height beyond the end of the electrodes (for generators of high nominal efficiency). Under these

conditions, and if the electrodes are not less than 1 per cent of the channel height long, they have an effective length for current about 0·4 channel heights greater than their actual length.

212. (**649**) FISHMAN, F., LOTHROP, J. W., PATRICK, R. M. and PETSCHEK, H. E.
Supersonic Two-Dimensional Magnetohydrodynamic Flow. Appendix—Determination of the "Free Stream" Conditions in the Shock Tube.
USAF-supported application of a perturbation theory to the supersonic flow of a conducting fluid through the magnetic field of a circular solenoid. These calculations describe the lift and drag forces on the solenoid as well as the gas conditions everywhere in the flow field within the limit of weak interaction between the magnetic field and the flow. Calibrated view camera pictures of the light emitted by the gas are in agreement with predictions based on the perturbation theory. Experimental verification of the prediction that lift forces can be achieved with geometrically symmetric bodies by utilizing the Hall effect has been given. Estimates of the experimental lift forces indicate a lift coefficient of about 0·4 and a lift-drag ratio of approximately unity. For very strong magnetic fields the experimental flow pattern becomes similar to the flow pattern around a solid cylinder. The possibility of using magnetohydrodynamic forces in flight depends upon the fact that the gas behind a normal shock at hypersonic velocities is heated sufficiently to become a good conductor. Such a normal shock could be supported by magnetic field. In order to achieve magnetohydrodynamics forces in flight the interaction parameter based on conditions behind the shock wave must be large enough to support the shock. This occurs for drag coefficients near unity.

213. (**650**) FLEISCHMAN, O. and LIPPMANN, B. A.
Remarks on Alfvén's Perturbation Method.
"Alfvén's perturbation method (*Cosmical Electrodynamics*, Oxford, 1950) for treating the motion of a point charge in a magnetic field consists of three elements: (1) The field is regarded, in zero order, as homogeneous. In the next order, the zero-order motion is replaced by its averaged effect, a magnetic dipole, and the interaction of this "equivalent dipole' with the inhomogeneities of the field constitutes the perturbation. (2) The moment of the 'equivalent dipole' is constant. (3) If the field is axially symmetric, the 'equivalent dipole' moves on the surface generated by rotating a line of force about the polar axis. Alfvén develops his method by the analysis of several special cases. In this report, we have re-derived his perturbation scheme from a viewpoint that emphasizes general dynamical principles. Thus: (1) is derived directly from Hamilton's principle, (2) is proved by the adiabatic theorem, after noting that the moment of the 'equivalent dipole' is an action variable, while (3) is related to the conservation of angular momentum. Our remarks under (2) and (3) are intended as an extension of Alfvén's discussion."

214. (**654**) FOURES-BRUHAT, Y.
Fluides Chargés de Conductivité Infinie.
L'auteur établit les équations des chocs pour un fluide relativiste doué de conductivité électrique infinie. Elle en déduit par considération des chocs infiniment faible, l'equation qui détermine les hypersurfaces constituant les traits d'ondes du premier ordre, et calcule la vitesse de propagation de ces ondes par rapport au repère propre.   (H. Cabannes)

215. (**658**) FRAENKEL, L. E.
A Shallow-Liquid Theory in Magnetohydrodynamics.
The nonlinear and linear shallow-water theories, which describe long gravity waves on the free surface of an inviscid liquid, are extended to the case of an

electrically conducting liquid on a horizontal bottom, in the presence of a vertical magnetic field. The dish holding the liquid, and the medium outside it, are assumed to be non-conducting. The approximate equations are based on a small ratio of depth to wavelength, on the properties of mercury, and on a moderate magnetic field strength. These equations have a magneto-hydraulic character, for in the shallow liquid layer the horizontal fluid velocity and current density are independent of the vertical co-ordinate. Some explicit solutions of the linear equations are obtained for plane flows and for axi-symmetric flows in which the velocity vector lies in a vertical, meridian plane. (ASTIA)

216. (**668**) FRIEDLANDER, F. G.
   Sound Pulses in a Conducting Medium.
A mathematical treatment of the propagation of small disturbances in a perfectly conducting compressible fluid in a magnetic field which is uniform when undisturbed. Only the case where Alfvén modes are not excited is considered. A study of the propagation speeds of fast and slow magnetoacoustic waves in different directions show that from an instantaneous points source two wave fronts spread out. The outer front is a rotationally symmetrical convex surface flattened in the direction of the applied field; the inner fronts are conoidal, with concave bases and zero opening angle, so that meridian sections have cups at the vertex of the conoid. For the case of an arbitrary initial pressure and zero initial velocity and field perturbations, a formal solution of the equations of motion is derived. If the initial pressure disturbance is highly localized, an approximate treatment of this formal solution gives estimates of the size of the propagating pressure disturbances associated with wave fronts. Surprisingly, the largest part of this disturbance is the part associated with the vertex of the conoid; it falls away as $\tau^{-\frac{3}{2}}$, in contrast with τ^{-1} for the other parts.

217. (**669**) FRIEDRICHS, K. O.
   Nonlinear Wave Motion in Magnetohydrodynamics.
It is shown that the basic equations governing magneto-hydrodynamics have essentially the same mathematical character as those governing gas dynamics, so that the same mathematical methods can be employed. This is illustrated by considering simple problems of one-dimensional hydromagnetic wave motion. Fast and slow disturbance waves, transverse waves and Alfvén waves, contact disturbances, conservation laws, shocks, fast and slow simple waves, transverse waves and contact layers, and the resolution of a shear flow discontinuity, are discussed. (TIL/MOS)

218. (**672**) FRIEMAN, E. A. and KULSRUD, R. M.
   Problems in Hydromagnetics.
Authors give survey of selected topics of continuum hydromagnetics. Review is divided in three sections. The first and shortest treats motion of magnetic lines, an energy conservation theorem, and general question of hydromagnetic equilibrium. Second part, by far the best, is completely devoted to hydromagnetic stability. Authors derive criteria for stability by normal mode and energy methods. Few examples are given. In the third part hydromagnetic waves are discussed at length. Study is confined to infinitesimal amplitudes. Authors derive properties for reflection, refraction, and transmission of such waves. (O. K. Mawardi)

219. (**683**) GABOVICH, M. D. and PASECHNIK, L. L.
   Anomalous Electron Scattering and the Excitation of Plasma Oscillations.
We have studied the interaction of an electron beam with an independently formed plasma, an interaction leading to an appreciable change in the electron energy and to the excitation of plasma oscillations. The observed data can

be interpreted qualitatively by assuming that the electrons form clusters and that these clusters interact coherently with the plasma.

220. (**684**) GAILITIS, A.
Influence of a Magnetic Field on the Boundary Layer in a Diffuser.
Considers motion of a slightly conducting liquid in a diffuser whose walls are inclined poles of a magnet and obtains expressions for boundary-layer velocities for the inward and the outward motion of the liquid.

221. (**685**) GAJEWSKI, R.
Magnetohydrodynamic Waves in Wave Guides.
Propagation of magnetohydrodynamic waves is investigated in a fluid bounded by a cylindrical surface of constant, but not necessarily circular, cross section. The fluid is assumed to be non-viscous and perfectly conducting with a constant magnetic field applied parallel to the walls of the cylinder. It is shown that the following types of waves can propagate in such a wave guide: (1) transverse waves propagating without dispersion with the velocity of Alfvén waves; (2) a longitudinal wave, identical with the wave of the principal mode for an acoustic wave guide; (3) waves having both longitudinal and transverse components propagating with a dispersion, their group and phase velocity being close to the respective velocities for an acoustic wave guide; (4) waves having both longitudinal and transverse components propagating with a small dispersion, their group and phase velocity being close to the velocity of Alfvén waves. When the applied frequency is too low, damping of certain modes appears for waves of type (3), only; the cut-off frequencies turn out to be slightly higher than the corresponding cut-off frequencies for an acoustic wave guide.

222. (**689**) GARTENHAUS, S. and TANNENWALD, L. M.
The Collapse of an Axially Symmetrical Pinch.
Derivation of equation of motion of an axially symmetric pinch surface, according to the Rosenbluth independent particle model, is obtained. Exact solutions are found in parametric form for a class of boundary conditions. A brief discussion of the magnitude of the axial thrust expected from the collapse of an axially symmetric body of plasma is appended. (Lockheed)

223. (**691**) GAUGER, J., VALI, V. and TURNER, T. E.
The Arc-Driven Shock Tube.
Several techniques have been proposed for space vehicle propulsion systems using magnetohydrodynamic effects. This paper describes experiments being conducted on capacitor-discharge shock tubes which yield shock velocities up to 6 cm/μsec in air. These shocks are produced by discharging a large bank of energy-storage capacitors through an electrode system designed to use the magnetic energy associated with the discharge currents. The dependence of shock velocity on the energy of the capacitor system, driving currents during the discharge, is discussed as well as ambient pressure in the shock tube. (Lockheed)

224. (**692**) GAUGER, J., VALI, V. and TURNER, T. E.
Laboratory Experiments in Hydromagnetic Propulsion.
Several techniques have been proposed for space ship propulsion systems. This paper describes experiments conducted on capacitor discharge shock tubes which yield shock velocities up to 6 cm per microsec in air, or specific impulses near 6000 seconds. (Lockheed)

225. (**694**) GELLER, R.
The Production of Stable High Frequency Plasmoids at the Plasma Resonance Frequency.
I. High frequency plasmoids are produced in various shapes of containing vessel, and measurements made on the electron density, n, and electron temperature,

using single and double probes. It is found that at electron densities of the order 10^7 cm^{-3}, the density adjusts itself to maintain resonance between the applied field and the plasma frequency $\omega_0 = (4\pi ne^2/m)^{\frac{1}{2}}$. (H. Gabriel)

II. Production de plasmoides de haute fréquence stables à la frequence de resonance du plasma. On obtient de plasmoides H.F. stables de densité $n \cong 10^7$ electrons/cm^3 et de temperature $T =$ quelques 10^5°K. On constate que n s'accorde à une valeur telle que l'éxcitation H.F. puisse entretenir la resonance électronique du plasmoide dont la pulsation est donné par

$$\omega_0 = \sqrt{4\pi \frac{ne^2}{m}}.$$

226. (**695**) GELLER, R.
Behaviour of High-Frequency Plasma in the Presence of a Magnetic Field.
An instability is observed when the resonance frequency of electrons in the plasma is approximatively equal to the electron gyromagnetic frequency.
(C. G. Morgan)

227. (**696**) GEORGE, K. A.
Plasma Heating by Current-Saturation.
States that the process which produces runaway ions in tocoidal discharges might be exploited to increase the density of the plasma.

228. (**697**) GEORGHITA, S. I.
Sur le Mouvements Stationnaires des Fluids Incompressibles dans les Milieux Poreux non-Homogènes.
The author presents some new approximations for different types of flow in porous non-homogeneous media. In particular, he deals with the following case: (a) non-existence of free-surfaces; (b) uni-dimensional motion; and (c) observations concerning motion in non-homogeneous media. Explicit solutions are presented.
(K. Bhagwandu)

229. (**698**) GEORGHITA, S. I.
Sur le Mouvements non-Linéaires dans les Milieux Poreux.
The author studies fluid motion in porous media typified by non-linear partial differential equations. A procedure, of the Janzen-Rayleigh type, is proposed as a possible means of obtaining solutions to these equations. The strong non-linearity is relaxed in certain cases by means of symmetry considerations. Some examples are presented, and a certain generalization of the equation of Boussinesq is also obtained. It should be noted, however, that the author does not present any rigorous justification of his boundary-conditions. (K. Bhagwandu)

230. (**700**) GERMAIN, P.
Introduction to the Study of Magnetoaerodynamics.
The review article consists of two parts. The first deals with general concepts: the motion of charged particles in a steady electromagnetic field, the hydrodynamic description of an ion-electron mixture, Maxwell's equations, the generalized Ohm's law, and the characteristic orders of magnitude (especially lengths) in a plasma. The second part deals with some special situations in a "perfect plasma" (one obeying the simplest form of Ohm's law): one-dimensional flow including shock transitions, flow through a tube, stability of flows, laminar boundary layer theory, motion of a solid sphere through a fluid. The discussion of one-dimensional flow appears to be original. There are 16 references. (O. Penrose)

231. (**702**) GERMAIN, P.
Sur la Structure de Certaines Ondes de Choc dans un Fluide Conducteur en Présence d'un Champ Magnétique.
Extension au cas où le fluide est électrisé et soumis à un champ magnétique des résultats classiques sur la structure d'une onde de choc, en supposant que la loi

d'état du fluide vérifie les inégalités de Weyl et en ne faisant aucune hypothèse sur les coefficients de viscosité, de conductibilité et de conductivité. 3 références bibliographiques. (SDIT)

232. (**708**) GERSHUNI, G. Z. and ZHUKHOVITSKII, E. M.
Stationary Convective Flow of an Electrically Conducting Liquid between Parallel Plates in a Magnetic Field.
An analysis is presented on the induced velocity, temperature and magnetic field distribution between two vertical plates at different temperatures when an external magnetic field is applied perpendicular to the plate. The fluid is viscous, electrically and thermally conductive. Neglecting displacement currents in Maxwell's field equations and viscous dissipation in the energy equation, author solves for the free convective velocity temperature and magnetic field between the two plates in terms of the distance between plates, the Grashof number and the Hartmann number. (S. Eskinazi)

233. (**709**) GERSHUNI, G. Z. and ZHUKHOVITSKII, E. M.
Stability of the Stationary Convective Flow of an Electrically Conducting Liquid between Parallel Vertical Plates in a Magnetic Field.
Translation. Investigation of the effect of a constant magnetic field on the hydrodynamic stability of flow. The equations for the amplitudes of the perturbations are solved by approximations, using the method of Galerkin. The study shows that a magnetic field greatly increases the stability of the stationary flow. In the case of a longitudinal field, the instability is always in the form of a "standing" perturbation. The critical Grashof Number and the critical wave number for standing and running perturbations have been determined as functions of the field strength. (Aero/Space)

234. (**712**) GHAI, M. L.
Space Propulsion Engines—A Problem in Production of High Velocity Gases.
A basic problem of space propulsion engines is to generate gases at very high velocities—about 8 to 100 times the gas velocities generated by the conventional jet engines. Three electric propulsion engines inherently capable of producing the required velocities are presented—the electro-thermal propulsion or the arc jet engine, the plasma propulsion or the magnetohydrodynamic engine, and the ion propulsion engine.

235. (**713**) GIAMBIRASIO, G.
On the Electrical Behaviour of an Ideal Plasma.
The solution of the equation for the current in an ideal plasma when the electric field, in a direction perpendicular to a constant magnetic field, is abruptly increased from zero to a constant value, is obtained using Laplace transforms. An exact solution and approximate solutions for some simple cases are obtained and discussed. An expression and the corresponding RLC network are found for the specific impedence of the plasma.

236. (**714**) GIANNINI, G. M.
The Plasma Jet and its Applications.
A general account of the plasma jet and its applications. (TIL/MOS)

237. (**716**) GIBSON, G. and LAUER, E. S.
Radiation Damping of an Electron in a Uniform Magnetic Field.
Analytic solutions are given for the pair of differential equations obtained from classical theory which express the time rate of change of the angle between the momentum vector and the magnetic field vector, and the time rate of change of the energy of the electron.

238. (**718**) Giellestad, G.
On Equilibrium Configurations of Oblate Fluid Spheroids with a Magnetic Field.
It is shown that a homogeneous incompressible oblate fluid spheroid of infinite electrical conductivity can be of equilibrium configuration if it has a uniform internal magnetic field and an external dipole field. The condition for stability is established, and the equilibrium spheroids are discussed briefly. It is shown that an oblate spheroidal cloud in an interstellar magnetic field in a spiral arm, as estimated by Chandrasekhar and Fermi, will be stable if the density is at least fourteen times larger than the average density of the surrounding interstellar matter, while it will be unstable and contract to a disklike shape or disintegrate if the density is less than fourteen times the average density.

239. (**727**) Ginzburg, V. L. and Eidman, V. Y.
The Radiation Reaction in the Motion of a Charge in a Medium.
The radiation reaction force is computed for a charge that moves in a medium which, for generality, is taken to be anisotropic and gyrotropic. The radiation force in the medium can be important in cases in which the particle moves in a magneto-active plasma, in channels and slits in dielectrics, or in wave guides. At velocities greater than the phase velocity of light in the medium, the radiation force that affects the oscillation because of the anomalous Doppler effect has a different sign than that due to dissipation associated with the normal Doppler effect. The total radiation force which affects the amplitude of the oscillations of the particle in an isotropic medium corresponds to dissipation for motion at velocities greater than the velocity of light. However this dissipation force may be appreciably smaller than the dissipation associated with motion at velocities smaller than the velocity of light. In an isotropic medium the oscillations can be strengthened instead of attenuated. The reduction in the radiative dissipation force may be related to the peculiarities of the anomalous Doppler effect as found in the quantum-mechanical analysis and instability of particle beams which move at velocities greater than velocity of light.

240. (**730**) Globe, S.
Laminar Steady State Magnetohydrodynamic Flow in an Annular Channel.
The problem considered is the steady flow of an electrically conducting, incompressible fluid, in the annular space between two infinitely long circular cylinders, under a radially impressed magnetic field. The general magnetohydrodynamic equations are simplified by the conditions of the problem to three equations in pressure, velocity, and magnetic field. One equation gives the pressure variation in the radial direction; the other two are coupled equations for the velocity and magnetic field, which are functions of the radial variable only and may be solved for in closed form. In the limiting case where the radii of the annulus become infinite, but their difference remains finite, the solution converges on the expression for magnetohydrodynamic flow between infinite planes under a transverse magnetic field.

241. (**731**) Globe, S.
Magnetohydrodynamic Pipe Flow. I. Laminar Flow in an Annular Channel.
The problem considered is the steady flow of an electrically conducting, incompressible fluid, in the annular space between two infinitely long circular cylinders, under a radially impressed magnetic field. The general magnetohydrodynamic equations are simplified by the conditions of the problem to three equations in pressure, velocity, and magnetic field. One equation gives the pressure variation in the radial direction; the other two are coupled equations for the velocity and

magnetic field, which are functions of the radial variable only and may be solved for in closed form. In the limiting case where the radii of the annulus become infinite, but their difference remains finite, the solution converges on the expression for magnetohydrodynamic flow between infinite planes under a transverse magnetic field.

242. (732) GLOBE, S.
The Suppression of Turbulence in Pipe Flow of Mercury by an Axial Magnetic Field.

An experimental investigation has been made of the effect of an axial magnetic field on transition from laminar to turbulent flow and on the turbulent friction factor for pipe flow of mercury. Magnetic flux densities up to 5700 gauss were obtained with a water-cooled solenoid. Pipes of glass and aluminium of approximately 0·1-in. and 0·2-in. diameter were used. The maximum Hartmann number (product of field flux density, hydraulic radius, and the square root of the electrical conductivity divided by the kinematic viscosity) was about 20. Measurements were made of the pressure gradient and velocity of flow. The transition Reynolds number was determined from the curve of friction factor against Reynolds number. The results show an increasing value of minimum transition Reynolds number with Hartmann number: at the highest value of the Hartmann number the minimum transition Reynolds number was increased to about 1·8 times the value of zero magnetic field. The results can be correlated with an empirical modification of Stuart's stability theory for plane Poiseuille flow. The magnetic field also brought about a decrease in the turbulent friction factor and corresponding shear force at the wall. For Reynolds numbers just above transition the decrease in friction factor was about 30 per cent. As the Reynolds number increased, the magnetic field brought about less of a decrease in the turbulent friction factor. For a Hartmann number of 20, there was no effect of the magnetic field above a Reynolds number of about 11,000.   (Appl. Mech. Rev.)

243. (734) GLOTOVA, G. I., GRANOVSKII, V. L. and SAVOSKIN, V. I.
Comparison of the Decay Rates of Plasma in Hydrogen and Deuterium.

The de-ionization rate in hydrogen and deuterium at pressure $p = 15$ to $600\ \mu$ Hg, tube diameters $d = 3.2$ to 6.5 cm, and values of the proceding current $I_0 = 60$ to 1500 mA was studied by means of oscillographic observation of the ion current in a negative probe. Under the condition employed the relative de-ionization rate in H and D decreased with time. The dependence of the rate of the process on the pressure is a non-monotonic function and goes through a maximum at p.d. $\sim 10^{-1}$ mm Hg/cm. The ratio of the de-ionization "time constants" (initial as well as final) in deuterium and hydrogen, TD/TH, is close to 1·4, i.e. $\approx (mD/mH)^{\frac{1}{2}}$ at all pressures both in the diffusion regime ($p < p_m$), and also in the recombination that under these conditions takes place primarily by means of triple collision with neutral molecules ($M^+ + e + M$).

244. (739) GOLD, T.
Motions in the Magnetosphere of the Earth.

The conditions determining the dynamical behaviour of the ionized gas in the outer atmosphere of the earth are discussed. It is proposed to call this region which the magnetic field of the earth dominates the "magnetosphere." Observations by van Allen and others [*Nature (London)*, Vol. 183, 430, 1953] indicate that this zone reaches out to between 5 and 10 earth radii, depending on the degree of magnetic disturbances. It is shown that the existence of an insulating layer at the base of this region, namely the non-ionized atmosphere, completely changes the type of control exerted by the magnetic field, allowing a class of motions to occur freely without the need to overcome any magnetic forces. The extent to which such motions may occur is discussed, and some of the indications from airglow and magnetic observations are mentioned. The theory predicts that, at the level of the F2 layer and above, most motions will show strict symmetry between the two base points of a magnetic line of force.

245. (**744**) GOLITZYNE, G. S.
One-Dimensional Motion in Magneto-Hydrodynamics.
A perfect conducting gas is assumed. The Riemann invariants for several gases are computed and some non-stationary problems solved. A new method is proposed for determining the approximate general solution of the equations. Some types of motion in the presence of shock waves are considered.   (TIL/MOS)

246. (**745**) GOLITZYNE, G. S.
Plane Problems in Magnetohydrodynamics.
The conditions for potential motion are deduced and such motions investigated. The investigations reduce to the usual hydrodynamical problems. The Prandtl-Mayer problem for a conducting gas in a magnetic field, its generalizations and applications are studied in detail.   (TIL/MOS)

247. (**746**) GOLITZYNE, G. S. and STANIUKOVICH, K. P.
Some Problems of Magnetogasdynamics with Account of Finite Conductivity.
Translation. Analysis of several problems of one-dimensional motion for a medium possessing arbitrary conductivity. It is shown that, if conductivity is taken into account, the equations of magnetogasdynamics become parabolically degenerate. The set of equations is replaced by an approximate but completely hyperbolic set for which the characteristics are found. It is shown that the equations of a stationary one-dimensional flow have a singularity where the flow velocity is equal to the local sound velocity. Conditions of the transition of the flow velocity through this critical value under the action of a magnetic field have been studied. Small oscillations in a conducting medium shock waves, and the structure of the shock are investigated.   (Aero/Space)

248. (**747**) GOLITZYNE, G. S. and STANIUKOVICH, K. P.
Some Remarks on the Structure of Shock Waves.
It is shown that at a maximum of the entropy in a shock wave the fluid velocity relative to the shock equals the local speed of sound. This result is stated to be true also for hydromagnetic and for relativistic shocks and (at two places) for detonation fronts. Simple methods of estimation are used to show that for strong magnetic fields the shock thickness is decreased by an increase of conductivity or of magnetic field.

249. (**749**) GORDEEV, G. V.
The Influence of End Boundaries upon the Rotation of Plasma in a Magnetic Field.
Calculates the angular velocity of, and the radial current density in a simple conducting fluid placed between two finite coaxial cylindrical conductors placed in a strong uniform magnetic field everywhere parallel to the axis of the conductors. Considers only the balance of the electromagnetic forces with the viscous forces. Assumes a steady state, that the viscosity and conductivity are constant scalar quantities and that the fluid velocities are zero at all the boundaries.
(R. Pease)

250. (**753**) GORDEEV, G. V. et GOUBANOV, A. J.
On the Question of the Acceleration of a Plasmic in a Magnetic Field.
Etude de l'accélération, provoquée par un champ magnétique axial extérieur, d'un plasma confiné entre deux électrodes cylindriques coaxiales et infinies. 2 références bibliographiques.   (SDIT)

251. (**754**) GORDEEV, G. V. and GOUBANOV, A. J.
On the Acceleration of a Plasma in a Magnetic Field.
The acceleration of a plasma between two infinite coaxial cylindrical electrodes due to an external axial magnetic field is considered. Authors compute the stationary plasma flow taking account of friction with the electrode, the dependence of flow velocity on magnetic flux and the radii of the electrodes, and the energy required to maintain the flow. The calculations show that it is possible to achieve supersonic plasma flow velocities with parameters which are realizable in practice.
(Appl. Mech. Rev.)

252. (**756**) GOROWITZ, B. and HARNED, B. W.
Measurements of Velocity and Momentum with a Pulsed T-tube Plasma Generator.
In preliminary studies concerning the use of plasma acceleration for propulsion purposes, a series of measurements was made of velocity and momentum of plasma bursts both in single-shot and pulsed operation over a range of pressures and input energies for various magnitudes and directions of magnetic field at the gaseous discharge. The effect of magnetic field on acceleration of the plasma and its contribution to the momentum transferred to a ballistic pendulum are discussed. Extrapolation was made of power input for the small thrust obtained to that required for a one pound thrust over the range of pressures and efficiencies investigated. (ASTIA)

253. (**758**) GOTO, K.
Relativistic Magneto-hydrodynamics.
Utilisation des méthodes employées par Eckart, Taub et Synge en hydrodynamique relativiste pour établir les équations des écoulements de particules électriquement chargées, se déplaçant à une grande vitesse dans un champ magnétique intense.
8 références bibliographiques. (SDIT)

254. (**759**) GOTO, T., SATO, M. and UCHIDA, T.
On the Mechanism of the Pinch Effect.
Phenomenological analysis of the fast pinch effect is presented and compared with some existing experimental data. It is argued that several results consistent with experiments can be derived from a general basic picture of the fast contracting process, independent of its detailed mechanism. To establish a consistent model of the pinch mechanism, it is therefore necessary to get more detailed experimental information about the dynamical behaviour of the plasma column under various initial conditions. Dimensional considerations are added in the appendix.

255. (**760**) GOULARD, R.
Optimum Magnetic Field for Stagnation Heat Transfer Reduction at Hypersonic Velocities.
The application of a magnetic field to the stagnation area of a blunt body has two contrary effects: It reduces convective energy transfer, but increases radiation energy transfer. Consequently, for very high speeds, when this latter effect is existent but not dominant ($q_R{}^{(o)} < 0.4 q_c{}^{(o)}$), an optimum magnetic field exists which insures minimum energy transfer. At still higher speeds, radiation is dominant, and the application of a magnetic field always increases the energy transfer to the stagnation area or the nose. This argument closely parallels the well-known argument on the existence of an optimum radius. The existence of an optimum magnetic field is shown, in fact, to depend on the choice of a nose radius below its optimum value. (ARS J.)

256. (**769**) GRAD, H.
Notes on Magneto-Hydrodynamics: IV Ohm's Law.
In this note the question of the formal nature and domain of validity of Ohm's law is considered. One of the complicating factors turns out to be the presence of

two entirely distinct mechanisms, namely collisions and gyro oscillations, which tend to validate Ohm's law under entirely distinct conditions. An important formal point is the clarification of the concept of different electrical conductivities parallel and perpendicular to the magnetic field. It is shown that there are two possible definitions for "conductivity," one of which has the conventional property that its transverse component varies as $1/B^2$ for large B, while the other (more natural) definition implies a conductivity which is essentially independent of B. Of course, proper use of either definition, in combination with the Hall effect must yield the same results.

257. (**770**) GRANOVSKII, V. P., RIUMINA, K. P., SAVOSKIN, V. I. and TIMOFEEVA, G. G.
Observations of the Pinch Effect at Decreasing Currents.
Image-converter photographs have been taken of transient states of pulsed discharges in H_2 and Hg at pressures of 10^{-2} to 10^{-3} mm Hg. The peak pulse currents were 1·3 to 5·5 kiloamperes and the pulses were 300 μsec long. Electrodynamic deformations (contraction and kinking) are observed at negative values of di/dt. It is found that these deformation effects first disappear (as manifested by the straightening and expansion of the column) at points of high local gas density (anode or cathode, depending on the experimental conditions).
(Appl. Mech. Rev.)

258. (**773**) GREEN, H. S.
Ionic Theory of Plasmas and Magneto-hydro-dynamics
I. This paper aims at removing certain sources of confusion in plasma theory by deriving a complete set of macroscopic equations based on the ionic theory. Relativistic and quantum effects are usually neglected, and an approximation equivalent to that of the macroscopic theory of irreversible processes is adopted. But there is no other approximation, and in particular multiple interactions are fully accounted for. The theory of the dielectric constant and permeability of plasmas is sketched, and there follows an ionic derivation of the equations of continuity and of energy and momentum transport, based on an exact separation of the long-range and short-range forces. It is shown how the short-range forces contribute to the pressure, the energy flux, and the flux of entropy. The ionic basis of the theory of irreversible processes is discussed, and its relevance to the generalization of Ohm's law. In an appendix, the formal statistical thermodynamics of plasmas is developed in a way which avoids certain difficulties associated with the long-range interactions. II. Equations of change, fluxes as functions of gradients and forces, and polarization and magnetization as functions of correlations between positions and velocities of neighbouring particles are derived for case in which the relativistic and quantum effects are negligible and the changes in macroscopic variables are small over distances of the order of the correlation length. A development of the statistical mechanics of plasmas in equilibrium, required for the calculation of the polarization of a plasma in equilibrium, is included as an appendix. The derivation of the equations of change is facilitated by separating exactly effects of long-range and short-range forces; the aforementioned application of statistical mechanics is facilitated by avoiding the technical difficulties encountered in evaluating the partition function for a plasma. As a significant part of the paper, author attempts to clarify certain confusions found in the literature of plasmas, particularly confusions regarding the induced charge and current densities and the generalization of Ohm's law. Although good backgrounds in electrodynamics and in thermodynamics (classical, statistical, and irreversible) are required for a complete understanding of this paper, reviewer believes that any investigator of plasmas would find something of interest in this paper.
(E. Knuth)

259. (775) GREENBERG, O. W. and SEN, H. K.
Hydrodynamic Model of Diffusion Effects on Shock Structure in a Plasma.
Diffusion effects on the structure of a steady, plane shock in a proton-electron plasma have been studied using a simplified, two-fluid, hydrodynamic model in which diffusion is the only shock broadening mechanism. Charge separations occur inside the shock because of the mass difference between protons and electrons. The shock is shown to have electric field and density oscillations as a function of distance through the shock. The peak electric fields are large: the peak electric field inside a weak shock of Mach 1·169 reaches 41,700 v/cm for typical quiescent plasma conditions. The distance in which electric field changes occur is of the order of ten Debye lengths of the quiescent plasma. The present work is limited to shocks of Mach number less than 2.

260. (777) GREENSPAN, H. P.
On the Flow of a Viscous Electrically Conducting Fluid.
Magnetohydrodynamic flow of a viscous incompressible fluid of constant properties past a flat plate is considered. The applied magnetic field is parallel to the free stream direction and the plate is at zero angle of attack. A number of explicit solutions of the linearized theory are presented for the flow past a semi-infinite plate which is either sucking or injecting a conducting fluid into the main stream. Unlike the case of super-Alfvén flow (where the free stream velocity is greater than the Alfvén wave speed) no solution exists in the problem of sub-Alfvén flow past a semi-infinite flat plate which is either impermeable or injecting fluid. Special solutions do exist for certain values of the suction velocity. The sub-Alfvén flow past a long finite impermeable plate is studied in some detail and the magnitude of the viscous wake is compared to the similar type upstream disturbance produced by the forward propagation of Alfvén waves. In the case of infinite conductivity, it is found that the upstream disturbance is approximately one plate length long measured from the leading edge. The inadequacies and failures of the linearized theory of the super-Alfvén are discussed.

261. (778) GREENSPAN, H. P.
Flat Plate Drag in Magnetohydrodynamic Flow.
In sub-Alfvén magnetohydrodynamic flow past a flat plate (the free fluid velocity is less than the Alfvén wave speed) the vorticity generated within the fluid is propagated upstream by Alfvén waves and produces a forward disturbance which in form is very similar to the viscous wake. The structure and strength of the wake and precursor are herein examined and compared for large Reynolds numbers and finite conductivity. As the conductivity increases, a larger proportion of the total vorticity is propagated upstream so that precursor becomes more pronounced and the wake weakens. Explicit formulas for the skin friction and drag coefficient are determined for arbitrary values of the conductivity, and the results clearly exhibit the effects of the intersection of fluid flow and magnetic field.

262. (779) GREENSPAN, H. P. and CARRIER, G. F.
The Magnetohydrodynamic Flow Past a Flat Plate.
Analysis of the uniform steady flow of an incompressible, viscous, electrically conducting fluid distorted by the presence of a symmetrically oriented semi-infinite flat plate. The ambient magnetic field is coincident with the ambient velocity field. The description of the resulting fields depends on the physical co-ordinates measured in units of Reynolds Number and on the two parameters ε and β. This description of the fields is approximated in three different ways and essentially covers the full range of ε and β. In particular, when $\beta \geqslant 1$, no steady flow which is uniform at large distances from the plate exists.   (Aero/Space)

263. (**787**) GROSS, R. A.
    A Note on One-Dimensional Plasma Motion.
Author derives the change of a number of physical quantities from the magneto-
hydrodynamic equations, as a function of heat added during the motion. He shows
that the behaviour is characteristically different depending on whether a generalized
Mach number (taking into account the magnetic effects upon the propagation of
disturbances) is larger or smaller than unity.   (W. Elsasser)

264. (**788**) GROSS, R. A., CHINITZ, W. and RIVLIN, T. J.
    Magnetohydrodynamics Effects in Combustion.
One dimensional steady flow with heat addition in the presence of a plane magnetic
field transverse to the direction of motion is studied. The basic equations are
derived and solved for a variety of ideal conditions. Particular emphasis is given
to the singular solution (the analogue of the Chapman-Jouguet detonation). The
presence of a magnetic field alters the classical conditions. The effects of variable
fluid properties and finite electrical conductivity are discussed. The electrical
conductivity of the product gases of hydrogen-air detonations is presented. The
experimental implications of this analysis are examined and lead to the conclusion
that large magnetohydrodynamic effects in combustion can be produced in the
laboratory under special conditions.

265. (**789**) GROSS, R. A., CHINITZ, W. and RIVLIN, T. J.
    Magnetohydrodynamic Effects on Exothermal Waves.
Elementary magnetohydrodynamic effects on exothermal, plane, supersonic waves
are examined. One-dimensional steady flow with heat addition in the presence of
a plane magnetic field transverse to the direction of motion is studied. Basic
equations are derived and solved numerically for several ideal conditions which
correspond to gaseous detonations and thermonuclear shocks. The magnetic
field acts on the flow in a way which tends to counteract the heat-addition effects.
The singular solution still exhibits the classical Chapman-Jouguet conditions.
Some properties of high-temperature gas mixtures are presented including the
electrical conductivity of air shocks and fuel-air detonations. Experimental
implications of the analysis and numerical results are discussed.

266. (**790**) GRUBIN, E. S., HARRACH, W. G. and ORR, W. R.
    Feasibility Study for a Hypervelocity Projector.
This feasibility study describes the basic thermodynamic, hydrodynamic and
electrical augmentation principles of a laboratory hypervelocity projector with a
theoretical capability of accelerating a 25 grain particle to a velocity of 50,000 fps.
A detailed analysis is presented of the propellant gas properties, as a function of
time and position, for the non-steady ballistic expansion of a perfect gas hydrogen
column by the conventional method of characteristics. A characteristics solution
of the equations of motion for a real, virial gas is developed, and the results are
found to diverge appreciably from the perfect gas case. From the initial gas
conditions of primary interest, 30,000 atm and 6000°K, the expansion was examined to determine the feasibility of energy addition by electrical means to augment
the normally adiabatic process.

267. (**792**) GUERCHMAN, B. N.
    *Contribution a l'Étude de la Théorie Cinétique de Propagation des Ondes Magnéto-
    hydrodynamiques dans le Plasma.*
Propagation dans un plasma homogène suivant une direction arbitraire par rapport
au champ magnétique permanent. Détermination de l'amortissement provoqué
par le mouvement thermique des particules. 12 références bibliographiques.
        (SDIT)

268. (**795**) GUMAN, W. J.
Further Comments on Ionizing Shock Waves in Monoatomic Gases.
Reply to Alpher criticism (*J. Fluid Mech.*, Vol. 2, No. 2, p. 123, 1957) to Guman
Note (*J. Appl. Phys.*, Vol. 27, p. 663, 1956), in which a technique was briefly out-
lined for determining gas dynamical parameters across either normal or oblique
stationary shock waves in the presence of ionization in monoatomic gases.

269. (**812**) HAALAND, C. M.
Confinement of Charged Particles by Plane Electromagnetic Waves in Free Space.
A survey of the present position and possibilities in this field.   (H. Gabriel)

270. (**818**) HAIN, K. and LÜST, R.
Stability of Axially Symmetrical Plasma Configuration in Volume Flow.
In German. Small perturbation techniques are used to investigate plasma configurations containing currents inside the plasma and possessing cylindrical
symmetry. The problem is reduced to an eigen-value problem. Considering a
special configuration with a relatively strong current along the axis, it is shown
that this configuration is unstable for long wavelength perturbations.

(D. Ter Haar)

271. (**820**) HAINES, M. G.
The Joule Heating of a Stable Pinched Plasma.
The hydromagnetic equations are employed to obtain the conditions necessary
for a pressure balance in a pinched discharge in ionized deuterium. The time
dependent energy equation is integrated to give the time taken to heat the plasma
by Joule heating with bremsstrahlung radiation losses only, and with a pressure
balance maintained at all times. This heating time is shown to be dependent on
the radius, line density, and final temperature of the plasma. The current density
distribution during the heating process is calculated, showing only a small diver-
gence from uniformity. The condition for no run-away electrons to be present at
any time during the heating process is shown to place a restriction only on the
minimum line density of the particles. The effects of an unbalance of pressure,
causing a change in the outside radius of the plasma during the heating process, is
discussed. Finally, the utilization of a transient energy source and its relation to
discharge parameters is considered.

272. (**822**) HAINS, F. D., YOLER, Y. A. and EHLERS, E.
Axi-Symmetric Magneto-Gas Dynamic Channel Flow.
Analysis of the channeling effect of the magnetic field produced by a circular loop
of wire on the steady state flow at low magnetic Reynolds Numbers of an electrically conducting compressible gas in a circular channel of constant radius, coaxial
with the magnetic field. Formal solutions are given for subsonic and supersonic
flow, linearized for small values of the magnetic interaction parameter. Shock-
tube investigations of wall pressures and wall temperatures are discussed.

(Aero/Space)

273. (**824**) HALL, L. S., GARDNER, A. L. and FUNDINGSLAND, O. T.
*Analysis of the Interaction of Electromagnetic Radiation with a Plasma in a
Magnetic Field.*
Equations are developed to analyse the problem of the interaction of electro-
magnetic radiation with a semi-infinite plasma in a homogeneous static magnetic
field and analytic expressions are derived describing this behaviour. Appended

also is a derivation of the plasma conductivity tensor (including effects of ion motion) for any plasma and static magnetic field geometry.

274. (**826**) HAQUES, G.
>   *Flow of a Conducting Fluid in the Presence of the Magnetic Field Created by a Line Electric Current, and its Determination by the Method of Rheoelectric Analogies.*

The steady flow of a conducting fluid in an external magnetic field is treated theoretically, the induced current being treated as a perturbation. The pressure perturbation is shown to satisfy an equation of the type of Poisson's equation, which can be solved by a resistance network analogue. This method is used to study flow in the field of a line current, and numerical results are presented graphically.

275. (**830**) HARRIS, E. G. and SIMON, A.
>   *Coherent and Incoherent Radiation from a Plasma.*

The Vlasov equations have been derived previously by starting from the Liouville equations and treating both plasma particles and electromagnetic field statistically. A by-product of this derivation was an equation for $F^\lambda(q^\lambda, p^\lambda)$, the probability density in the phase space of one of the radiation field oscillators. These functions are now used to define an entropy for the electromagnetic field. If the phases and amplitudes of all electromagnetic waves are precisely defined (coherent radiation), the field entropy is negatively infinite. Any incoherence increases the entropy. A direct consequence of the F^λ equation is that the field entropy is a constant of the motion. This is analogous to Newcomb's proof that the particle entropy is constant. It follows that incoherent radiation cannot be calculated from the Vlasov equations.

276. (**832**) HARRISON, E. R.
>   *Experiments with Plasma Beams.*

Some experiments are described in which a continuous discharge is used as a source of charged particles. The different behavior of the beams, when the pressure increases, is clearly described.

277. (**835**) HART, P. J.
>   *Effect of Gas Pressure and Cone Angle on the Velocities of Electrically Excited Shock Waves.*

Velocities of shocks from sparks between a central electrode and an outer cylindrical electrode, separated by a conical insulator, depend on the cone angle, on the nature and surface condition of the insulator, and on pressure. At low pressure ($\sim 0\cdot03$ mm Hg) the highest velocities are for large angles. Effects are explained by Joule heating and direction of magnetic field of the spark.

278. (**840**) HASIMOTO, H.
>   *Viscous Flow of a Perfectly Conducting Fluid with a Frozen Magnetic Field.*

We consider the steady, incompressible, viscous flow of a perfectly conducting fluid past bodies and show that certain surprising results can be explained as unusual interpretations of familiar solutions for nonconducting flows.

279. (**844**) HELFER, H. L.
>   *Magneto-Hydrodynamic Shock Waves.*

An interpretation of the de Hoffman-Teller shock-wave equations for an infinitely conducting medium is given analogous to the classical interpretation of the ordinary hydrodynamic shock-wave equations of Rankine and Hugoniot. Two cases of interest are considered as a consequence of this theory. It is shown that weak magnetic fields in interstellar clouds will be amplified, and, if external mechanisms are available to reduce the compressional effects of shock waves, the field will reach a value $H \sim (8\pi p)^{\frac{1}{2}}$, where p is the pressure. Also, some aspects of the internal motions of prominences are considered; it is shown that $H \sim 0.1$ gauss will yield results in accord with the observational material.

280. (859) HESS, R. V.
Some Basic Aspects of Magnetohydrodynamic Boundary-Layer Flows.
In several recent papers on magnetohydrodynamic stagnation flow, the meaning of the simplifying assumptions used has been improperly interpreted. It is shown that for the particular law of deformation of the magnetic field postulated in some papers the magnet would have to be situated in the flow away from the body to take up the induced forces resisting the flow. Conditions for the existence of magnetohydrodynamic potential flow are also discussed. Certain large differences in heat-transfer rates found in the literature are shown to be mainly due to different interpretations of re-entry conditions rather than due to more subtle reasons. A simplified approach for boundary-layer flow is developed.   (NASA)

281. (867) HINES, C. O.
On the Rotation of the Polar Ionospheric Regions.
The possibility of magnetic coupling between the polar regions of the earth's ionosphere and the interplanetary gas has led to the suggestion that the polar ionosphere may not rotate with the earth. The depth to which the effects of the interplanetary drag might penetrate is examined here with the aid of two simple models. The results are not conclusive but they do indicate that heights as low as the E region may be involved.

282. (870) HOFFMANN, F. W. and TELLER, E.
Magneto-Hydrodynamic Shocks.
A mathematical treatment of the coupled motion of hydrodynamic flow and electromagnetic fields is given. The motion is described by a plane shock wave. Various orientations of the plane, of the shock and the magnetic field are discussed separately, and the extreme relativistic and unrelativistic behaviour is examined. Special consideration is given to the behaviour of weak shocks, that is, of sound waves.

283. (873) HOH, F. C. and LEHNERT, B.
Diffusion Processes in a Plasma Column in a Longitudinal Magnetic Field.
Earlier results, by Lehnert on the diffusion processes in the positive column in a longitudinal magnetic field have been confirmed in a new series of measurements over a wide range of data. Experiments with helium, argon, krypton, nitrogen, and hydrogen are described. In the case of helium good agreement is obtained between the collision diffusion theory and the experiment up to a certain critical magnetic field. For stronger fields the potential drop along the column indicates a much higher diffusion-rate across the magnetic field than that expected from the binary collision theory. Account is taken in the theory, of the presence of molecular ions and of charge exchange collisions. Abnormal voltage characteristics indicating an increased diffusion rate above a certain magnetic field strength have also been investigated in argon, krypton, nitrogen, and hydrogen. The transition from the normal to the abnormal branch of the characteristics seems to depend neither on the length of the discharge tube nor on the length of the magnetic field, provided that these lengths exceed some fifty tube diameters. On the other hand, the transition depends upon the gas density, the nature of the gas, the tube radius, and

also slightly, upon the discharge current. The transition is also indicated by an increasing noise level above the transition point. Finally, the product of the magnetic field strength and the tube radius seems to be constant at this point.

284. (**874**) HOLTER, O., JENSEN, E., *et al.*
Theoretical Researches in Magneto-Hydrodynamics.
Researches were made in the general field of magneto-hydrodynamics by the Institute of Theoretical Astrophysics, Oslo. The subjects covered are plasma oscillations in the classical sense; general theory of wave propagation in a plasma; the form and importance of viscous forces in plasma phenomena when magnetic fields are active; plasma shock waves; and forces in a plasma conditioned by certain deviations from thermal equilibrium, in particular deviations from equipartition of kinetic energy. (ASTIA)

285. (**879**) HU, P. N.
An Outline of the Basic Theory of Magneto-Hydrodynamics.
A survey of the basic theory of magneto-hydrodynamics is given together with a review of the fundamental concepts of electrodynamics and the motion of a charged particle. The basic equations used for a viscous, heat-conducting, radiating, electrically-conducting, and compressible fluid are the Maxwell equations, the momentum equation, the continuity equation, the ideal gas law, the energy equation, and Ohm's law. The most general form of these equations is derived and then reduced to various approximate forms. The associated boundary conditions for the electric and magnetic fields, pressure, velocity, and heat energy are also derived. Solutions to several problems are noted. (ASTIA)

286. (**880**) HUBBARD, J.
The Instabilities of a Cylindrical Gas Discharge with Field Penetration.
Work in the U.S.A. has shown that a hydromagnetic model of the cylindrical gas discharge which neglects viscosity and finite electrical conductivity always predicts that the discharge will be unstable with finite field penetration when the internal and external axial fields are in the same direction. This is probably no longer so when finite viscosity and conductivity are introduced. This report describes a calculation of the stability with field penetration in which the effects of finite conductivity and viscosity are approximately taken into account. The numerical work was performed on the mercury computer and a wide range of field configurations was investigated. (TIL/MOS)

287. (**882**) HUNZIKER, R. R.
The Flow About a Charged Body Moving in the Lower Ionosphere.
Analysis using a simple gas model composed of electrons, ions, and neutral particles; a hydrodynamic description is given on the basis of Maxwell's transfer equations for a mixture. The conditions under which local statistical equilibrium can be assumed are discussed, and different approaches to determine the gas dynamic force in the subsonic, supersonic, and hypersonic cases are indicated. The reciprocal action of the flow electric field on the body is also analysed, and a formula for the resultant electric force is given. Also includes calculation of the negative potential acquired by a plane body, and discussion of the solution of the external nonlinear problem which characterizes the electric potential and the electron distribution. (Aero/Space)

288. (**885**) IAKOVLEV, L. G.
Wave-Front Velocity in Electrodynamics Containing Higher Derivatives.
The wave-front velocity in Maxwell-Lorentz electrodynamics and in the non-linear electrodynamics has been the subject of several studies. The author proposes to use the method of Levi-Civita to analyse electrodynamics with higher derivatives.

289. (**887**) Inglis, D. R.
Theories of the Earth's Magnetism.

Proposed mechanisms for generating a terrestrial magnetic field are considered for some oversimplified flow patterns in an attempt to indicate what features of the flow provide the most important possibilities for field generation. It is suggested that, without a field to absorb the energy, the flow would be accelerated indefinitely. The generating mechanisms discussed include two induction theories, the dynamo theory of Elsasser and Bullard, and the "twisted-kink" theory of Alfvén. Other mechanisms discussed depend either on the thermo-electric effect with junctions at the core-mantle interface or on a combination of thermoelectric and Hall effects in the core and mantle.

290. (**894**) Jacobs, J. A. and Obayashi, T. J.
A Dynamo Theory of Magnetic Storms.

Renewed interest in the dynamo theory of disturbances has arisen from the discovery of a conspicuous current system at the time of sudden commencement. Assuming a reasonable conductivity change it has been possible to determine a consistent wind system which can produce the current system. Agreement with data obtained from actual geomagnetic variations is satisfactory, the wind system being the combination of a diurnal and a semi-diurnal mode. (1) Magnetism, terrestrial disturbances. (2) Magnetohydrodynamics. (3) Ionospheric winds.

291. (**896**) Jancel, R. and Kahan, T.
Analysis of the Coupling of Ordinary and Extraordinary Electromagnetic Waves in a Lorentzian Plasma and its Applications to the Ionosphere.

Les Auteurs appliquent les résultats d'une précédente communication à l'analyse de la propagation des ondes électromagnétiques dans un plasma inhomogène (variation de la densité avec l'altitude) et anisotrope (présence d'un champ magnétique) ainsi qu'à l'analyse du couplage des rayons ordinaire et extraordinaire dans ce milieu.

292. (**905**) Jancel, R. and Kahan, T.
Développement d'une Solution Générale de l'Equation de Boltzmann en Présence d'un Champ Electrique et Magnétique.

Les auteurs proposent un développement général en harmoniques sphériques et en série de Fourier d'une solution de l'équation intégro-différentielle de Boltzmann pour le cas d'un plasma lorentzien soumis à l'action d'un champ électrique oscillant et d'un champ magnétique constant, compatible avec les conditions de symétrie du problème étudié.

293. (**907**) Janes, G. S.
Production of High Velocity Shock Waves and their Interaction with Magnetic Field.

Production d'ondes de choc atteignant des vitesses de 18 cm/s dans une chambre en Pyrex contenant H_2 ou D_2 fortement ionisés et soumis à un champ magnétique axial pulsé. (C.N.R.S.)

294. (**910**) Janes, G. S. and Patrick, R. M.
The Production of High Temperature Gas by Magnetic Acceleration.

A study was made of gaseous magnetohydrodynamics under conditions where the ions Larmor radius is of the order of a millimetre while the mean free path for collisions is larger, of the order of a centimetre. This requires a temperature of

10^6 °K at particle densities of a few times 10^{16} per cm³. Physical phenomena in this region are interesting for fusion power applications and have more recently exhibited possible applications in space flight propulsion.

295. **(916)** JIGOULEV, V. N.
Contribution à l'Etude d'une Espèce de Mouvements en Magnétohydromécanique.
Cas d'un écoulement plan à symétrie axiale ayant les vecteurs-vitesse perpendicu‧laires aux lignes de force du champ magnétique. 2 références bibliographiques.
(SDIT)

296. **(925)** JOHNSON, J. L., OBERMAN, C. R., KULSRUD, R. M. and FRIEMAN, E. A.
Some Stable Hydromagnetic Equilibria.
Authors obtain hydromagnetic equilibria for a variety of situations which have approximately zero pressure and uniform axial magnetic field. Criteria for ascer‑taining the stability of these equilibria are derived by means of energy principle. In particular, if helically invariant fields are present, stable equilibria with non-zero pressure and net axial current can be found. (Appl. Mech. Rev.)

297. **(934)** JUKES, J. D.
The Structure of a Shock Wave in a Fully Ionized Gas.
The structure of a plane shock wave moving through a completely ionized plasma of protons and electrons is calculated. It is assumed that the two species of particles behave as two gases, each separately in a quasi-equilibrium state corresponding generally to two different temperatures. Navier-Stokes type equations with coeffi‑cients of viscosity and thermal conductivity appropriate to the two species are solved by numerical iteration. For very strong shocks it is found that both the velocity of electrons and protons and the temperature of the protons change in a distance about twice the mean path for momentum transfer between protons in the hot (shocked) gas. The electron temperature changes in about eight of these mean free paths, causing a relatively wide zone of hot electrons at low density ahead of the usual velocity shock-front. The density and temperature gradients of protons and electrons create an electric field.

298. **(936)** JUNGCLAUS, G.
Laminar Boundary Layers in Magnetohydrodynamics.
In German. Laminar boundary layers are treated in incompressible and electric‑ally conducting liquids under the influence of magnetic fields. The pressure normal to the boundary layer is taken as constant so that the usual boundary-layer theory is applicable. A very simple solution is given for strong magnetic fields. The conditions are given for similarity solutions for arbitrary strength of the magnetic field. Some of these solutions are also presented. (Appl. Mech. Rev.)

299. **(938)** JUNGCLAUS, G.
Laminare Grenzschichten in der Magnetohydrodynamik (Les couches limites laminaires en magnétohydrodynamique).
Etude des couches limites laminaires des écoulements de fluides incompressibles à conductivité électrique sous l'influence de champs magnétiques. Conditions requises pour que la pression verticale par rapport à la couche limite soit constant et permette l'établissement sous une forme habituelle d'une théorie de la couche limite. Solutions dans les cas de champs magnétiques intenses et quelconques.
5 références bibliographiques. (SDIT)

300. **(944)** KAGAN, U. M.
Le Mouvement des Ions dans le Plasma.
Données expérimentales sur le mouvement des ions obtenues par une méthode spectroscopique et interprétation analytique. 15 références bibliographiques.
(SDIT)

301. (**945**) KAHALAS, S. L.

Magnetohydrodynamic Wave Propagation in the Ionosphere.

The propagation of magnetohydrodynamic waves in a compressible fluid is discussed with reference to the ionosphere. An investigation of the damping for a gas of finite conductivity shows that different wave modes may be heavily attenuated in certain directions of propagation. Also, the slow wave of the magneto-acoustic mode is shown to exhibit preferentially less damping for propagation along the magnetic field lines. An examination of the Hall and electron pressure terms shows that they may be neglected for low enough wave frequencies. The coupling of electromagnetic to magnetohydrodynamic waves at a plasma-vacuum boundary is considered. The coupling coefficient is estimated to be 1 per cent.

302. (**946**) KAHALAS, S. L. and KASHIAN, H. C.

On the Approach of Electrons to Equilibrium.

Author computes change of electronic distribution function with time until Maxwellian distribution is reached. Author also shows how specific cases may be treated when electrons attach to neutral molecules, forming negative ions.

303. (**947**) KAHN, F. D.

Velocity Changes of Charged Particles in a Plasma.

Mechanisms for the acceleration and deceleration of fast charged particles traversing a plasma are discussed. The deceleration mechanisms are (i) the excitation of a plasma excitation increasing exponentially with time by a stream of fast protons acting coherently, and (ii) the production of a wake in the plasma by single fast particles acting incoherently. The acceleration mechanism is the action of the fluctuating electric field in the plasma. The deceleration mechanism (i) is shown to require a velocity spread of the protons which is much smaller than the difference between electron and proton mean velocities, so much so that the mechanism is unlikely in astronomical applications. Deceleration mechanism (ii) is shown to be sufficiently weak for quite a low level of plasma excitation to accelerate fast particles. (A. Herenberg)

304. (**948**) KAHN, F. D.

The Collision of Two Ionized Streams.

It is shown that the interpretation of two streams is arrested, as a rule, not because of individual collisions between particles belonging to opposite streams, but because the whole system of charged particles is unstable. The smallest wavelength of an unstable oscillation is λ_{min}, where

$$\lambda_{min} = \sqrt{\left(\frac{\pi m_0 U^2}{2Ne^2}\right)\left(1 - \frac{U^2}{c^2}\right)^{-\frac{3}{4}}}.$$

Here $\pm U$ are the velocities of the undisturbed streams, and N is the density of electrons in each. A further calculation for the non-relativistic case deals with the amplification of the plasma oscillations present in two colliding streams. It is shown that these grow rapidly and that $\tau_{crit} \sqrt{(m_0 V^2/\pi Ne^2)}$ is the distance of interpretation achieved before the counterstreaming of the electrons is brought to a halt. The value of τ_{crit} depends only insensitively on the ratio of the internal plasma energy densities T_{pl} to the kinetic energy densities T_{kin} in the streams. For example, $\tau_{crit} = 9 \cdot 0$ when $T_{pl} : T_{kin} = 1 : 10$ and $\tau_{crit} = 19 \cdot 0$ when $T_{pl} : T_{kin} = 1 : 10^5$.

305. (**950**) KAITMAZOV, S. D. and PROKHOROV, A. M.
   Paramagnetic Resonance of the Free Radicals Obtained by Freezing a Plasma of H_2S.
Authors describe, with details, the results of the observation of the paramagnetic resonance spectrum of the dissociation products of the H_2S, previously passed into a quartz tube. (The power of the discharge was 120 W and the frequency was 4 Mc/s.)

306. (**951**) KAKUTANI, T.
   Effect of Transverse Magnetic Field on the Flow due to an Oscillating Flat Plate.
Determination of the velocity distributions, magnetic field, and related quantities (such as pressure, electric field and current density) for the flow of an incompressible, viscous, and electrically conducting fluid due to an infinite oscillating flat plate in the presence of a transverse magnetic field. General solutions are derived, and some special cases corresponding to limiting values of various parameters are discussed. It is shown that each of the velocity distributions and other related quantities consists of two different oscillations whose decaying factors differ from the corresponding wave numbers. (Aero/Space)

307. (**953**) KANAWAL, R. P.
   Flow Behind Shock Waves in Conducting Gases.
In this paper it is proved that in addition to generating vorticity, the shock waves in conducting gases generate electric current also. Secondly, it is shown that the expression for vorticity in conducting gases, in contrast to non-conducting gases, depends on the thermodynamic behaviour of the fluid. Furthermore, an interesting relation between the normal components of the vorticity and current density is discovered.

308. (**954**) KANEKO, S.
   The Maximum Disturbance Growth Rate for an Unstable Plasma Column.
Derivation of a dispersion relation for a self-pinched plasma column enclosed by a conducting wall for the case of a model with both surface sheet current and uniform volume current. The maximum disturbance growth rate for the instability is calculated on the basis of this dispersion relation. It is shown that both the uniform volume current and longitudinal magnetic flux outside the plasma column decrease the stability and make the growth rate faster, the effect of the magnetic flux being larger. (Aero/Space)

309. (**959**) KANTROWITZ, A. R.
   Application of Magnetohydrodynamics to Astronautics.
Magnetohydrodynamics has two presently visible applications to space flight. First, it seems quite likely that MHD methods of electrical propulsion will be very useful in the provision of exhaust jets in the specific impulse range 1500–5000 seconds. At higher specific impulses the competitive position between ion rockets and MHD is still to be determined. A discussion of various MHD devices to produce thrust in various specific impulse ranges will be given. Second, MHD plays a dominant role in the dynamics of interplanetary gas masses. Thus, the dynamics of interplanetary gas clouds will be important because these gas masses will transport the highly energetic particles which are dangerous to human beings. Experimental reproduction of the fast shock waves present in the interplanetary plasma will be discussed. Some preliminary laboratory results obtained with shock waves in the velocity range of 50 cm per microsecond will be given.

310. (**960**) KANTROWITZ, A. R.
   Flight Magnetohydrodynamics.
A brief discussion is given of the possible flight applications of magnetohydrodynamics and the conditions under which they might be practical.

311. (**961**) KANTROWITZ, A. R.
Magnetic Field Alters Aerodynamic Forces.

High temperature gases around bodies at very high speed are ionized and conducting. It is possible to alter the aerodynamic forces and heat transfer in the vicinity of a body in such a flow by introducing a magnetic field force. The magnetic Reynolds Number was derived, which plays the same role in Magneto-hydrodynamic flow as the Reynolds Number does in normal viscous flow. The same relationship indicated the need for large amounts of electrical energy to produce the necessary magnetic field strengths. This requirement led to the speculation of operating a moving conductor (coil) as a self-exciting generator to supply the electrical energy. The characteristics of such a generator are described. The flight regimes of magnetohydrodynamics in terms of altitude and velocity are described, by defining further relationship between magnetic force and dynamic pressures.

312. (**962**) KANTROWITZ, A. R. and JANES, G. S.
On Magnetohydrodynamic Propulsion.

USAF-supported study of the properties of plasma accelerators employing electrodes considered as circuit elements. It is shown that these devices have very low effective characteristic impedances, and that provision must always be made for recovery of the magnetic field energy before the plasma is expelled. These considerations, plus the assumption of electrode arc voltage drops, lead to a theorem relating the minimum instantaneous power, the efficiency, and the specific impulse.
(Aero/Space)

313. (**963**) KANTROWITZ, A. R. and PETSCHEK, H. E.
Introducing Magnetohydrodynamics.

Discussion of research being done in magnetohydrodynamics for possible applications to a space propulsion system, re-entry drag devices, and electric power generators. (IAS)

314. (**964**) KANTROWITZ, A. R., PATRICK, R. M. and PETSCHEK, H. E.
Collision Free Magnetohydrodynamic Shock Waves.

AFOSR-supported investigation in which it is assumed that the dissipation in a collision-free shock produces a random distribution of magnetohydrodynamic waves. These waves are then treated as the fundamental particles of the plasma. A rough kinetic theory is developed for estimating the heat conduction coefficient due to the waves. Using this heat conduction coefficient, the shock thickness is estimated to be about four times the characteristic ion Larmour radius. This prediction is in rough agreement with experimental results obtained in a MAST device. (Aero/Space)

315. (**971**) KAPLAN, S. A.
The Effect of Anisotropic Conductivity in a Magnetic Field on the Structure of a Shock Wave in Magnetohydrodynamics.

Assuming that all parameters change only in the x-direction, the anisotropy of the electrical conductivity causes an appreciable increase of thickness of the wavefront of a gas magnetic shock wave when the wave-front is inclined to the x-axis. The wave-front thickness is proportional to the square of the magnetic field intensity.

316. (**975**) KAPUR, J. N.
Superposability in Magnetohydrodynamics, II.

The results of Pt. I are used to discuss: (1) superposability of wave motions; (2) hydrostatic equilibrium of magnetic stars; (3) effects of viscosity in axially symmetric hydromagnetic flows; (4) axially symmetric force-free fields; (5) general force-free fields.

317. **(978)** von Kármán, T.
Applications of Magnetofluidmechanics.
Starting out as an "ideal intellectual playground for aerodynamicists and mathematicians," it now promises many practical applications in three different areas—flow modifications, containment, and propulsion.

318. **(980)** von Kármán, T.
Some Comments on Applications of Magnetofluidmechanics (Commentaires sur les applications de la mécanique magnétique des fluides).
Aperçu des applications possibles de l'aéromagnétodynamique: modifications d'écoulement, retenue des gaz ionisés très chauds et propulsion par ions, par accélération de particules chargées de grosseur colloidale et par accélération de plasmas. (SDIT)

319. **(981)** von Kármán, T.
Magnetofluidmechanics: A General Lecture.
Author's preference for use of term magnetofluidmechanics instead of magnetohydromechanics: résumé of main principles; applications of the science in astronautics. (TIL/MOS)

320. **(983)** Kash, S. W.
Electrical Propulsion Systems.
Discussions on space travel frequently mention ion-gun, plasma-jet, or fusion propulsion. These refer to suggested systems in which electric and magnetic forces are used to obtain thrust on a space vehicle. The purpose of this paper is to note and compare some of the physical concepts underlying these systems. The discussion includes a brief description of a hydromagnetic propulsion device.
(Lockheed)

321. **(984)** Kash, S. W.
The Pinch Tube as a Device for Plasma Propulsion.
One of the devices under study for the acceleration of plasma consists in essence o a linear pinch tube open at one end. The device can be used as a magnetic driver at one end of a shock tube or as a means of obtaining plasma thrust. For the latter application the system operates into a vacuum and a small amount of gas released at the closed end triggers the discharge and provides the plasma propellant. This report provides an estimate of the energy and impulse delivered to the plasma by such a device. (Lockheed)

322. **(985)** Kash, S. W.
Magnetically Driven Shock Waves: Experiments at Lockheed Missile Systems Division.
As part of a preliminary investigation of certain aspects of partially ionized gases at LMSD, a hydromagnetic shock tube similar to that originally used by Fowler has been employed. Activities so far have been confined to observation of the effects of magnetic propulsion on shock velocity, the development of instrumentation for measuring shock velocities, and an examination of the visible radiation emitted by the luminous shocks produced. (Lockheed)

323. **(987)** Kash, S. W., Gauger, J., Starr, W. and Vali, V.
Velocity Measurements in Magnetically Driven Shock Tubes.
In magnetically driven shock tube systems, the discharge is arranged in such a manner that the strong magnetic fields induced by the discharge current are used to impart energy or motion to the gas in the discharge region. Such systems provide a means of producing relatively high-temperature ionized gases, and should be useful for the studies of the properties of these gases. To determine the temperatures obtainable with air, a series of shock pulse velocity measurements were made over a range of densities. (Lockheed)

324. (**988**) KATO, Y.
   Interactions of Hydromagnetic Waves.
L'auteur considère des mouvements rectilignes d'un fluide compressible douné de
conductivité électrique infinie. Aprés avoir rappellé les équations de choc, il
étudie l'interactions d'une onde de choc et une discontinuité de contact, et
l'interaction d'une onde de raréfaction et une discontinuité de contact.

325. (**989**) KATO, Y. and TANIUTI, T.
   Hydromagnetic Plane Steady Flow of Compressible Ionized Gases.
The MHD in compressible gases of infinite conductivity is discussed under the
assumptions that the flow is isentropic and steady and that the directions of flow
velocity and of magnetic field are in the same plane. The hyperelasticity conditions
for the special case in which the flow is parallel to the direction of magnetic field are
analysed in detail.

326. (**991**) KAUFMAN, A. N.
   Effect of Charge Separation on Plasma Diffusion in a Strong Magnetic Field.
A low-density, fully ionized plasma, confined by a strong magnetic field, diffuses
across the field primarily by means of ion-electron collisions, the flux being proportional to the density gradient. Ion-ion collisions, on the other hand, produce a
flux two orders higher in the spatial variation of density. But the latter effect may
be comparable to the former, because of the large ion-electron mass ratio. It is
found that the ratio of the flux from ion-ion collisions to the flux from ion-electron
collisions is of the order of $(m_i/m_e)^{\frac{1}{2}}(R_i/D)^2$, where R_i is the ion gyration radius, and
D a characteristic distance of the density variation. Upon taking into account the
ion-electron collisions, and electron-electron collisions, it is found that the ratio
of the flux from like-particle collisions to that from unlike-particle collisions is of
the order of $(R_e/D)^2$, and is therefore generally quite negligible.

327. (**993**) KAUFMAN, A. N.
   Plasma Viscosity in a Magnetic Field.
The viscosity of a fully ionized plasma in a magnetic field is analysed from two
points of view: first, from a consideration of particle orbits; and second, from the
solution of a simplified Boltzmann equation. These semiquantitative methods are
studied in order to clarify the behaviour of the viscosity coefficients.

328. (**995**) KELLOGG, P. J.
   *Possible Explanation of the Radiation Observed by van Allen at High Altitudes in
   Satellites.*
Suggestion is made that the radiation at high altitudes results from the decay
electrons and protons from neutrons produced in the earth's atmosphere by cosmic
rays and stored in the earth's magnetic field. Order of magnitude estimates for
the densities to be expected are presented. Only scattering loss is considered.
Using a lifetime of 3×10^9 sec for loss through scattering, an upper limit of 10^{-2}
electrons/cm³ near the earth and $0{\cdot}05 \left(\dfrac{R_E}{r_0}\right)^3$ electrons/cm³ at large distances r_0 in
the equatorial plane is obtained. The proton density at large distances is
$0{\cdot}03 \left(\dfrac{R_E}{r_0}\right)^2$ cm⁻³, for a lifetime of 10^{12} sec. If plasma accelerations are not important, then the spectrum of electrons will be that of neutron beta decay. The
protons are produced by fast neutrons coming directly from nuclear stars and their
spectrum will be approximately that of the protons from stars. The electron density
is sufficient to give a counting rate a few times larger than is observed, while the
proton density is sufficient to give a counting rate 10^4 times higher than the observed
lower limit. The lifetimes of stored particles are therefore probably much less than

those given by scattering. There should be a strong latitude effect which is roughly estimated as proportional to $\cos^6\lambda$. Reasons are given for believing that collective effects will reduce the density below this near the poles. (ASTIA)

329. (**996**) KELLOGG, P. J. and LIEMOHM, H.
    Instability of Contrastreaming Plasmas.
The problem of instabilities in colliding hydrogen beams, which has been treated by Kahn and Parker in the special case of zero temperature is solved for the non-zero temperature case by taking Maxwell distributions for the equilibrium density functions. At sufficiently high temperature it is found that the random thermal motion will prevent growing oscillations. The boundary between the stable and unstable regions is plotted as a function of energy and density parameters. Certain phenomena associated with solar particle streams are discussed in terms of these results. (Physics Abstr.)

330. (**997**) KEMP, N. H.
    On Hypersonic Blunt-Body Flow with a Magnetic Field.
USAF-sponsored analysis of the effect of a magnetic field on the inviscid flow near the stagnation point of a blunt axisymmetric body in the practical case of small magnetic Reynolds Number. The method of analysis was introduced by Lighthill and assumes a spherical shock shape and incompressible flow. A prediction is made for the change in heat transfer and pressure drag caused by the field. (Aero/Space)

331. (**999**) KEMP, N. H.
    On Hypersonic Stagnation-Point Flow with a Magnetic Field.
Interest has recently arisen in magnetohydrodynamic effects in high-speed flight, especially at the nose of blunt bodies where ionization and gas conductivity are likely to be large enough so that a magnetic field can affect the flow. The purpose of this note is to present the effect of a magnetic field on the inviscid flow at the stagnation point of a blunt axisymmetric body in the practical case of small magnetic Reynolds Number. This will make possible a prediction of the change in heat transfer and pressure drag caused by the field. The method used to analyse the flow is that introduced by Lighthill, where a spherical shock shape and incompressible flow are assumed. (Aero/Space)

332. (**1000**) KEMP, N. H. and PETSCHEK, H. E.
    Theory of the Flow in the Magnetic Annular Shock Tube.
A theoretical description is given of the properties of the gas flow in the magnetic annular shock tube. This shock tube uses a magnetic field to drive a shock wave through an annular region, producing a very high temperature plasma. It is shown that this particular configuration allows a fairly precise calculation of the flow parameters. Numerical calculations of the significant flow properties for a complete range of the initial field strength and orientation have been made and are presented graphically. (ASTIA)

333. (**1001**) KEMP, N. H. and PETSCHEK, H. E.
    Two-Dimensional Incompressible Magnetohydrodynamic Flow Across an Elliptical Solenoid.
An analysis has been made of the two-dimensional flow of an incompressible, constant-conductivity fluid through an elliptically-shaped solenoid containing a constant magnetic field directed normal to the flow plane. The effect of both Hall current and ion slip has been included in the Ohm's Law used for the fluid. The analysis was performed by means of a perturbation procedure in two parameters,

one being the magnetic Reynolds Number R_m and the other the ratio of magnetic force per unit area to dynamic pressure, S. Calculations were carried through first order in each parameter, and closed-form analytic expressions were obtained for the force and moment on the solenoid, the current density, stream function, magnetic field and other pertinent physical quantities. It was found that in zero order, there is a force but no moment on the solenoid. In the first order in S, where the flow field changes but the magnetic field does not, there is a moment and a force, the latter being antiparallel to the zero order force. In the first order in R_m, where the magnetic field changes but the flow field does not, there is a moment, but no force. Thus, through first order, the lift to drag ratio is the same as in zero order. Graphs are presented which illustrate some of the effects of angle of attack, fineness ratio of the ellipse, Hall current and ion slip on the forces and moments.

334. (1002) KENDALL, P. C.
Hydromagnetic Oscillations of a Rotating Liquid Sphere.
The equation governing hydromagnetic oscillations of a liquid globe rotating in a uniform magnetic field is solved in cylindrical polar co-ordinates and the solution adapted to satisfy special boundary conditions. The period equation is obtained in the form of an infinite determinant. Numerical approximations, in the case when the coriolis force appreciably affects the motion, indicate that convergence is likely and confirm the order of magnitude of the period as obtained by Cowling (1) for the case of a liquid and a gaseous globe.

335. (1004) KERREBROCK, J. L.
Similar Solutions for Boundary Layers in Constant Temperature Magneto-Gasdynamic Channel Flow.
Deals with the problem of the growth of the boundary layers upon the accelerator walls; states that similar solutions exist for thermal and viscous boundary layers if M_∞^2 is small and the wall temperature is constant. By utilizing the concept of local similarity, it may be possible to extend the results to non-zero Mach numbers.

336. (1005) KERREBROCK, J. L.
La Diffusion dans les Gaz Neutres ou Ionisés a Gradients de Pression Extrêmement Elevés.
Etude de la diffusion dans les circonstances où—contrairement aux cas où l'on s'est placé jusqu'ici—la diffusion due à un gradient de pression est le facteur dominant parce que le gradient de pression et la diffusion qui en résultent sont normaux à la vitesse de l'écoulement principal, comme c'est le cas pour l'écoulement tourbillonnaire où il peut y avoir de forts gradients de pression produits par les vitesses tangentielles alors que la vitesse radiale est petite. Application à deux exemples: 1° les deux gaz en diffusion sont neutres (séparation des isotopes de l'uranium); 2° diffusion des électrons dans un gaz ionisé (problème aéromagnétodynamique). 7 références bibliographiques.   (SDIT)

337. (1007) KHALATNIKOV, I. M.
On Magneto-hydrodynamic Waves and Magneto Tangential Discontinuities in Relativistic Hydrodynamics.
Derivation of equations for the velocity of waves in the presence of a magnetic field making an arbitrary angle with the direction of propagation of the waves in a medium with an arbitrary equation of state. The properties of purely magnetic tangential discontinuities in relativistic hydrodynamics are also discussed.
                                                                    (Aero/Space)

338. (1008) KIEPENHEUER, K. O.

The Observability of Hydromagnetic Phenomena in the Sun.

Diagnostic information is limited by the restrictions of current observational techniques. Further measurements are required in particular of the temporal changes in solar phenomena, and of their field structures.

339. (1009) KIHARA, T.

Macroscopic Foundation of Plasma Dynamics

Discussion of basic equations, energy and momentum theories, and the law of similarity for plasma dynamics. The condition under which the current equation reduces to the usual form is considered, and one-dimensional transverse waves are treated as an example. Quasi-stationary phenomena are examined as a particular case; and it is shown that one of the usual basic equations of magnetohydrodynamics, Ohm's Law, does not hold in the simple case and must be revised. An axially symmetric solution is obtained and applied to a self-pinched column whose stability is explained in an elementary manner.   (Aero/Space)

340. (1013) KILLEEN, J., GIBSON, G., and COLGATE, S. A.

Boundary-Layer Formation in the Pinch.

A study is made of various processes that occur prior to the pinch effect when an electric field is applied to a deuterium gas. The variables of the problem are the percentage of ionization, the electron and ion temperatures, the resistivity of the gas, and the current density. A one-dimensional problem is considered in which the above variables are determined as functions of one-space dimension and the time. The equations determining these variables are: the heat developed and the current flow through the gas equals the rate of increase of the internal energy of the plasma; the equation describing the rate of ionization; the equation describing the rate of transfer of energy from electrons to ions; and the electromagnetic field equations. These equations are a generalization of the plasma equations solved by Wyld and Neston in which that spatial dependence is included, i.e., a current layer is calculated instead of assuming a constant current. The equations are solved numerically using an IBM704 computer.

341. (1014) KIM, Y. B. and PLATNER, E. D.

Flux Concentrator for High-Intensity Pulsed Magnetic Fields.

Use of multiturn coil structure in the production of several hundred kilogauss pulsed fields is discussed with specific emphasis on coil life. The magnetic force that shortens the coil life is reduced by introducing a flux concentration device. Into the multiturn coil is inserted a rigid, slotted metal slug that generates induction current in such a way as to shift the magnetic flux from the multiturn to the central vacuum region and serves as a flux concentrator. Electromagnetically and mechanically this scheme is a convenient synthesis of the multiturn and single turn coils. The advantage of this scheme is most apparent for tape-wound coil structures, and a quantitative analysis of the flux pattern relevant to this coil system is given. An analog computer is employed in solving the time dependence of the field. The results are documented by experimental tests carried out with a $3000\mu F$, 4 kV capacitor bank.   (ASTIA)

342. (1019) KIRKO, I. M.

Phénomènes Magnétohydrodynamiques à l'Echelle Mondiale.

Principes généraux et possibilités d'applications pratiques.   (SDIT)

343. (1020) KIRZHNITS, D. A.

Correlation Energy of an Inhomogenous Electron Gas.

The influence of a non-uniform distribution of particles on the electron correlation energy is investigated. It is found that this influence is so large that the corresponding expressions obtained on the basis of the uniform distribution mode 1.2 are not valid for a real system. The principal part of the correlation energy of the electrons in the crystalline lattice (without consideration of interaction with the vibration of the latter) has been found for high pressures, low temperatures, and large values of the nuclear charge. Estimates are given for the correlation energy of uncompressed matter.

344. **(1022)** KISCOVODSKY, A. D.

Contribution à la Théorie des Ondes Superficielles en Magnétohydrodynamique.
Détermination du champ des vitesses, du champ magnétique, du profil et de la vitesse de l'onde superficielle; relation entre ces facteurs et le champ magnétique interne. 5 références bibliographiques. (SDIT)

345. **(1023)** KISELEV, M. I.

Sur le Calcul des Ondes de Choc dans l'Hydrodynamique Magnétique.
In Russian. On montre le procédé de simplification des calculs des paramètres des ondes en question par abaissement d'une unité de l'ordre des équations algébriques se rencontrant dans les travaux de Hoffmann et Teller (*Phys. Rev., U.S.A.*, 1950, 80, 692) et de Helfer (*Astrophys. J., U.S.A.*, 1953, 117, 177). (C.N.R.S.)

346. **(1024)** KISELEV, M. I. and TSEPLIAEV, V. I.

Oblique Shock Waves in a Plasma with Finite Conductivity.
The structure of an oblique shock wave in a plasma with finite conductivity is considered neglecting its viscosity and thermal conductivity. The conditions of applicability of the approximations are obtained. An estimate of the width of the wave front is given. The limiting angle for the propagation of an oblique shock wave is obtained in a plasma of infinite conductivity.

347. **(1032)** KLIMONTOVICH, Y. L.

Charged Particle Energy Losses due to Excitation of Plasma Oscillations.
Beam electrons and plasma oscillations are regarded as two subsystems. A kinetic equation describing the interaction between the beam and plasma is obtained on the assumption that the beam does not change the properties of the plasma and that the plasma state is specified by its equilibrium parameters. The expression for the decelerating force calculated on the basis of this equation includes losses due to electron-electron collisions as well as those due to excitation of plasma oscillations. A more general case is considered in which neither of the subsystems is in thermal equilibrium. The solution of a set of non-linear equations for the beam electron distribution function and the electric potential is considered for this particular case. The results are used to account for the rapid energy transfer from beam electrons to plasma electrons, which was first observed by Langmuir.

348. **(1033)** KLIMONTOVICH, Y. L.

Relativistic Transport Equations for a Plasma.
A connexion is established between the definitions of the probability of a state and the distribution function given by various authors based on the transport equation for a charged particle in an external electromagnetic field. A random function which determines the number of particles in a volume element in phase space is introduced. The electromagnetic field strengths, or the numbers of oscillators, are also considered as random functions. The set of equations for these functions serves as the basis for deriving a chain of equations connecting moments of the random functions or the corresponding distribution function of different orders. Through an approximation to this chain of equations we obtain a set of relativistic self-consistent equations. Relativistic expressions are given for the dispersion equations for the transverse and longitudinal plasma waves. A variational principle for a relativistic plasma is considered.

349. (**1035**) KLIMONTOVICH, Y. L.
Space-Time Correlation Functions for a System of Particles with Electromagnetic Interaction.

A closed set of equations is obtained for the random functions $Nqp(t)$. This set determines the number of particles at a given point p, q in phase space-time t, and the vector and scalar potentials A, q. Chains of coupled equations for the moments of the random functions have been obtained by averaging from this set of equations. The equations are solved under the assumption that the random process in the system is stationary and uniform. Expressions are obtained which permit determination of space-time correlation functions of currents, densities, and vector potentials from a knowledge of simultaneous (equilibrium) correlation functions. Expressions are obtained for correlation functions of "extraneous" random electromagnetic field and currents. In the absence of space dispersion these expressions become the familiar formulae derived by Leontovich and Rytov phenomenologically. An explicit expression is obtained for the complex dielectric constant of the medium.

350. (**1036**) KLINE, M.
Magneto-Hydrodynamics.

The object of the Magneto-hydrodynamics research group of the Division of Electromagnetic Research Group of the Institute of Mathematical Sciences NYU during the period 1.10.1953–31.10.1956, has been to investigate the motion of charged particles of an ionized fluid in the presence of external electric and magnetic fields. (TIL/MOS)

351. (**1040**) KOGAN, M. N.
Les Ondes de Choc en Magnétohydrodynamique.

Etude de l'onde de choc en fonction des caractéristiques du courant et du champ magnétique. 3 références bibliographiques. (SDIT)

352. (**1041**) KOGAN, M. N.
Ondes de Choc dans la Gazdynamique Magnétique.

In Russian. Etude analytique de la nature des polaires de choc pour les différents paramètres du courant et du champ magnétique. (C.N.R.S.)

353. (**1042**) KOGAN, M. N.
Magnetodynamics of Plane and Axisymmetric Flows of a Gas with Infinite Electrical Conductivity.

Translation. Analysis showing that there exist two hyperbolic flow regimes, one of which occurs at subsonic velocities. In this flow regime, shock waves are inclined upstream. For certain values of the ratio between magnetic and hydrodynamic pressures, there exists an elliptic type of flow at supersonic velocities. In this regime weak shock waves do not occur, but strong shock waves are present whose angles of inclination start from the perpendicular. The simple waves for the hyperbolic regimes are constructed and the solutions are presented for the problem of flow around bodies in the linearized and second-order approximations. (Aero/Space)

354. (**1047**) KOLB, A. C.
Magnetically Confined Plasmas.

The propagation of high-velocity shock waves in an axial magnetic field generated by single-turn coils connected in parallel to a condenser bank is investigated. Time-resolved photographs show that the plasma behind the shock front is driven away from the tube walls by the magnetic pressure. This compression heats the ionized gas and maintains a high shock velocity during the transit of the front through the coil. The compressed plasma appears to be stable and undergoes radial oscillations that follow the current oscillations. The interpretation and significance of these observations are controlled. Thermonuclear fusion research is discussed.

355. (**1049**) KOLB, A. C.
Production of High-Energy Plasmas by Magnetically Driven Shock Waves.
High-voltage (5–100 kilovolts) with peak currents in 0·3 to 5 microseconds have been used to produce shock waves in deuterium plasmas. The discharge is struck in a transverse magnetic field and the resultant Lorentz force drives the plasmas out of the region of the discharge into a quartz side arm. Velocity measurements of the magnetically driven plasma are discussed in relation to the parameters of the discharge. These measurements indicate that deuterium plasma with ion energies 100 eV/ion at densities 5×10^{16} ions/cm^3 can be produced by this method.

356 (**1052**) KOLB, A. C.
High Temperature Plasmas.
(Article in Report of NRL Progress, June, 1957.) Methods have been developed for producing very high temperatures with shock waves. The methods involve the acceleration of a plasma by the interaction of magnetic fields with a high-current, pulsed gas discharge. With these techniques, ion energies greater than 100 eV/ion have been produced in a deuterium plasma.   (TIL/MOS)

357. (**1058**) KOLLER, A.
The Confinement of Plasma by a Magnetic Field.
The fundamental characteristics of plasma flow, based on the behaviour of a single particle, are outlined. The various methods of applying magnetic fields, their limitations, power requirements and possibilities, for controlling dimensions and continuity of the plasma are described. Some examples are given of time dimensions and temperatures involved in these processes.

358. (**1059**) KOLOMENSKII, A. A.
The Radiation emitted by an Electron Moving Uniformly in an Electron Plasma Situated in a Magnetic Field.
An electron plasma in a magnetic field behaves like a double-refracting gyrotropic crystal possessing an axis of symmetry directed along the magnetic field H, and the value of the refractive index depends on the frequency of the propagated wave, the angle between the direction of propagation and the direction of H, and the so-called gyroscopic frequency, and differs for the ordinary and extraordinary waves. The condition for occurrence of the Cherenkov effect, which cannot be brought about in electron plasma without the presence of a magnetic field since the phase velocity would have to be greater than the velocity of light, is found to be related to both the anisotropic and to the gyrotropic medium under consideration.   (TIL/MOS)

359. (**1060**) KOLOMENSKII, A. A. and FONG SOY-CEN
Cyclic Motion of Charged Particles in an Electric Field.
Expressions are obtained for the cyclic motion of charged particles in an electric guide field. This field can be produced by a system of appropriate lenses (weak-focusing or strong-focusing). Resonance acceleration is considered; in particular we consider phase stability (phase focusing). This is analogous to the usual phase focusing in magnetic field. An investigation is made of the effect of electro-magnetic radiation (including quantum fluctuations) on the motion of electrons in the electric field. The case in which part of the particle trajectory is in an electric field and part in a magnetic field is also treated.

360. (1063) KOMEL'KOV, V. S.

Selfconstricting Discharges in Deuterium at High Rates of Current Growth.

Results of investigation of selfconstricting discharge are described for rates of current size in the range 7×10^{11} to $1 \cdot 4 \times 10^{12}$ amp/sec, and for current amplitudes up to 2×10^6 amp. The initial deuterium pressure in the chambers varied between $0 \cdot 1$ and 10 mm of Hg. The highest gas temperature that was possibly attained was about 200 eV.

361. (1065) KONTOROVICH, V. M.

On the Interaction between Small Disturbances and Discontinuities in Magnetohydrodynamics and on the Stability of Shock Waves.

Translation. Presentation of a geometrical method for the construction of waves (reflected and refracted) diverging from a surface of discontinuity and produced by the incidence of a plane monochromatic wave on a plane stationary surface of discontinuity in a medium described by the equations of magnetohydrodynamics. On the basis of the results obtained, the stability of shock waves with respect to splitting up is investigated for obliquely incident disturbances. The change in frequency resulting from the interaction of small disturbances with shock waves is considered. (Aero/Space)

362. (1066) KONTOROVICH, V. M.

Stability of Shock Waves in Relativistic Hydrodynamics.

Stability against perturbations of the discontinuity surface is investigated for shock wave in an arbitrary medium, described by relativistic equations for an ideal fluid.

363. (1067) KONYUKOV, M. V.

Non-linear Langmuir Electron Oscillations in a Plasma.

An exact solution has been obtained for the non-linear oscillations of the electron density in a plasma at zero electron temperature. The initial conditions necessary for these oscillations are determined.

364. (1068) KONYUKOV, M. V.

On the Theory of a Positive Column in a Longitudinal Magnetic Field.

This article considers decantactions of the positive columns in a gas discharge located in an external magnetic field directed along the discharge axis.

365. (1076) KOROBEINIKOV, V. P. and RIAZANOV, E. V.

Solution des Equations de la Magnétohydrodynamique pour un Gradient de Température Egal à Zéro.

Etude des mouvements unidimensionnels d'un gaz parfait, conducteur d'électricité, à ondes cylindriques et planes, compte tenu d'une conductibilité infinie et en négligeant la viscosité, le champ magnétique étant perpendiculaire à la trajectoire des particules du gaz. 2 références bibliographiques. (SDIT)

366. (1079) KOTCHINA, N. N.

Solutions Exactes des Equations de Mouvement en Magnétohydrodynamique, à la Limite des Mouvements Analogiques.

Application de la théorie des écoulements des fluides instationnaires unidimensionnels aux problèmes de magnétohydrodynamique. 5 références bibliographiques. (SDIT)

367. (1080) KOTCHINA, N. N.

Shape-Preserving, Exact Solution of the Equations of Magnetohydrodynamics.

Author considers one-dimensional, unsteady motion of an ideal electrically conducting gas in presence of magnetic field; a particular shape-preserving solution for the case of planar symmetry and one for the case of planar or axial symmetry are given. The conditions at the shock-wave front and the equation of a line of weak disturbance are written for both cases. More complicated solutions of the form of the foregoing are considered and analogy with the case in which the magnetic field is absent is examined. (R. Nardini)

368. (**1083**) Koulikovski, A. G.
Mouvements à Déformation Homogène en Magnétohydrodynamique.
Étude analytique des mouvements d'un milieu visqueux conducteur de chaleur à conductivité électrique finie. 3 références bibliographiques. (SDIT)

369. (**1084**) Koulikovski, A. G. and Lubimov, G. A.
Les Problemes les plus Simples Comportant une Onde de Choc Ionisant un Gaz Dans un Champ Electromagnétique.
Cas d'une onde de choc forte se propageant à travers un gaz froid non conducteur et se trouvant dans un champ électromagnétique: ionisation du gaz et interaction avec le champ. Cas d'un écoulement autour d'un dièdre. 3 références bibliographiques. (SDIT)

370. (**1085**) Koulikovski, A. G. and Lubimov, G. A.
Remarques Concernant la Structure d'une Onde de Choc Magnétohydrodynamique Orthogonale.
Structure d'une onde de choc avec thermo- et électro-conductivité mais sans viscosité. 3 références bibliographiques. (SDIT)

371. (**1089**) Kovrizhnykh, L. M.
Effect of Inelastic Collisions on the Velocity Distribution of Electrons.
The velocity distribution function for electrons in a weakly ionized plasma was found, taking into account inelastic collisions. It is shown that the inelastic collisions lead to a sharp drop in the distribution function for electron energies exceeding the excitation (or ionization) energy.

372. (**1090**) Kovrizhnykh, L. M.
Velocity Distribution of Electrons in a Strong Electric Field.
A method is developed for determination of a non-stationary solution of the Boltzmann equation in the case of strong electric fields. An expression is derived for the electron distribution function in a completely ionized plasma located in a strong electric field. It is shown that in a first approximation the distribution is Maxwellian, superimposed on the general translation motion of the electron gas. In a first approximation the translational velocity increases linearly with time whereas the temperature remains constant.

373. (**1091**) Kovrizhnykh, L. M.
Motions of a Plasma Loop in an Axially Symmetric Magnetic Field.
Problems related to the dynamics of a plasma loop in an inhomogeneous axially symmetric magnetic field.

374. (**1092**) Kovrizhnykh, L. M.
Oscillation of a Completely Ionized Plasma in a Cylindrical Cavity.
Within the framework of magnetohydrodynamics, under the assumption of ideal conductivity, a study has been made of oscillation of a cylindrical cavity in a completely ionized plasma located in a magnetic field. It is shown that such a system is stable and that under certain conditions no waves can propagate along the cavity.

375. (**1093**) Kovrizhnykh, L. M.
On the Dynamics of a Bounded Plasma in an External Field.
Some problems relating to the dynamics of a quasi-neutral plasma formation situated in the field of a plane electromagnetic wave are considered. The method of successive approximations is employed. It is shown that within the limits of the assumptions underlying the analysis a plasma bunch tends to spread out.

376. (**1098**) Kraichnan, R. H.
Relation of Fourth to Second Moments in Stationary Homogeneous Hydromagnetic Turbulence.

The hypothesis that the fourth moments of the field amplitude distribution are related to the second moments as in a normal distribution is examined to determine whether it is consistent with the equations of motion for stationary, homogeneous, and incompressible hydromagnetic turbulence. An application of this hypothesis to the two-point, two-time amplitude distribution of the velocity field and magnetic field leads to a gross violation of energy conservation at high Reynolds numbers. This result holds also in the non-magnetic case. An estimate of the magnitude of the violation yields a rate of energy generation of order $E = E_i/\tau_i$, where E_i is the energy contained in the inertial range and τ_i is a period characteristic of modes in the inertial range. The results obtained are discussed in relation to a recent theory of turbulence formulated by Chandrasekhar.

377. (**1101**) Kraus, L. and Yoshihara, H.
Electro-Gasdynamic Motion of a Charged Body in a Plasma.

Analysis of some aspects of the coupling between fluid motion and the electrostatic properties of a plasma. The basic equations are described and the theory illustrated by treating the very simple case of supersonic flow of a plasma past a two-dimensional slender dielectric body. (IAS)

378. (**1102**) Kraus, L. and Watson, K. M.
Plasma Motions Induced by Satellites in the Ionosphere. Appendix—Damping when the Density is High.

Analysis on the electrohydrodynamic phenomena associated with the high-velocity motion of a charged body in a plasma. It is shown that the effect of the electric field due to the charge on the body in inducing collective motion leads to similar results both for high- and low-density gases. By using a linearized theory, formulas are obtained for the electrohydrodynamic drag and for the increased ionization in the Mach cone behind the body. (IAS)

379. (**1107**) Krook, M.
Structure of Shock Fronts in Ionized Gases.

Author shows how equations for the electric field and moments of the ion and electron velocity distribution functions can be reduced to a determinate set of ordinary differential equations by assuming that the distribution functions are the sum of two modified Maxwell distributions. A formal method of solution is described, and results are obtained for moments of first and second order. A discussion of these and of solutions for moments of higher order is left to a subsequent paper. (P. Saffman)

380. (**1108**) Krumigue, U.
Rotation d'une Sphere Conductrice dans un Fluide Visqueux Conducteur en Présence d'un Champ Magnétique.

Calcul du moment de freinage provoqué par le champ magnétique. 5 références bibliographiques. (SDIT)

381. (**1110**) Kruskal, M. D. and Kulsrud, R. M.
Equilibrium of a Magnetically Confined Plasma in a Toroid.

General properties of plasma in static equilibrium are derived from equations of magnetostatics. These properties are expressed as integrals over surfaces of constant pressures, which are shown to be topologically toroidal under general assumptions. A variational principle for such equilibrium conditions is derived. One of its consequences is characterization of equilibria by value of certain invariants. Conditions are then obtained for steady state of a plasma slowly diffusing across a magnetic field out of a topologically toroidal region. (Appl. Mech. Rev.)

382. (**1113**) KRUSKAL, M. D. and TUCK, J. L.
The Instability of a Pinched Fluid with a Longitudinal Magnetic Field.
Analysis of the stability of a pinched plasma equilibrium with a longitudinal magnetic field superimposed on the characteristic azimuthal magnetic field of the pinch current. The linearized solutions are developed as helical perturbations of the plasma surface. The behaviour of these is given for the different cases of a uniform longitudinal field, a longitudinal field zero inside the plasma, and for helices of the same and opposite sense to the helix which describes the total magnetic field. It is concluded that the longitudinal field has the effect of stabilizing short-wave perturbations, but that some long-wave perturbations remain unstable no matter how large the externally imposed longitudinal magnetic field.

(Aero/Space)

383. (**1114**) KRUSKAL, M. D., JOHNSON, J. L., GOTTLIEB, M. B. and GOLDMAN, L. M.
Hydromagnetic Instability in a Stellarator.
Authors investigate the stability of a column of plasma in the presence of a large magnetic field parallel to the column and its discharge current. For small perturbations, various helicoidal unstable modes are found. The external conductors have negligible effects on the stability of the column. In the case of the stellarator, a gradual twist of the cylindrical co-ordinates must be introduced. This leads to a critical discharge current for the appearance of helicoidal unstable motions. The experimental results are in good agreement with the theory for the first mode. The stability of higher modes is affected by the current distribution, and there is no evidence that they have serious effects. (R. Betchov)

384. (**1116**) KRUSKAL, M. D. and OBERMAN, C. R.
On the Stability of Plasma in Static Equilibrium.
Criteria for stability of a system of charged particles are derived from Boltzmann equation in small m/e limit. These criteria are obtained from examination of variation of energy due to a perturbation subject to constraint that all time-independent constants of motion have their equilibrium values. Authors find that first-order variation of energy vanishes, while second-order variation yields quadratic form in displacement variable. Positive definiteness of form is sufficient condition for stability. Authors also state theorem comparing their stability criterion with that of conventional hydromagnetic theory where heat flow along magnetic lines has been neglected. (Appl. Mech. Rev.)

385. (**1120**) KRZYWOBLOCKI, M. Z. and NUTANT, J.
On the Similarity Rule in Magneto-Gasdynamics.
Adiabatic flow is considered to be a flow of an inviscid, non-heat conducting fluid with heat addition by means of sources, i.e. injection of heat. If, in addition, the flow takes place in an electromagnetic field, the sources of heat may be referred additionally to the Joule heat. This case is considered in the present paper. The governing fundamental equations are: the first law of thermodynamics, Newton's equation of motion, pressure-density-entropy relation, Bernoulli's equation of energy, Maxwell's equation and Ohm's law. The two dimensional equations of the velocity potential and of the stream-functions are transformed into the hodograph plane. Assuming a simplified pressure-density relation, a similarity rule is derived in the flow in question. This is applied to some particular problems.

386. (**1123**) KUDRIAVTSEV, V. S.
Energy Diffusion of Fast Ions in an Equilibrium Plasma.
In Russian. Author considers the problem of the energy diffusion of fast ions injected into an equilibrium plasma. The initial conditions for the energy distribution of the injected ions is a monochromatic distribution with the values exceeding the mean thermal energy in the plasma. The distribution over the

velocity directions is isotropic. The kinetic equation for a completely ionized plasma in the absence of external field is taken from the well-known Landau paper (*Zh. Eksp. Teor. Fiz.* **7**, 203, 1937). The influence of the mutual particle collisions is assumed to be small and the time-variation of the distribution function of these particles is determined by the collisions with the ions and electrons of the equilibrium plasma distributed according to a Maxwellian law. This leads to an expression for the particle flux in the velocity space and to an equation for the energy density distribution. The latter equation is solved by means of the Laplace transform and an approximate assumption for the form of the energy density. The final expression for the energy density describes the energy distribution of the ions injected into the plasma being in an equilibrium state. The result for an arbitrary initial distribution can be found by using the superposition principle since the equations are linear. (M. Krzywoblocki)

387. (**1125**) KULIKOVSKII, A. G.
   On the Flow of a Conducting Fluid Around a Magnetized Body.
In Russian. When a stream in which there is no magnetic field passes over a magnetized body, it cannot penetrate the region occupied by the magnetic field if the electrical conductivity of the field is infinite. In this case, there will be a cavity outside the body and the free streamline will cover both the magnetized body and the cavity. In this paper, author first discussed the fundamental equations for such a free streamline problem. Since such a free streamline problem does not give a unique solution, author imposed some additional conditions on the magnetic field in order that the solution of the problem may be uniquely determined. Finally, author gave some simple examples of the free-stream problems such as (1) flow around a plane magnetic dipole perpendicular to the flow, (2) supersonic flow around a wedge along whose surface a current of constant density flows parallel to the edge of the wedge, and (3) supersonic flow around a cone along whose surface flows a current of constant density directed perpendicularly to the cone generators. (S. Pac)

388. (**1126**) KULIKOVSKII, A. G.
   Study of Riemann Waves in Magnetohydrodynamics.
Study of Riemann waves in magnetohydrodynamics for the case of arbitrary field distribution in relation to the wave front leading to new mechanic effects.

(IAS)

389. (**1128**) KULIKOVSKII, A. G. and LYUBIMOV, G. A.
   The Simplest Problems Involving Shock Waves Which Ionize Gases in an Electromagnetic Field.
By considering in some detail the shock wave associated with a moving piston, relations are obtained between the speed of the piston, the wave velocity and the difference of densities on either side of the shock front. Results are applied to shock waves propagating about a wedge.

390. (**1129**) KULSRUD, R. M.
   Effect of Magnetic Fields on Generation of Noise by Isotropic Turbulence.
Lighthill's (1952) and Proudman's (1952) results on the generation of aerodynamic noise by isotropic turbulence are generalized to include magnetic effects. It is found that if there are only turbulent magnetic fields present and no constant magnetic field, the magnetic turbulence generates sound very efficiently and increases considerably the generation of sound by kinetic turbulence. If there is a constant magnetic field, hydromagnetic waves are generated instead. For the modified sound mode of the hydromagnetic waves, a result similar to the case of no general field is obtained. No energy is generated into the Alfvén and modified Alfvén waves unless the energy density of the magnetic field is greater than the energy density of the kinetic turbulence. Expressions are found for the rate of noise

generated per unit mass, and these results are applied to the problem of heating the chromosphere and the corona.

391. (**1130**) KULSRUD, R. M.
General Behaviour of Hydromagnetic Fluids.
Eléments de la théorie de l'aéromagnétodynamique. (SDIT)

392. (**1132**) KUNEN, A. E. and McILROY, W.
The Electromagnetic Pinch Effect for Space Propulsion.
The phenomenon of the electromagnetic pinch effect is used to accelerate ionized gases for space propulsion. Electrical energy, initially stored in capacitors, is discharged across two nozzle-shaped electrodes wherein the radial pinch is converted to axial motion of the affected gases instead of confinement at the axis. The gas dynamics of a pinch using the hydrodynamical model of a "magnetic piston" driving a shock wave, is combined with the electrodynamics of the circuit to calculate the behaviour of the discharge. Experiments on three different electrode designs are discussed and the results obtained are compared with the calculated values. The results of the study are applied to one particular space propulsion system.

393. (**1133**) KUNKEL, W. B.
Some Considerations Concerning Magnetohydrodynamic Exhaust Control for Rocket Guidance.
Some of the requirements for magnetohydrodynamic steering of rocket exhausts are discussed. It is concluded that the present exhaust temperatures (near 3000°K) are too low and the gas densities (near atmospheric) too high to make the scheme more than barely marginal even if adequate seeding with cesium is assumed. It is further found that the presence of halogens in the exhaust renders the method impossible because of the large fraction of alkali halides formed. (ASTIA)

394. (**1139**) LADYJENSKAIA, O. A. and SOLONNIKOV, V. A.
Etude de la Possibilité de Résolution des Problemes Instationnaires de la Magnéto-hydrodynamique.
Etude de l'interaction du champ magnétique et d'un fluide conducteur, visqueux et incompressible, en mouvement. 1 référence bibliographique. (SDIT)

395. (**1140**) LADYJENSKII, M. D.
Problèmes de l'Ecoulement autor de Corps en Magnétohydrodynamique.
Ecoulement autour d'un corps soumis à un champ magnétique interne provoqué par un courant de fluide conducteur, pour un nombre de Reynolds magnétique infini ou très élevé. Détermination des forces magnétiques agissant sur le corps. Cas d'un champ électrique interne superposé à un champ magnétique. 4 références bibliographiques. (SDIT)

396. (**1142**) LAI, W., SLOAN, D. H. and TALBOT, L.
Preliminary Design and Tests of a Plasma Jet.
Preliminary design and test results are presented for a plasma jet which incorporates rotation of the gas which surrounds the arc and issuing of the plasma through a hollow electrode. A combination of a $\frac{3}{4}$-in.-diam. cored C cathode and a water-cooled Cu anode in the form of a truncated cone were used. Between the cathode and anode are three water-cooled electrodes which are electrically isolated and neutral in operation. Argon passes through a Cu tube with four in-line holes oriented in a manner to cause the gas to rotate. The results of tests under three different conditions are tabulated. Potential difference, current, and arc length are interdependent as with a free arc.

397. (**1150**) LANDSHOFF, R. K. M.
> *Scaling Laws as an Aid to Experimental Studies.*

Quantities which describe a flow pattern can be combined to form expressions having the dimensions of frequencies, velocities, lengths or energies. The article lists those combinations which are of significance in magnetohydrodynamics and certain dimensionless ratios between them. Flow patterns can differ in scale and still be similar in structure provided these ratios are the same. (Lockheed)

398. (**1151**) LANDSHOFF, R. K. M., ed.
> *Magnetohydrodynamics.*

I. A selection of well-integrated essays from the Lockheed Missiles and Space Division sponsored Magnetohydrodynamics Symposium. The volume covers both theoretical work and laboratory experiments. (Lockheed)

> LANDSHOFF, R. K. M.
> *La magnétohydrodynamique.*

II. Aperçu général sur la magnétohydrodynamique ou science des fluides réagissant à l'action d'un champ magnétique, ce qui nécessite qu'ils soient hautement conducteurs et contiennent par conséquent une densité suffisante d'électrons rapides, ceux-ci pouvant provenir soit de l'ionisation du fluide par la chaleur, soit d'une source envoyant des électrons dans un fluide froid. Domaines de la magnétohydrodynamique. (SDIT)

399. (**1152**) LANDSHOFF, R. K. M., ed.
> *The Plasma in a Magnetic Field: A Symposium on Magneto-Fluid-Dynamics.*

Volume of 130 pages records ten papers which were presented at a Lockheed-sponsored symposium in December of 1957. Section 1 presents two theoretical papers which treat the plasma from a kinetic point of view. Chandrasekhar gives a careful treatment of adiabatic invariants in the motions of charged particles, a subject of great importance in the design of magnetic mirrors and mirror-type machines. Rosenbluth presents a hydromagnetic basis for the treatment of plasmas and shows these equations to be valid even when effective particle collisions are so infrequent as to be completely negligible. Section 2 has four papers on the confinement and instabilities of a plasma interacting with a magnetic field. Colgate discusses the mechanism of ion acceleration by dynamic pinch instabilities which led to the observation of large bursts of "false" neutrons. Karr presents experimental studies of the pinch effect done at Los Alamos Scientific Laboratory. Data are given for the stability studies of the straight pinch and the current distribution within the pinch discharge. Weibel gives an interesting analysis of the possibility of the confinement of a plasma column by radiation pressure. Part of this treatment includes the study of charge separation. Parker considers some plasma instabilities in an interplanetary magnetic field. Section 3 presents four papers dealing with the fluid mechanics aspects of transferring energy from the magnetic field into the plasma. Blackman and Niblett give interesting experimental results using an electrodeless discharge hydromagnetic shock tube. Shocks up to Mach 30 are produced and ionization times measured for argon and air. Kash *et al.* give some data on velocity measurements obtained in a T-type and a conical electrode-type shock tube. Scott *et al.* present interesting results of channeling a strong shock by means of an external magnetic field. In the given configuration, the magnetic interaction did not contribute any noticeable heating of the shock-produced plasma. Liepmann gives the main features and results for the Couette flow problem of a real gas in the presence of a magnetic field and briefly discusses hydromagnetics of Stokes flow. This small volume is a worthy addition to the fast-growing literature of magneto-fluid-dynamics. (R. Gross)

400. (**1155**) LANDSHOFF, R. K. M.
   A Review of Magnetohydrodynamics.
This review covers the fundamental laws; the modification of Ohm's law; such magnetohydrodynamic phenomena as equilibrium, stability, steady flow, small amplitude waves, shock waves, transient flow, flow stability, and turbulence; and large mean free path. (Lockheed)

401. (**1159**) LARENZ, R. W.
   On the Magneto-Hydrodynamics of Compressible Media.
In a consequent theory of the compressible plasma, the charge separation must be taken into account, especially in the case of macroscopic velocities comparable to or larger than the velocity of sound. Charge separation is considered for a two-component plasma, and the system of magneto-hydrodynamic equations is so transformed as to contain only two quantities. (TIL/MOS)

402. (**1160**) LARENZ, R. W.
   Plasma Flows of Large Amplitude and Charge Separation.
To justify the incorporation of charge separation in the magneto-hydrodynamics of compressible media, one-dimensional sound wave-like motions are examined. Specific flows are obtained, described as "ion-" and "electron-sound" of large amplitude and periodic and aperiodic structure which, under suitable conditions, may lead to local virtually complete charge separation. Pressure forces were found to be important in limiting the charge separation, which is determined as a function of temperature. (TIL/MOS)

403. (**1162**) LARISCH, E. and SHEKHTMAN, I.
   Propagation of Detonation Waves in the Presence of a Magnetic Field.
It is shown that relativistic detonation wave in a magnetic field possesses properties similar to those of the ordinary waves. Solutions of the equations at the discontinuity are presented for the relativistic and non-relativistic cases.

404. (**1169**) LAZUKIN, V. A.
   Oscillations of a Plasma in a Magnetic Field at Frequencies Close to the Cyclotron Frequency.
A description is given of a method used to observe oscillations of a plasma in a longitudinal magnetic field at frequencies several times smaller than the ion cyclotron frequencies. The method makes it possible to observe the oscillations spectrum in the form of a series of narrow lines with very high signal-to-noise ratio. It is suggested that the observed oscillations are analogous to the wave known from the hydromagnetic analysis.

405. (**1170**) LAZUKIN, V. A.
   Some Features of Multiplet Ferromagnetic Resonance in Ferrites.
Preliminary results are presented of the observation of multiplet ferromagnetic resonance in inhomogeneously magnetized single-crystal and polycrystalline ferrite samples. The inhomogeneous magnetized samples required for the observation of this effect were produced mainly by the inhomogeneity of the demagnetizing fields of the investigated samples. Some features are noted of the absorption spectra observed under various conditions.

406. (**1171**) LEADON, B. M.
   Plane Couette Flow of a Conducting Gas Through a Transverse Magnetic Field.
The general equations of a plane Couette flow of an electrically conducting, variable property gas in the presence of a uniform transverse magnetic field are analysed under several sets of simplifying assumptions. Significant effects upon the

skin friction are found in all cases, but heat transfer is found to be affected only through property value variations and the recovery factor not affected at all. Strong effects upon both velocity and temperature profiles are evident in all cases and a "separation" profile occurs at strong values of the magnetic parameter. When interpreted as a boundary layer flow with plate spacing varied arbitrarily so as to preserve constant mass flow, the results for a constant property, variable conductivity fluid are in good agreement with a boundary layer analysis. This assumption may be of use in obtaining preliminary estimates of variable property flows. (Convair)

407. (**1177**) LEEUW DE, J. H.
The Interaction of a Plane Strong Shock Wave with a Steady Magnetic Field.
Appendix A, B: One-Dimensional Flow with Momentum Loss for an Ideal Gas.
Appendix C: Description of Some Interaction Experiments.
Theoretical investigation of some aspects of the interaction of a magnetic field and the flow of ionized and electrically conductive argon, as it may be produced in the shock tube by strong shock waves. Three different configurations are considered. The axial components of the ponderomotive forces that act on the gas as a result of its motion through the magnetic field are calculated for each of the configurations considering the shock tubes as having non-conductive walls. The behaviour of the gas under the action of the ponderomotive forces is determined by considering the flow to be one-dimensional. Results indicate that the use of ideal gas relations is inadequate to give even an approximate indication of the real flow. Includes determination of limiting conditions beyond which shock waves cannot be reflected off the magnetic field. It was found that, at a given pressure level, reflected shock waves can occur only over a limited range of Mach Numbers of the incident shock wave. (Aero/Space)

408. (**1181**) LEHNERT, B.
Magnetohydrodynamic Waves in Liquid Sodium.
Liquid sodium, because of its higher electrical conductivity and lower density, is more suitable than mercury for magnetohydrodynamic experiments. Torsional waves in liquid sodium have been generated in a cylindrical vessel with the axis parallel to a homogeneous magnetic field, and resonance phenomena have been investigated at constant frequency and variable magnetic fields strength. The agreement between theory and experiment is satisfactory. It is shown that even with sodium, damping plays an important role under laboratory conditions. The calculations of this paper are also used to improve the results of earlier investigations with mercury.

409. (**1182**) LEHNERT, B.
Magnetohydrodynamic Waves under the Action of the Coriolis Force, I.
In the sun, magnetohydrodynamic waves with wavelengths larger than about a hundredth of the solar radius will be strongly influenced by the Coriolis force if a dipole field with a polar strength of less than 25 gauss is assumed. For small amplitudes, a plane Alfvén wave will be split up into two circularly polarized, transverse waves, travelling with velocities C_1 and C_2 in the direction of the wave normal and with moduli $|C_1| > |V_z| > |C_2|$, where $V_z = V \cos \psi$, $V = B(\mu\rho)^{-\frac{1}{2}}$ being the Alfvén velocity and ψ the angle between the wave normal and the magnetic field, B. Further, there is no equipartition between the kinetic and the magnetic energies. These facts will modify Alfvén's theory of sunspots as far as the periods are concerned; and disturbances of large linear dimensions will be distorted, owing to dispersion. Alfvén's conclusions based on the geometry of the solar magnetic field and his hypothesis on the creation of disturbances due to the

presence of instability regions in the solar core are not affected by the discussion of this paper.

LEHNERT, B.
Magnetohydrodynamic Waves under the Action of the Coriolis Force, II.
The phase velocity of a single plane magnetohydrodynamic wave in a rotating liquid is independent of the amplitude. The non-linear interactions between the components of the spectrum of a complex travelling disturbance vanish only in a non-rotating fluid without dissipation. A criterion for the approximate validity of the principle of superposition is given for small values of the Coriolis force and the dissipation. In a rotating medium in a magnetic field a disturbance will not necessarily travel along the magnetic field lines. The anisotropic group velocity for a wave packet is given. In solar physics the effects of anisotropic dispersion and non-linearity are significant for disturbances with wavelengths of the order of a hundredth of the solar radius, if a dipole field with a polar strength of less than 25 gauss is assumed.

410. (**1183**) LEHNERT, B.
    The Decay of Magneto-Turbulence in the Presence of a Magnetic Field and Coriolis Force.
The final period of decay of magneto-turbulence in an external, homogeneous magnetic field is considered and it is shown that it develops pronounced axisymmetric properties, turbulence elements with finite wave numbers in the direction of the field being damped strongly under normal physical conditions. The turbulence consists of aperiodic motions as well as wave motions. An introduction of an angular velocity, inclined to the field, destroys the axisymmetry and modifies the damping effects and periodicity. The influence of the magnetic field on the damping is counteracted by the Coriolis force. A linear stationary theory on the action of the field gives results consistent with those of the theory of decay. From the results of both theories an explanation is given of the observed inhibition of turbulence in mercury by a magnetic field.

411. (**1195**) LENCHEK, A. M.
    Radiowave Propagation in Interplanetary Magnetic Fields.
Certain solar and interplanetary magnetic fields and electron densities are suggested as measurable by means of the rotation of the plane of polarization of radiowaves. A convenient source of polarized radiowaves might be the Crab Nebula. The magnitude of the rotation is calculated for several possible models of a general solar field and for a corpuscular beam. Numerical estimates indicate that, particularly in the case of a non-turbulent solar beam, measurable effects may be obtained. The polarization of the Crab Nebula as a function of wave frequency is discussed. The theory of the Faraday effect for the general case of magnetic field arbitrarily oriented with respect to the direction of propagation is developed.

(ASTIA)

412. (**1197**) LEONTOVICH, M. A. and OSOVETS, S. M.
    On the Mechanism of Current Constriction in High-Current Gas Discharges.
A theory is given of the mechanism of the current constriction caused by electrodynamic forces.

413. (**1201**) LEWELLEN, W. S.
    An Inviscid Boundary Layer of Magnetohydrodynamics.
A boundary-layer approximation for fluids with large electrical conductivities is applied to the two-dimensional, steady, inviscid, incompressible magnetohydrodynamic equations for the case of a uniform magnetic field parallel to the free stream. Two approaches to the solution of the magnetic boundary layer are used. In the first, the approximate integral method is used to derive equations analogous

to the von Kármán integral momentum equation of viscous theory. These equations are integrated for flow of the type $U_1 = Cx^n$. In the second approach the exact magnetic-boundary-layer equations are transformed, for similar flows, into a system of ordinary differential equations. The solution of these equations is found in the form of a power-series expansion in a parameter equal to the Alfvén speed divided by the free-stream velocity. Numerical results are given for several cases of similar flow. In sub-Alfvénic flow, evidence points to a boundary layer growing in the direction opposite to the flow.

414. (**1202**) Li, H., Michelson, I. and Rabinowicz, J.
Studies in Magneto-Aerodynamics. I: One-Dimnesional Flows. II: Stability of Laminar Boundary Layer.

Examination of the governing equations of magneto-aerodynamics for the weak interaction approximation. It is found that, for the case where $R_v R_H \ll 1$, it is possible to treat the magneto-aerodynamic interaction as a simple additional body force. The approximate equations for weak interaction are derived and applied to several one-dimensional flows including the propagation of small disturbances and the one-dimensional channel flow. The neutral stability of the boundary layer for a flat plate in the presence of a magnetic field is determined. Results indicate that the application of a magnetic field is unstabilizing in the case of the boundary layer flow with a transverse magnetic field fixed relative to the plate.

(Aero/Space)

415. (**1206**) Lin, S. C.
Note on a Class of Exact Solutions in Magneto-Hydrodynamics.

Paper shows how the partial differential equations governing the magneto-hydrodynamic flow of an incompressible fluid can be simplified for a particular class of solutions. For these solutions the velocity and magnetic fields, and the pressure gradient are allowed to vary in a general manner with time and one space co-ordinate, but can only vary in a linear way with the other two space co-ordinates. A simple non-magnetic example of this type of motion is steady laminar flow about a rotating disc, where the velocity components take on a variation in the direction normal to the plate, but have only linear variations with radius. Author states that some specific solutions to this set of magneto-hydrodynamic equations are being obtained and will be published later. (R. Siegel)

416. (**1207**) Lin, S. C. and Cambel, A. B.
Magnetohydrodynamic Flow Regimes

Some flow parameters are derived for simple cases and the associated flow regimes delineated. The parameters include magnetic Mach number, magnetic Mach angle and the Cowling number (ratio of Alfvén velocity to flow velocity, squared).

417. (**1208**) Lin, S. C. and Lamb, L.
Electrical Conductivity of Thermally Ionized Air Produced in a Shock Tube.

The electrical conductivity of shock-heated air at equilibrium temperature from 3500°K to 6200°K, and at densities of the order of 0·01 NTP, has been measured, using the shock wave–magnetic field interaction technique. (Cornell Aer. Lab.)

418. (**1210**) Lindberg, L., Witalis, E. and Jacobsen, C. T.
Experiments with Plasma Rings.

Presents measurements of transient magnetic flux carried by a ring shaped plasma ejected from a coaxial plasma gun across a static radial magnetic field.

(C. Morgan)

419. (**1212**) Linhart, J. G.
Accelerated Self-Constricted Electron Streams in Plasma.

Analysis considering the mechanism of radial oscillations in a neutralized cylindrical electron stream of an accelerating electric field. The method is based on the two-fluid model of plasma. Analytical expressions for amplitude oscillations and numerical solutions for large amplitudes are derived. It is found, when electron–positive ion collisions are taken into account, that for dense streams in low electric fields the radial oscillations (pinch oscillations) can destroy the streaming character of the electron flow and thus prevent its acceleration. (IAS)

420. (**1213**) LINHART, J. G.
Plasma Confinement by External Magnetic Fields.
The energy loss due to particle losses from a magnetic bottle are calculated. These are much greater if "flute instabilities" can form, which they cannot in a cusp geometry. For a stable system, the particle loss is shown to be negligible for a D-T reactor at a temperature of 10^9 °K. The conditions under which runaway electrons can be produced are derived. Equations for wave propagation on a cylinder of plasma are obtained for the three cases in which the confining field is longitudinal, azimuthal and helical.

421. (**1221**) LIUBARSKII, G. J. and POLOVIN, R. V.
The Disintegration of Unstable Shock Waves in Magnetohydrodynamics.
Magnetohydrodynamic shock is known to be unstable if the magnetic field is normal to the shock and its strength lies within the region $c_2\sqrt{4\pi\rho_2} < H_x < 4c_2\sqrt{4\pi\rho_2}$, where c_2 and ρ_2 are the acoustic speed and the density of the flow upstream of the shock. The present paper is an extension of the previous work and deals with the disintegration of such an unstable shock where the magnetic field has only a weak component tangential to the plane of the shock. A first-order approximation with respect to the weak tangential component of the magnetic field was carried out. The result shows that the initial shock wave splits, in addition to a contact surface, into four discontinuities: a fast and a slow magnetoacoustic shock travelling downstream, an Alfvén discontinuity, and a fast magnetoacoustic shock travelling upstream. The distances between these discontinuities grow continuously in time. The process of disintegration of the initial shock is accompanied by an increase in entropy. Following these arguments, the discontinuities formed from the disintegration of the initial shock are shown to be stable. (C. Chang)

422. (**1223**) LIUBARSKII, G. J. et POLOVIN, R. V.
Dissociation des Ondes de Choc Instables en Magnétohydrodynamique.
Etude du mécanisme de la dissociation de l'onde en une série d'ondes comportant les ondes magnétoacoustiques. 12 références bibliographiques. (SDIT)

423. (**1224**) LIUBARSKII, G. J. and POLOVIN, R. V.
Simple Magnetosonic Waves.
In Ukrainian. It is shown that, just as in ordinary gasdynamics, the phase velocity of simple magnetosonic waves increases as the density increases under compliance with $[v_{\rho\rho}]_s > 0$. This fact is used for a qualitative investigation of time variation of simple waves. Conditions are found for formation of discontinuities, which agree with a known gasdynamics criterion, too. It is shown that self-similar waves are always rarefaction waves. Time dependence of density is given in a Lagrangian representation. (P. Schwaar)

424. (**1226**) LOCK, R. C.
The Stability of the Flow of an Electrically Conducting Fluid Between Parallel Planes under a Transverse Magnetic Field.
The stability under small disturbances is investigated of the two-dimensional laminar motion of an electrically conducting fluid under a transverse magnetic field. It is found that the dominating factor is the change in shape of the undisturbed velocity profile caused by the magnetic field, which depends only on the

Hartmann number M. (Hartmann number $M = \mu Ha \times \sqrt{(\sigma/\rho\nu)}$, where $H =$ magnetic field, $\mu =$ magnetic permeability, $\sigma =$ electrical conductivity, $\nu =$ kinematic viscosity, $2a =$ distance apart of parallel planes.) Curves of wave number against Re for neutral stability are calculated for a range of values of M; for large M values the calculations are similar to those which determine the stability of ordinary boundary-layer flow. The critical Re is found to rise very rapidly with increasing M, so that a transverse magnetic field has a powerful stabilizing influence on this type of flow. (TIL/MOS)

425. (**1227**) LODIJENSKY, M. D.
Ecoulement Hypersonique Autour de Corps en Magnétohydrodynamique.
Equations générales. Ecoulement autour d'un dièdre et d'un cone. 5 références bibliographiques. (SDIT)

426. (**1229**) LONG, R. R.
Steady, Finite Motions of a Conducting Liquid.
In certain cases of steady motion of a conducting fluid in a magnetic field the primitive equations may be integrated once, yielding a second order, partial differential equation in the stream function. This equation is highly non-linear in general but for certain choices of basic flow and magnetic fields it is tractable. Several arbitrary functions of integration have to be evaluated to make the analysis useful. This may be done in a region that remains undisturbed. A short discussion is given to suggest a procedure for deciding in a special case whether this undisturbed region is upstream or downstream. (ASTIA)

427. (**1233**) LOOS, H. G.
The Punch Method of Compressing, Heating and Confining a Plasma.
A method of compression, heating and confinement of a plasma by means of a suddenly applied magnetic field of external origin is explored. The basic cylindrical configuration does not show any instabilities in the hydrodynamic approximation. The number N_i of ions per unit length along the tube is shown to be related to the amount of separation between plasma and field that is achieved in times small compared with the decay time of the field. Furthermore, this number N_i determines how many large angle collisions an ion will undergo with other ions during the decay time. Order of magnitude calculations have been made of the energy required for heating by isentropic compression and of the energy and voltage required for shock heating. (ASTIA)

428. (**1234**) LOOS, H. G.
Some Dynamics Problems of the Punch Method of Heating and Acceleration of Plasmas.
A few dynamics problems encountered in punch discharges are discussed. The fully ionized plasma is supposed to interact with the magnetic field only at the plasma boundary; the analysis is limited to time intervals in which the effect of ion-ion collisions may be neglected. The type of discharge for the basic cylindrical punch geometry depends solely on two non-dimensional parameters. A scaling law is derived for changes for which these two parameters remain the same. For compressions or expansions that take place in a time short compared with the ion-ion collision time, but which diffraction pattern and of the X-ray line are used as reference angle (or wave-length) positions. Certain disadvantages are also pointed out: (1) the lattice parameter so determined refers necessarily to the centroid of the crystal pattern, (2) in order to keep the Bragg law simple and to avoid double-valued lattice parameters, the centroid proposal implies that X-ray wavelengths in general should refer to the centroid of the respective lines, and (3) there is an inherent experimental imprecision in the determination of the

173

centroid of any line or pattern having long tails that fade gradually into the ubiquitous background. The third point is argued qualitatively in terms of the general signal-to-noise ratio. This inherent imprecision is largely avoided if the peak position of the line is used as the reference position (defined as the intersection of the line profile with the curve drawn through the bisecting points of the horizontal chords of the line) and if the parameter position of the crystal pattern is taken as the bisector of the chord. These reference positions also avoid the Bragg law complication.

429. (**1238**) LOUGHHEAD, R. E.
Solution of Problems Involving the Hydromagnetic Flow of Compressible Ionized Fluids.
The characteristic forms of the hydromagnetic equations for a compressible fluid are examined from the viewpoint of obtaining by the method of finite differences numerical solutions for continuous initial value problems involving unidimensional motion of the fluid.

430. (**1241**) LOW, F. E.
A Lagrangian Formulation of the Boltzmann-Vlasov Equation for Plasmas.
Development of a variational principle for the Boltzmann-Vlasov equation for an ionized gas in an electromagnetic field. (IAS)

431. (**1242**) LOWRY, E. S.
Geometrical Representation of the Maxwell Field in Minkowski Space.
The electromagnetic field tensor of a classical particle is associated with the orientation and density of a family of two-dimensional surfaces radially distributed about the world line of a particle in Minkowski space.

432. (**1245**) LUDFORD, G. S. S.
The Structure of a Hydromagnetic Shock in Steady Plane Motion.
This paper considers the transition solutions (depending on one co-ordinate x only) of the equations of steady plane motion of an electrically conducting perfect viscous gas in the presence of a magnetic field in its own plane, on the basis of classical continuum theory.

433. (**1246**) LUDFORD, G. S. S.
The Propagation of Small Disturbances in Hydromagnetics.
Paper deals with the propagation of small initial disturbances in a conducting gas under the influence of a uniform external magnetic field. The starting point is the usual system of equations of magneto-gasdynamics, with the coefficients μ (permeability), ε (di-electric constant) and σ (conductivity) being constant and the charge density different from zero. Introducing a deviation from a given uniform state and neglecting squares, author obtains a system of nine-first-order linear partial differential equations. The first problem solved is that of plane waves, with the initial set splitting into two sets, leading to a quartic and a quintic for the frequency. From the roots, three give pure decay, and the remaining six three possible modes of propagation of sinusoidal disturbances (one is an Alfvén wave). As the next item author shows that the general linearized equations can be split into two sets of four and five, which lead to partial differential equations of the order two and four, respectively. The boundary-value problem of standing waves in the fluid confined in a rectangular box made of a perfectly conducting material is discussed next. Three types of waves appear: those corresponding to an infinity of frequencies associated with the Alfvén velocity, and two others distinguished by their symmetry properties. The distributions of frequencies are sketched for the two extreme cases of very weak and very strong external fields. The limiting forms of the waves for the two extreme cases are also considered; a discussion of the general initial-value

174

problem and of the determination of Fourier coefficients referring to the standing waves closes the paper. (M. Krzywoblocki)

434. (1248) LUDFORD, G. S. S.

Rayleigh's Problem in Hydromagnetics: Impulsive Motion of a Pole-Piece.

Consideration was given to the motion of an incompressible, viscous, electrically conducting fluid contained between the parallel, plane, pole-pieces $y = O, h$, of a permanent magnet which provides a uniform external field in the y-direction. Starting at time $t = 0$, with fluid at rest, the magnet is made to move uniformly in the negative x-direction. A simple exact solution is presented for which the transition from zero to infinite conductivity is traced and the modifying effects of viscosity determined.

435. (1251) LUDFORD, G. S. S. and MURRAY, J. D.

On the Flow of a Conducting Fluid Past a Magnetized Sphere.

In the steady flow of an incompressible, inviscid, conducting fluid past a magnetized sphere, the first-order effects of the magnetic field and the conductivity are studied. Paraboloidal wakes of vorticity and magnetic intensity are formed, the non-conservative electromagnetic force is logarithmically infinite on the sphere. For the case of a dipole of moment M at the centre of a sphere of radius a, the drag coefficient is

$$C_D = \frac{144\mu'^2}{5(2\mu + \mu')^2} \beta R_{M'}$$

where μ and μ' are the permeabilities of the fluid and sphere, respectively, β is the ratio of the representative magnetic pressure $\mu M^2/2a^6$ to the free-stream dynamic pressure, and R_M is the magnetic Reynolds number.

436. (1252) LUDLOFF, H. F.

Magnetic Boundary Layer.

Velocity field of two-dimensional supersonic flow of a conducting fluid past a thin airfoil carrying a weak magnetic field can be determined by solving a linearized momentum equation after the magnetic field has been determined from the linearized induction equation. The solution of the latter equation in terms of modified Bessel functions indicates that the magnetic field that is axisymmetric about the airfoil when the magnetic Reynolds number is vanishingly small (i.e. without fluid flow) is blown downstream to form a thin "magnetic boundary layer" for large magnetic Reynolds number. This insight illustrates the often-quoted theorem that the magnetic flux is partly carried with the fluid and partly dissipated through it. (I. Tani)

437. (1253) LUK'YANOV, S. YU. and SINITSYN, V. I.

Spectroscopic Investigation of an Intense Pulsed discharge in Hydrogen. III: Determination of the Parameters of a High-temperature Plasma.

The results of a spectroscopic measurement of the parameters of a high-temperature plasma are presented. It is shown that at the time of maximum compression the density of charged particles along the axis of the discharge is 35–40 times greater than the original density of neutral atoms. The ionic temperature reaches one or two million degrees.

438. (1261) LUNDQUIST, S.

On the Stability of Magneto-Hydrostatic Fields.

The stability of static magnetic fields in an electrically conducting liquid is investigated. The result of the study is applied to the stability of twisted cylindric magnetic fields. It is shown that instability may be caused by the twisting of a homogeneous field.

439. (**1268**) Lüst, R.
Some Theoretical Aspects of Magnetohydrodynamics and Thermonuclear Fusion.
The problem of confining a plasma in a magnetic field is considered from the standpoints of hydromagnetic pressure balance, stability and individual particle losses. Previous work on these topics is considered together with some new work along similar lines by the Göttingen group. (A. Gabriel)

440. (**1273**) Lykoudis, P. S.
Channel Turbulent Flow of an Electrically Conducting Fluid in the Presence of a Magnetic Field.
Analysis considering a system of two concentric cylinders with an annulus thickness very small compared to their average radius. An electrically conducting fluid may flow in a direction parallel to the axis of the cylinders and perpendicularly to a radial magnetic field; in this case the induced current lines will be circles lying on a plane perpendicular to the stream lines. With regard to the flow, the assumption is made that the fluid is incompressible with constant scalar transport properties. (Aero/Space)

441. (**1277**) Lyubimov, G. A.
Onde de Choc d'un Gaz à Coefficient de Conductivité Discontinu dans un Champ Electromagnétique.
Cas de la discontinuité de la conductivité sur le front de l'onde de choc. (SDIT)

442. (**1279**) Lyubimov, G. A.
Stationary Flow of an Ideally Conducting Gas Around a Corner.
The problem of the flow as in the title is investigated for an arbitrary external magnetic-field distribution relative to the flow. A system of cylindrical co-ordinates is introduced in which the axis is directed along the edge of the corner, and following particular solutions depending only on the azimuthal angle ϕ are considered: (1) two progressive flows parallel to the plane $\phi = \phi_0$; (2) a solution which may be termed a Prandtl-Meyer rotational wave: density is constant, velocity and magnetic field change direction; (3) flow around an infinitely conducting corner: all unknown quantities are expressed as functions of the density, which may be determined numerically from a complicated differential equation; (4) flow around a non-conducting corner: the corresponding differential equations must apparently be integrated numerically. (R. Nardini)

443. (**1282**) Maecker, H.
Plasma Streams in Arcs Due to Self-Magnetic Compression.
Presents experimental evidence for existence of a cathodic plasma stream and for the mechanism of its development. Demonstrates the critical importance of the plasma stream for the formation of the central core in the column of a heavy-current carbon arc and the mechanism of all heavy-current arc discharges. (TIL/MOS)

444. (**1290**) Manheimer-Timnat, Y. and Low, W.
Electron Density and Ionization Rate in Thermally Ionized Gases Produced by Medium Strength Shock Waves (Densité des électrons et vitesse d'ionisation dans les gaz ionisés thermiquement produits par des ondes de choc d'intensité moyenne).
Description d'une méthode de mesure de ces valeurs, basée sur l'atténuation des micro-ondes; résultats obtenus pour l'air dans le domaine des nombres de Mach de choc de 8,2 à 10,4 et pour de l'azote contenant 0,25% d'oxygène aux nombres de Mach de 7,4 à 8,8. 20 références bibliographiques. (SDIT)

445. (**1295**) Margenau, N., Dezlodzh, E. and Stillinger, D.
Conductivity of Weakly Ionized Gases.
The classical derivation for the complex conductivity of an ionized medium, as a function of frequency, is considered first; discrepancies are discussed between the

formula so obtained depending on several approximations, and the experimental data. This leads to a new derivation of the conductivity formula (based on the Boltzmann statistics) and to reconsiderations of approximations usually made. In the last part of the paper the results obtained are applied to the case of upper atmospheric layers and Lorentz's approximation is compared with that based on the assumption of constant mean free path. Several graphs show conductivity computed on these two assumptions, as function of frequency for various values of electron temperature. (J. Skwirzynski)

446. (**1300**) MARONI, P.
Phénomenes des Décharge dans les Plasmas Lorentziens: Etude de la Distribution Electronique en Présence d'un Champ Magnétique.
On étudie les divers cas de sèparation des variables d'une équation aux dérivées particlles à laquelle obéit la fonction de distribution électronique d'un plasma lorentzien établie par M. M. Jancel et Kahan. On procède à l'integration complète dans le cas où la fréquence de collisions est constante.

447. (**1301**) MARSHALL, W.
The Growth in Time of a Hydromagnetic Shock.
In a previous report (A.E.R.E. T/R 01718) the structure of steady hydromagnetic shocks was discussed theoretically and it was shown that the situation most likely to be met with experimentally was that in which an ordinary hydrodynamic shock was preceded by a region of width $\approx \dfrac{c^2}{4\pi\sigma u_1}$ cm, where σ is electrical conductivity and u_1 the velocity of the shock, in which the magnetic field changed slowly. In this report the time development of such a shock is considered and an estimate of the time required to set up the steady state is given. It is shown that the magnetic field increases rapidly in front of the shock until the steady state is set up; when this is done the shock has travelled about $16 \times \dfrac{c^2}{4\pi\sigma u_1}$ cm. The time required to set up a steady state behind the shock is longer. The field is shown as a function of the distance from the hydrodynamic shock for various times. (AERE)

448. (**1304**) MARSHALL, W.
The Structure of Magnetohydrodynamic Shocks.
The structure of a plane flow in an ionized gas in the presence of a magnetic field which is perpendicular to the line of flow is examined theoretically. It is shown that the nature of the flow depends upon the magnitude of a parameter B which is determined by the electrical conductivity, i.e. by the temperature and number density of electrons, in the undisturbed gas. (TIL/MOS)

449. (**1306**) MARSHALL, J.
Performance of a Hydromagnetic Plasma Gun.
The coaxial gun operates without an auxiliary magnetic field and accelerates several litres of hydrogen plasma to a velocity of $\sim 1\cdot5 \times 10^7$ cm sec^{-1}, transferring approximately 40 per cent of the input energy to kinetic energy of the plasma jet. Under certain conditions a plasma free of electrode materials is obtainable.

450. (**1309**) MATSUSHITA, S.
On Artificial Geomagnetic and Ionospheric Storms Associated with High-Altitude Explosions.
Geophysical effects of nuclear explosions at Johnston Island on August 1 and 12, 1958, were studied by means of I.G.Y. geomagnetic and ionospheric data collected in the Pacific area and the American continent. The explosion heights are estimated at 70 to 80 km and about 40 km respectively. Immediately after each explosion, three phenomena occurred. (1) Strong counterclockwise circular electric currents were formed in the vicinity of Johnston Island at 80 to 100 km height. They

caused the immediate occurrence of artificial magnetic storms in the central Pacific. (2) High-energy particles moving along the magnetic lines of force caused auroras seen from Asia, and also caused the main parts of the magnetic storms observed at Asia. (3) X-rays due to the explosion caused the increase of the D-region absorption observed at Mani. Irregularities of the electron density in the F-layer at Mani and the maximum geomagnetic change at Honolulu were caused by a shock wave from the explosion. The degree of ionization in a wide area in the central Pacific increased to about ten times normal within 35 min after the first explosion and within about 6 hr after the second. Then a strong radio absorption continued for many hours.

451. (**1310**) MAWARDI, O. K.

Magnetohydrodynamics: A Survey of the Literature.

Revue faisant ressortir la théorie des milieux continus davantage que la théorie cinétique des gaz. Elle se divise en: équations générales du mouvement d'un fluide conducteur: théorie dynamique des ondes magnétohydrodynamiques de petite amplitude; magnétohydrostatique; instabilités hydromagnétiques: ondes de chocs hydromagnétiques. (C.N.R.S.)

452. (**1312**) McCUNE, J. E.

On the Motion of Thin Airfoils in Fluids of Large but Finite Electrical Conductivity.

A two-dimensional, small-perturbation theory for the steady motion of thin lifting airfoils in an incompressible conducting fluid, with the uniform applied magnetic field perpendicular to (and in the plane of) the undisturbed, uniform flow field, is described. The conductivity of the fluid is assumed to be such that the magnetic Reynolds number ($\equiv R_m$) of the flow is large but finite. Within this assumption, a theory based on superposition of sinusoidal modes is constructed and applied to some simple thin airfoil problems. It is shown that with this particular field geometry the Alfvén wave mechanism is important in making possible very deep penetration into the flow field of currents and their associated vorticity. It is also shown that the current penetration for an airfoil is much larger than for a wavy wall of wavelength equal to the airfoil chord. A value of $R_m = 5$ is found to be a good approximation to infinity; use of the present technique for values of R_m on the order of unity is permissible. These results provide an indication of what is meant by large magnetic Reynolds number in two-dimensional magneto-aerodynamics.

453. (**1317**) McILROY, W.

Magnetohydrodynamics is an Old Field with New Implications for Engineers.

Discussion on the principles of magnetohydrodynamics and some applications such as the "pinch effect."

454. (**1318**) McILROY, W.

Research in Magnetohydrodynamics.

Presents some fundamental ideas and the basic theory of this field. Applications are described, including the induction flowmeter and the electromagnetic pump. The pinch process is briefly treated. Finally, a short discussion of investigations concerning the future is presented; such items as reduction of aerodynamic heating at the nose of a re-entry missile, the possibilities of a plasma engine for flight into outer space, and the regeneration of electricity from the fluid are considered. (TIL/MOS)

455. (**1322**) MEECHAM, W. C.

Some Exact Solutions of the Navier-Stokes and the Hydromagnetic Equations.

Some exact, closed-form solutions of the Navier-Stokes equations for incompressible flow and of the hydromagnetic equations for high-conductivity, incompressible flow are presented. They can be considered to be generalizations of Taylor's solutions. The solutions are two dimensional and cellular containing a single-space Fourier component; the spatial behaviour is chosen in such a way that the nonlinear inertial term and the pressure term cancel one another, leaving a linear system to be solved. The time behaviour of the solutions is quite general. The solutions to the hydromagnetic equations are such that the velocity and the magnetic fields are parallel and decoupled. The velocity behaves as it does in the purely mechanical case while the magnetic field simply decays in time; there is no source term for it in the present treatment.

456. (**1327**) MEYER, F.
The Stability of a Plasma in Crossed Magnetic Fields.
(In German.) The stability of a plasma in crossed magnetic fields is investigated for the following equilibrium configuration. A plasma with an interior horizontal magnetic field is supported against gravity by a horizontal vacuum magnetic field which is inclined at some angle α to the interior field. This example is an extension of the case α = 0 investigated by Kruskal and Schwarzschild. It is found that for all disturbances with small wave-lengths, including those disturbances which give the Kruskal-Schwarzschild instability, stability can be restored by using a non-zero α. Perturbations of sufficiently large wavelengths are found unstable for every α and every ratio of field strength.   (Appl. Mech. Rev.)

457. (**1328**) MEYER, F. and SCHMIDT, H. U.
Toruslike Configurations of a Plasma in Equilibrium with an Exterior Magnetic Field without Azimuthal Current.
(In German.) The authors attack the problem of the existence of toruslike configurations of a plasma in an equilibrium with an exterior magnetic field. The starting point is the Maxwell equations with the pressure of the gaseous medium being constant over the entire external surface of the torus. As the first problem, authors solve the following question: Do toruslike surfaces exist with meridianal, closed and equally distributed current lines? To answer this, authors consider the geometry of the toruslike surface and establish a differential equation based on the equation of the length of an arc. The first answer is that there cannot exist a torus configuration with plane, closed current lines, whose planes pass through the z-axis. To find the possible configurations, they solve the equation in question by means of characteristics which are identical with the lines of the magnetic field. The current lines can be closed plane curves but their planes cannot pass through one and the same axis. The disturbances in the distribution of the initial values propagate always along characteristics. The plasma cross section must have maxima and minima. Authors construct a few possible toruslike configurations, show their azimuthal and meridianal cross-sections and prove that they always must possess an azimuthal component of the current. Finally they constructed a paper model of a torus, whose picture shows many interesting details. This is a nice contribution to the field in question.   (M. Krzywoblocki)

458. (**1329**) MEYER, R. C.
On Reducing Aerodynamic Heat-Transfer Rates by Magnetohydrodynamic Techniques.
Paper considers theoretically the reduction of stagnation point heat transfer on a blunt body at hypersonic speeds by the use of a magnetic field. The modifications to the flows inside and outside the viscous boundary layer are considered, and it is concluded that the effect on the external flow is primarily responsible for the reduction of heat transfer. The existence of a magnetic-fluid boundary layer is demonstrated for fluids of high electrical conductivity, and it is shown that the theory for

this layer resembles that for a viscous boundary layer. For a flat plate, a simple investigation suggests that magnetic techniques are unlikely to have a significant effect on heat transfer unless the electrical conductivity of air is artificially enhanced. A critical review of this and other papers on the effects of magnetic fields on boundary-layer flows is given by Hess in NASA Memo 4-9-59L. (D. Holder)

459. (**1332**) MEYER, R. X.
Magnetohydrodynamics and Aerodynamic Heating.
The basis equations and some fundamental concepts of magnetoaerodynamics are discussed. As an application, the problem of the flow near the stagnation point of a body of revolution is reviewed and an exact solution is given. Data are presented for the heat transfer coefficient at the stagnation point, and for its gradient in the stagnation point region. The magnetic field strength required to accomplish an appreciable reduction of aerodynamic heating in hypersonic flight is discussed, for the case in which ionization is due to thermal motion. Alternatively, methods which involve electrical breakdown of the air are considered. (ARS J.)

460. (**1333**) MEYER, R. X.
Magnetohydrodynamics in the Limit of Small Inertial Forces.
The continuum theory of electrically conducting fluids is considered for the case in which inertial forces are negligible compared with pressure gradients and ponderomotive forces. The pressure is constant along field lines, and the flow of an ideal gas is isothermal. The field lines are found to be characteristics for the determination of the stream function. An application to the fluid mechanics of plasma propulsion and electromagnetic shock tubes is indicated. The rate of leakage of an ionized gas through a two-dimensional "magnetic-piston" is computed in detail.

461. (**1334**) MEYER, R. X.
Magnetohydrodynamics and its Application to Propulsion and Re-Entry.
The first part of this paper is largely a review of some of the basic concepts of magnetohydrodynamics in the regime of continuum fluid mechanics. The acceleration of plasmas to high velocities by means of magnetic fields is considered. The use of magnetic fields for the purpose of reducing aerodynamic heating at re-entry is discussed, and some theoretical and experimental data which have been previously reported, are reviewed. In a second part of this paper, the theory of the Newtonian approximation to magnetohydrodynamic flow is developed. Results are presented, concerning the magnetohydrodynamic flow in the shock layer of a re-entry body. A similarity solution of the resulting equations is obtained for a circular cone in the case of finite and variable electrical conductivity.

462. (**1335**) MEYER, R. X.
The Quasi-Newtonian Approximation.
The theory of the Quasi-Newtonian approximation to magnetohydrodynamic flow is developed. Results are presented, concerning the flow of an ionized gas in the shock layer of a re-entry body. A similarity solution, valid for arbitrarily varying conductivity, is obtained for a circular cone at zero angle of attack.

463. (**1336**) MEYER, R. X.
A Magnetohydrodynamic Model for a Two-Dimensional Magnetic Piston.
USAF-supported calculation of the mass flow rate of gas leaking through the magnetic piston in the regime of continuum flow. The analysis is confined to a plane geometry rather than to a rotationally symmetric one. The principal assumption throughout the analysis consists in neglecting the kinetic energy of the gas (in a co-ordinate frame attached to the piston) compared with its internal energy and compared with the energy of the magnetic field. The gas therefore

"percolates" through the field somewhat analogously to a liquid percolating through a porous medium. This assumption is verified numerically and a typical example is considered. (Aero/Space)

464. (**1337**) MEYER, R. X.
Magnetohydrodynamic-Hypersonic Flow in the Quasi-Newtonian Approximation.
The theory of the Quasi-Newtonian approximation to magnetohydrodynamic flow is developed. Results are presented, concerning the flow of an ionized gas in the shock layer of a re-entry body. A similarity solution, valid for arbitrarily varying conductivity, is obtained for a circular cone at zero angle of attack.
(ASTIA)

465. (**1352**) MILLER, M. A.
Acceleration of Plasmoids by High-Frequency Electric Fields.
The possibility of accelerating completely ionized quasi-neutral plasmoids in moving high-frequency potential wells is indicated. If such wells are formed by two fields or by using a waveguide of variable cross-section, certain features of linear and cyclical plasma accelerators are analysed.

466. (**1355**) MITCHNER, M.
Magnetohydrodynamic Flow in Shock Tube.
The effect of a transverse magnetic field on the motion of a perfectly conducting fluid in a shock tube is examined. A generalized form of the Riemann invariant for the continuous motion of such a fluid is combined with the conservation equations for a magnetohydrodynamic shock to obtain an exact description of the fluid motion in a shock tube in terms of arbitrary initial conditions. The fluids are assumed to have constant specific heat ratios. Qualitatively, the effect of the magnetic field is equivalent to that of a pressure, but quantitatively the effect is always greater than merely the hydrodynamic pressure equivalent of the appropriate Maxwell stress. A magnetic field in the high pressure region alone can produce shocks having Mach numbers for typical laboratory conditions, of the order of hundreds, and in general is in agreement with available experimental results. A magnetic field in the low pressure region results in weaker, but higher velocity shocks. (ASTIA)

467. (**1357**) MITCHNER, M.
Steady Two-Dimensional Flow with a Transverse Magnetic Field.
Equations are developed for the steady, two-dimensional, isentropic and irrotational flow of a perfect electrically conducting fluid in a transverse magnetic field. For very strong magnetic fields the magnetohydrodynamic equations are identical to the corresponding hydrodynamic equations specialized to a gas with a ratio of specific heats equal to two and with the sound velocity replaced by the total disturbance velocity. The effect of the magnetic field on the Bernoulli equation is examined, and the characteristic curves in the hodograph plane calculated for the case of supersonic flow. A magnetic field is shown to cause a more rapid expansion for flow around a convex curved wall, and to cause the shock produced in flow around a concave curved wall to move upstream. For comparable Mach numbers these effects are relatively small, even for very strong fields. (ASTIA)

468. (**1365**) MOROZOV, A. I. and SOLOV'EV, L. S.
The Integrals of Drift Equations.
The motions of particles in a slowly time- and space-varying electromagnetic field can be approximately described by the "drift equations." The authors derive trajectories of such particles by assuming that the particle velocity component perpendicular to the magnetic field intensity vector is constant. The resultant differential equation for particle position has then the usual Lagrangian form. The solution of such an equation is studied for simple types of magnetic fields (i.e. for

rectangular axial and screw symmetries). As an illustration, the authors consider trajectories in a magnetic field due to superposition of circular, variable and constant currents: (1) "locked" particles, moving almost entirely in the direction of circular current, and (2) "escaping" particles, following the lines of force of the magnetic field. Trajectories of both types of particles are studied.

469. (1375) NAKAGAWA, Y.
   Heat Transport by Convection in Presence of an Impressed Magnetic Field.
The effect of an impressed magnetic field on heat transport by convection, which arises from instability in a layer of an electrically conducting fluid, bounded between two constant temperature surfaces, is examined. It is shown that such a field reduces the amount of heat transported by convection, and that when the strength of the magnetic field is increased, such reduction becomes proportional to $(\pi^2 Q)^{-1}$, where $Q = \sigma\mu^2 \cos^2 \vartheta H^2 d^2/\rho v$, d is the depth of the layer, ρ the density, H the strength of magnetic field, ϑ the inclination of the direction of H to the vertical, and σ, μ and v are the coefficients of electrical conductivity, magnetic permeability, and kinematic viscosity, respectively, for all types of the boundary conditions. It is also shown that in the neighbourhood of the marginal state of stability, a simple formula characterizes the heat transport by convection.   (L. Kovasznay)

470. (1376) NAKAGAWA, Y.
   Experiments on the Instability of a Layer of Mercury Heated from Below and
   Subject to the Simultaneous Action of a Magnetic Field and Rotation, Part II.
Continuation and further elaboration of the experiment reported earlier (AMR **11** (1958), Rev. 2172). Surface motion of the rotating pool of mercury placed in the magnetic field of a cyclotron magnet is observed and the cellular structure is analysed. When increasing the magnetic field, a sudden change in scale of the cells is observed at a characteristic value of the non-dimensional parameter.

471. (1378) NAKAGAWA, Y.
   Theoretical and Experimental Study of Heat Transfer by Cellular Convection in
   the Presence of Impressed Magnetic Fields.
Results are given for the heat transfer by combined conduction and cellular convection through a horizontal layer of electrically conducting fluid. In the experiments a mercury layer was used, with the lower bounding surface heated, and the upper one cooled, by constant temperature baths. The mercury chamber was placed in a vertical magnetic field. The heat flow through the layer is given as a function of Rayleigh number. Very good agreement with theory is obtained in the range up to twice the critical Rayleigh number given by the linear theory for marginal stability.   (R. Siegel)

472. (1379) NAPOLITANO, L. G.
   Contribution à l'Etude de la Magnétohydrodynamique.
Etude concernant les gaz complètement ionisés et tendant à établir les équations de la magnétohydrodynamique avec rigueur et cohérence tout en obtenant une généralité telle que ces équations soient utilisables pour l'étude des problèmes géophysiques, astrophysiques ou aéronautiques. Application des hypothèses simplificatrices de Cowling et Spitzer. Fluides continus et discontinus. Equation de l'entropie. 9 références bibliographiques.   (SDIT)

473. (1381) NAPOLITANO, L. G.
   Discontinuity Surfaces in Magneto-Fluid-Dynamics.
This report is concerned with the macroscopic study of magneto-fluid-dynamic discontinuities for negligible relativistics effects. Jump conditions relating the end states on the two sides of discontinuity surfaces of arbitrary geometry are derived for both the steady and unsteady cases. Applications are presented in

182

connection with (*a*) the magneto-fluid-dynamic counterpart of the Truesdell-Lighthill-Hayes problem of determining the vorticity jump across a shock and (*b*) the existence of magneto-fluid-dynamic slip and/or contact surfaces.

(Appl. Mech. Rev.)

474. (**1386**) NAPOLITANO, L. G.

Magnetofluidmechanics of Two Interacting Streams.

The interaction of two electrically conducting streams of different velocity in the presence of magnetic fields has been analysed. Boundary layer type equations are derived for the interaction of semi-finite streams under conditions of constant fluid properties and laminar flow for two special cases—where the field is (*a*) stationary with respect to a fixed frame of reference, and (*b*) stationary with respect to the slower stream. Extensions of the analysis to more complex cases are suggested.

(TIL/MOS)

475. (**1389**) NAPOLITANO, L. G.

Superfici di Discontinuità in Magnetofluidodinamica.

(In Italian.) Derivation of the basic equations for discontinuities in magneto-fluiddynamics, and discussion of their solutions in relation to contact and vortical discontinuities. The electric conductivity is considered to be infinite, constant, and variable with the absolute temperature. It is found that contact discontinuities are always possible in the first two cases, whereas vortical discontinuity surfaces are possible only when the magnetic field has no component normal to the surface itself (Hn $= 0$). For $\sigma = \sigma$ (T) vortical discontinuity surfaces are always possible, and their characteristics, when Hn $= 0$, depend upon the surface geometry and the tangential component of the electric field. The existence of contact surfaces implies the existence of discontinuities in the magnetic field unless the tangential component of the electric field vanishes. (Aero/Space)

476. (**1394**) NARDINI, R.

Sulla Mutua Azione fra Fenomeni Acustici ed Idromagnetici.

Study of the interaction of acoustic and hydromagnetic phenomena. (IAS)

477. (**1400**) NAZE, J.

Sur certain Ecoulements quasi Rectilingnes d'un Fluide Doué de Conductivité Electrique Finie.

This note begins with a treatment of the same problem as was studied by Resler and Sears. Here the "one-dimensional flow" approximations are made in such a way that the current is proportional to $\partial H/\partial x$, where x is the co-ordinate along the channel and H is the magnetic field strength. Relations are obtained for the velocity as functions of x when the cross-sectional area is prescribed. The stability is then studied by the same technique as in the paper reviewed below. Again it is concluded that only decelerating transonic flow is unstable. This stability investigation is subject to the same criticism as in the review below. The reviewer also disagrees with the treatment of the steady-flow problem and suggests that the meaning of "one-dimensional" has been misconstrued. For the channel of nearly uniform area the current cannot be given by $\partial Hy/\partial x$; in fact the other term of curl H, viz. $\partial Hx/\partial y$ is much greater for steady flow. That this latter derivative does not appear in the analysis is due to the one-dimensional approximation, i.e. to the fact that an average has been taken across the section of the channel. Thus the reviewer cannot accept the results of this note nor those of a previous investigation [*C.R. Acad. Sci., Paris*, **246** (1958) 3316–3319] where a fluid of infinite conductivity was considered. For the same reason, exception is taken to the author's description of the Resler-Sears work, viz. ". . . les fluctuations des champs dues ou mouvement du fluids sont négligées . . ." A similar statement also appears in her review [MR 19, 1226] of the Resler-Sears paper. (W. Sears)

478. (**1401**) NAZE, J.
Etude de la Stabilité des Ecoulements de Resler-Sears.
In two recent papers [*J. Aero. Sci.*, **25** (1958) 235–246; *Z. Angew. Math. Phys.* **96** (1958) 503–518; MP 19, 1226; 20 No. 616] Resler and the reviewer studied steady flow of electrically conducting perfect gases in channels of nearly uniform cross-section, under the influence of applied electric E and magnetic H fields. This paper represents an attempt to study the stability of such flows. This involves the consideration of waves propagating along the channel. Unfortunately, the author has taken H to be unperturbed by such waves, which is not appropriate for the unsteady case, and therefore arrives at a characteristic velocity (sound speed) independent of H. The correct value has been given by van de Hulst [*Proc. Astrophysical Symposium, Paris*, 1949] and others. Using this result she has studied the stability in the manner of R. E. Meyer [*Quart. J. Mech. Appl. Math.* **5** (1952) 257–269; MR 14, 329]. She concludes that flow decelerating through the sonic speed is unstable while in all other cases studied in the original reference (excepting of course those exhibiting choking) the electromagnetic effect increases the stability.

(W. Sears)

479. (**1407**) NEUFELD, J. and RITCHIE, R. H.
Passage of Charged Particles Through Plasma.
The passage of charged particles through plasma is investigated by means of straightforward application of Maxwell's equations for a dispersive medium. The case is considered when the Debye screening loses its significance.

480. (**1408**) NEURINGER, J. L.
Optimum Power Generation Using a Plasma as the Working Fluid (Méthode optimale de génération d'énergie électrique utilisant un plasma comme fluide de travail).
Description et discussion d'une méthode ne faisant intervenir aucun élément mobile et basée sur le principe de l'induction électromagnétique. 4 références bibliographiques. (SDIT)

481. (**1410**) NEURINGER, J. L. and McILROY, W.
Incompressible Two-Dimensional Stagnation-Point Flow of an Electrically Conducting Viscous Fluid in the Presence of a Magnetic Field (Écoulement bidimensionnel, incompressible, à point d'arrêt d'un fluide visqueux conduisant l'électricité, en présence d'un champ magnétique).
Étude théorique du rôle favorable que peut jouer sur la trainée de frottement l'existence d'un champ magnétique d'intensité raisonnable, lors de la rentrée dans l'atmosphère d'un engin à longue portée qui engendre, par suite de sa vitesse, une coiffe de gaz ionisés entre l'onde de choc détachée et le nez du solide. Naissance d'une science appliquée nouvelle: la "magnétohydrodynamique." 3 références bibliographiques. (SDIT)

482. (**1411**) NEURINGER, J. L. and McILROY, W.
Hydromagnetic Effects on Stagnation-Point Heat Transfer.
Authors calculate the reduction in heat transfer at a two-dimensional stagnation point in an incompressible, constant property fluid due to a magnetic field aligned with the free-stream direction. The work is an extension of the analysis reported in *J. Aero. Sci.* **25,** 3, 194–198, Mar. 1958, wherein the reduction of the skin friction due to the magnetic field was evaluated. In the latter analysis the change in the imposed magnetic field induced by the electric currents in the fluid is fully taken into account. However, in the heat-transfer solution, the effect of the magnetic field is introduced only insofar as it influences the flow velocity components, the

effects of Joule heating and viscous dissipation being neglected as small. Results of machine computations show that the stagnation point heat transfer can be reduced by as much as 28 per cent by a magnetic field of reasonable strength in a fluid of relatively small electric conductivity. The same problem has been solved by Rossow in a slightly different way. In Rossow's solution the change in the imposed magnetic field induced by the electric current is neglected in the momentum equations, but the Joule heating and viscous dissipation terms are retained in the energy equation. The numerical results of the two analyses are the same for practical purposes. (H. Stine)

483. (**1414**) Newcomb, W. A.
> *Magnetic Differential Equations.*

A necessary and sufficient condition is derived for a magnetic differential equation $B \cdot \nabla = 0$ to have a single-valued solution r, where B is the field of a magnetohydrostatic equilibrium state or, more generally, any field with a system of toroidal magnetic surfaces.

484. (**1416**) Nguyen, X. X.
> *The Electromagnetic Energy-Momentum Tensor in the Presence of Charged Matter, in the Case of the Non-Linear Coupling Equations of the Born-Infeld Theory.*

The energy-momentum of the electromagnetic field, in the presence of charged matter can be represented by various tensors, symmetric and asymmetric. In the theory of Maxwell their choice is still not completely determined, but in the Born-Infeld theory these tensors reduce to a single symmetric tensor. (T. Carson)

485. (**1417**) Niblett, E. R.
> *The Stability of Couette Flow in an Axial Magnetic Field.*

Extension of Chandrasekhar's theory of the stability of viscous flow of an electrically conducting fluid between coaxial rotating cylinders with perfectly conducting walls to the case of non-conducting walls. It is found that their effect is to reduce the critical Taylor Numbers, and to increase the wavelength of the instability patterns. An experiment to measure the values of magnetic field and rotation speed at the onset of instability in mercury between Perspex cylinders is described.
(IAS)

486. (**1419**) Niblett, G. B. F. and Blackman, V. H.
> *An Approximate Measurement of the Ionization Time Behind Shock Waves in Air.*

I. A hydromagnetic shock tube has been used to obtain an approximate measurement of the time to reach equilibrium ionization behind shock waves of Mach number 11 to 17 moving into air at a pressure of about 1 mm of mercury. This ionization time decreases with increasing Mach number. Experimental results are presented as a graph of the ionization time *vs.* Mach number. The principal source of error in the measurement is the attenuation of the shock and the results indicate a lower limit for the ionization time in air.

II. Mesure approchée du temps nécessaire pour atteindre l'équilibre d'ionisation derrière une onde de choc, aux nombres de Mach de 11 à 17 et sous une pression de 1 mm de mercure, au moyen d'un tube de choc hydromagnétique. 7 références bibliographiques. (SDIT)

487. (**1420**) Niblett, G. B. F. and Green, T. S.
> *Radial Hydromagnetic Oscillations.*

This paper discusses the radial hydromagnetic oscillations of a plasma confined by an axial magnetic field. Oscillations of this type have recently been observed experimentally and typical high-speed streak photographs are presented and analysed. On the assumption that the plasma is confined in a thin cylindrical annulus, the non-linear equation of motion can be integrated analytically. The calculated period of the oscillations is independent of amplitude and is found to be in good agreement with experimental results. Damping of the oscillations by diffusion of the magnetic field is discussed and reference made to the possible significance of the oscillations as a means of transferring energy irreversibly to the ions.

488. (**1421**) NIBSBET, I. C. T.
Interfacial Instability of Fluids of Arbitrary Electrical Conductivity in Uniform Magnetic Fields.
The stability to small sinusoidal disturbances of an infinite plane interface separating an electrically conducting fluid from a lighter non-conducting fluid is investigated in the case where both fluids are incompressible and inviscid. Gravity and a uniform magnetic field act on the system and the fluids are in steady relative motion. The motion of the conducting fluid consists of a superposition of two modes, an irrotational mode corresponding to the solution obtained in classical hydrodynamics, and a rotational mode which consists in general of a damped magnetohydrodynamic wave, but which degenerates into a surface current as the conductivity becomes infinite and the magnetic field becomes parallel to the interface. The relative amplitudes of the two modes are determined by the condition that the surface current is otherwise zero, and an algebraic equation, in general of the tenth degree, is obtained for the exponential growth rate. This equation is analysed in two special cases: that in which both fluids are initially at rest (Rayleigh-Taylor instability); and that in which gravity is unimportant (Helmholtz instability). For the Rayleigh-Taylor case, conditions are derived which make the flow pattern and growth rate when the conductivity is finite, differ insignificantly from those calculated for infinite conductivity. A sufficient criterion, in most cases, is that the square root of the magnetic Reynolds Number should be large, but much larger magnetic Reynolds Numbers are required if the system is close to the position of critical stability. (ASTIA)

489. (**1422**) NIGAM, S. D. and SING, S. N.
Heat Transfer by Laminar Flow between Parallel Plates Under the Action of Transverse Magnetic Field.
Solution of the energy equation of magnetohydrodynamics is obtained for the heat-transfer problem corresponding to Hartmann's velocity profile for forced flow between two infinite parallel plates. The semi-infinite plates $z = \pm L$, $x \leqslant 0$, are kept at a constant temperature T_0 and the plates $z = \pm L$, $x \geqslant 0$ are kept at a different temperature T_s (constant). Solutions are found which are valid for the regions $x \leqslant 0$ and $x \geqslant 0$ respectively. These are joined smoothly at the plane $x = 0$ by imposing certain continuity conditions. Asyntotic solutions for large $M \geqslant 10$ are presented. A simplified case valid for large Péclet numbers is worked out numerically and the mean mixed temperature and local total Nusselt numbers are tabulated and shown graphically. These are compared with the corresponding values for the heat-transfer problem in which the magnetic field is absent and the fluid is electrically non-conducting. It is found that due to ionic-conductivity the mean mixed temperature at any point is decreased and consequently the local total Nusselt number is increased.

490. (**1424**) NISHIYAMA, T.
Electrostatic Interactions in an Electron-Ion Gas at High Density.
This paper is a continuation of work done by the author on the properties of electron-ion gas [*Prog. Theoret. Phys.* **6** (1951), 366–378; **14** (1955), 38–51; MR 13, 716; 18, 444]. The electron-ion interaction is studied here by three

methods: (*a*) the method of normal modes, similar to that of Sawada [*Phys. Rev.* (2) **106** (1957), 372–383; MR 19, 98]; (*b*) the sound approximation; (*c*) the collective description. Using (*a*) it is shown that the interaction between electrons and photons corresponding to the Bloch interaction for metals can be derived by eliminating the interaction between the electronic plasma and the ionic plasma. The method (*b*) turns out to be equivalent to the Gell-Mann-Breckner method [*ibid.* **106** (1957), 364–368; MR 19, 98]. The dispersion equations are also obtained in this approximation. In method (*c*) the interaction between holes and holes, and between excited electrons and excited electrons are taken into account, and some implications to super-conductivity are discussed.   (M. Moravcsik)

491. (**1427**) NOSTICK, W. H.
      Experimental Study of Ionized Matter Projected Across a Magnetic Field.
Describes the production of a "plasmoid" in field-free space and the effect of firing it across a magnetic field. Presents photographic evidence of (1) the toroidal structure of plasmoids and their magnetic and electrical properties, and (2) interaction of plasmoids with one another. Postulates a mechanism to explain the interaction effects. A "plasmoid" is defined as a plasma-magnetic entity (formed by firing a plasma gun into a d.c. magnetic field).   (TIL/MOS)

492. (**1428**) NOTCHEVKINA, I. I.
      Sur une Méthode Approchée pour l'Etude des Ecoulements Tourbillonnaires Plans en Magnétohydrodynamique.
In Russian. Etude analytique du mouvement tourbillonnaire, stationnaire d'un liquide compressible idéal se trouvant dans un champ magnétique perpendiculaire au plan d'écoulement.   (C.N.R.S.)

493. (**1429**) NOTCHEVKINA, I. I.
      On the Approximation Method in Investigation of Plane Rotational Flow in Magnetohydrodynamics.
Equations are transformed to a form which corresponds to the usual gasdynamic case without magnetic fields but with a different equation of state. The latter is simplified in a specific Mach number range (example given was for the range $1 \cdot 56 \leqslant M \leqslant 1 \cdot 9$) to yield a separable differential equation.   (H. Yoshihara)

494. (**1432**) OGUCHI, K.
      Blunt Body Viscous Layer with and without a Magnetic Field.
The present paper is mainly concerned with the solution for the viscous flow in the shock layer about the stagnation region of a sphere in hypersonic flow. The Reynolds Numbers considered are in a range too low to apply usual boundary layer theory within the shock layer, but are large enough that the shock wave may be regarded as a discontinuous surface. This viscous layer problem has been studied previously by Probstein. With the assumption of constant density in the shock layer an analytic solution is applied to this problem both with and without an applied magnetic field. This solution makes use of the fact that the ratio of the density ahead of the shock to that behind the shock (ε) is small. The solution has been found in analytic form to first order in ε. In the non-magnetic case numerical results for both the shock wave detachment distance and skin friction are presented for a value of $\varepsilon = 0 \cdot 1$ and they are shown to be in good agreement with the exact numerical calculations of Probstein and Kemp. Numerical results are also presented on the effect of an applied magnetic field on both the shock wave detachment distance and skin friction. It is found that for a fixed value of ε and Reynolds Number the skin friction decreases and the detachment distance increases for increasing value of the magnetic field parameter S which is proportional to the magnetic pressure divided by the total pressure.

495. (**1439**) ONG, R. S. and NICHOLLS, J. A.
On the Flow of a Hydromagnetic Fluid Near an Oscillating Flat Plate.
This note considers the MHD flow near an infinite plate which oscillates parallel to itself in a perpendicular magnetic field. This work is an extension of the problem analysed by Rossow [NACA Tech. Note 3971 (1957)]. As in the latter paper, the magnetic field is assumed constant and the manner in which currents are to be closed, etc., is left unresolved. (H. Greenspan)

496. (**1440**) ONG, R. S.
Characteristic Manifolds in Three-Dimensional Unsteady Magnetohydro-dynamics.
The technique developed in the general theory of discontinuities is applied to the basic equations of unsteady magnetohydrodynamics in order to find the conditions to be satisfied by the discontinuities in the derivatives of the significant flow and magnetic field parameters. In the formulation of the basic equations use is made of the "magnetohydrodynamic approximation." This amounts to the assumption that the magnetic energy is very large compared with the electric energy, or physically, that the displacement current is negligible. The fluid itself is considered to be infinitely conductive, inviscid, and compressible. With the aid of the relations satisfied by the jumps in the derivatives of the parameters the various characteristic manifolds are found. Finally, it is shown that these manifolds are hypersurfaces along which small disturbances and weak shocks are propagated.

497. (**1442**) OSBORN, A. B.
Plasma Jet for Laboratory Use.
The usual form of cathode for plasma jet apparatus is a graphite disk having a central hole through which the jet of plasma emerges. Burning of the graphite continuously enlarges the hole and necessitates frequent renewal of the disk. For small-scale work this inconvenience can be avoided by replacing the disk with a metal orifice plate (electrically neutral), and by using an external graphite rod as cathode. With the 7 kW apparatus described, the jet of plasma produced is some 5 cm long, with a maximum core temperature believed to be about 10,000°C. The maximum rate of heat transfer to a surface of 6 mm diameter is approximately 300 cal cm^{-2} sec^{-1}. By injecting various gases the atmosphere of the arc can be modified. Argon is notable for reducing the arc voltage by about 30 per cent, and for suppressing the usual crater formation at the anode.

498. (**1445**) OSTER, L.
Linearized Theory of Plasma Oscillations.
A study of longitudinal and transverse plane waves in a plasma in a zero or uniform magnetic field, first by a hydrodynamic method, and afterwards by an essentially equivalent kinetic method based on the assumption that the perturbed velocity distribution function is locally Maxwellian. There are 28 references.

499. (**1449**) PAI, S. I.
Cylindrical Shock Waves Produced by Instantaneous Energy Release in Magneto-gas Dynamics.
The behaviour of a cylindrical shock wave produced by instantaneous energy release along a straight line of infinite extent in a conducting gas subjected to a magnetic field with circular lines of force has been analysed. Initially the gas is at rest and has constant temperature. Both the initial density and the initial magnetic field H_{Θ_0} are assumed to be inversely proportional to some power of the radial distance r. It was found that similar solutions exist only if H_{Θ_0} is proportional to $1/r$. Similar solutions for various initial density distributions have been obtained. Numerical examples are given for constant initial density. The magnetic field has great influence on the pressure distribution but little influence on the density

distribution within the shock. The pressure near the shock front is increased by the magnetic field while that near the centre of the region is decreased. In general, the magnetic field increases the flow velocity within the cylindrical shock.

(ASTIA)

500. (**1450**) PAI, S. I.
>*Shock Wave Propagation in an Infinitely Electrically Conductive Gas with Transverse Magnetic Field and Gravitation.*

USAF-supported investigation of the one-dimensional flow produced by a strong shock propagating in a gas of infinite electrical conductivity in the presence of a transverse magnetic field and a gravity field, using the Lagrangian method. The method of series expansion is worked out in detail and applied to the case of shock waves in a gas of constant temperature and under constant transverse magnetic field. The effect of the magnetic field is to increase the velocity of the shock wave and the flow field influenced by the wave. The problem is also analysed by means of the Eulerian method. (Aero/Space)

501. (**1451**) PAI, S. I.
>*Energy Equation of Magneto-Gas-Dynamics.*

The general energy equation of a viscous, heat-conducting, and electrically conducting fluid in magneto-gas-dynamics has been derived. Various simplified forms of energy equations have been discussed, particularly for the cases with magneto-gas-dynamics approximations. The fundamental equations of magneto-gas-dynamics are also given.

502. (**1454**) PAI, S. I.
>*On Exact Solutions of One-Dimensional Flow Equations of Magneto-Gas-Dynamics.*

The magneto-gas-dynamic equations describing the steady one-dimensional flow of a viscous heat conducting, electrically conducting and compressible gas under planar magnetic field perpendicular to the velocity vector are treated. It corresponds to the problem of structure of shock wave in magneto-gas-dynamics.

(Cornell Aer. Lab.)

503. (**1455**) PAI, S. I.
>*L'écoulement Unidimensionnel Varié de la Magnétoaérodynamique des Fluides Compressibles.*

Etude de l'écoulement unidimensionnel varié d'un fluide compressible conducteur de la chaleur et de l'électricité dans un champ magnétique plan perpendiculaire au vecteur-vitesse. 5 références bibliographiques. (SDIT)

504. (**1455**) PAI, S. I.
>*One-Dimensional Unsteady Flow of Magneto-Gas-Dynamics.*

The one-dimensional unsteady flow of a viscous, heat conducting, electrically conducting and compressible gas under planar magnetic field perpendicular to the velocity vector is investigated. First the special case of an ideal gas which is inviscid non-heat-conducting and infinitely electrically conducting is considered in detail. An exact solution of this case has been found which shows the shock wave formation in magneto-gasdynamics. Next the characteristics of the one-dimensional magneto-gas-dynamics flow equations are discussed in detail.

505. (**1460**) PAI, S. I.
>*Laminar Jet Mixing of Electrically Conducting Fluid in a Transverse Magnetic Field.*

This note discussed a jet of electrically conducting incompressible viscous fluid issuing from a narrow two-dimensional slit. A weak magnetic field is applied perpendicularly to the slit. The stream function is expanded as a power series in the magnetic field, and the induced magnetic field is neglected altogether. A particular rate of decrease of the applied field with distance from the slit is shown to lead to a similar solution whose velocity distribution shape is independent of distance from the slit, the spread of the jet mixing region being derived for this case.

(A. Hezenberg)

506. (**1463**) Pai, S. I. and Speth, A. I.
    The Wave Motions of Small Amplitude in Radiation-Electro-Magneto-Gas Dynamics.

Study of the fundamental equations of radiation electro-magneto-gasdynamics. These equations are linearized under the condition that there exists an externally applied uniform magnetic field. Wave motions of infinitesimal amplitude, which may be divided into a transverse wave and a longitudinal wave, are analysed. Radiation phenomena exert influence only on the longitudinal wave, while the transverse wave is independent of the radiation field. The radiation effect is characterized by introducing a radiation parameter which is the ratio of radiation pressure to the gasdynamic pressure. For an ideal plasma, it may be expressed in terms of an effective radiation sound speed. (Aero/Space)

507. (**1464**) Palmer, J. L.
    Laminar Flow in Magnetically Focused Cylindrical Electron Beams.

The behaviour of a cylindrical electron beam in a magnetic field is discussed in terms of a laminar-flow model. By numerical integration of the equations of motion the maximum and minimum radii of excursion and the wavelength of the undulations for each electron are presented in graphical form for various boundary conditions on the electron beam. By the proper selection of the boundary conditions, e.g. magnetic field strength at the cathode, the graphs are utilized to describe Brillouin flow, space-charge-balanced flow, immersed flow, confined flow, and, in fact, any electron flow which satisfies the laminar flow criterion. The perturbations introduced by improper injection conditions for any of the flows mentioned can be read directly from the graphs. A study of the wavelength and the amplitude of such perturbations as a function of radial position in the beam determines if a given type of flow with given injection conditions satisfies the laminar flow criterion. The sensitivity of the various types of electron flow to misadjustments of the boundary conditions is clearly revealed by the graphs, e.g. the amplitude of the undulations in Brillouin flow is very sensitive to the adjustment of the magnetic field strength, whereas for immersed flow a similar deviation in magnetic field strength has very little effect on the amplitude of the undulations. (Appl. Mech. Rev.)

508. (**1471**) Parker, E. N.
    The Generation of Acoustic and Hydromagnetic Waves and the Acceleration of Cosmic Rays.

Studies the transport problem which arises through large amounts of energy being necessary for the acceleration of cosmic rays throughout the galaxy. The hydrodynamic and hydromagnetic equations are investigated from the viewpoint of energy propagation. It is shown that, with the conditions existing in the galaxy, all fluid motions reduce to hydromagnetic waves. A consideration of the interaction of charged particles with hydromagnetic waves shows that it is the fluid velocity, and not the wave velocity, that is responsible for the acceleration of cosmic rays by Fermi's mechanism. (TIL/MOS)

509. (**1473**) Parker, E. N.
    The Propagation of Hydromagnetic Waves and the Acceleration of Cosmic Rays.

We first calculate the dissipation of hydromagnetic waves in the interstellar medium, and the variation of amplitude and wavelength of such waves with changes in ρ and B_0. It is then shown that the galaxy is no more than 1 per cent efficient in the acceleration of cosmic rays because of the tremendous viscous losses in the interstellar medium, and that there is no hydromagnetic mechanism that can

190

convert the observed large-scale low-velocity fluctuations in the interstellar medium to the required small-scale high-velocity motions. The conclusion is that cosmic rays are not accelerated throughout the galaxy at the rate corresponding to the observed spectrum, but must be locally concentrated.

510. (**1474**) PARKER, E. N.
   Hydromagnetic Dynamo Models.

The purpose of this paper is to investigate the steady-state amplification of magnetic fields in a fluid. It is shown that a rotating sphere of conducting fluid can regenerate a dipole magnetic field. It is sufficient for the angular velocity of rotation to vary with distance from the axis of rotation and for cyclonic fluid motions to be present. The non-uniform rotation generates a toroidal field from the dipole field; the cyclones generate, from the toroidal field, loops of flux in the meridional plane which coalesce to amplify the dipole field. The rotating sphere is discussed in relation to the liquid core of the earth and the geomagnetic dipole field. If, instead of a rotating sphere, one has a prismatic volume of fluid, it is possible to construct migratory dynamo waves. The dynamo waves are discussed in relation to the solar convective zone; it is shown that such waves can account for many of the principal features of the observed solar magnetic activity.

511. (**1475**) PARKER, E. N.
   Mechanics of the Geomagnetic Dynamo.

After developing the formal integration of $\partial B / \partial t = \text{curl}(v \times B)$, it is shown that cyclonic convective motions in the core produce magnetic loops in meridional planes through interaction with the toroidal magnetic field. Expressing these loops in terms of the usual orthogonal vector modes, it is shown that they result in a predominantly dipole field. Together with the non-uniform rotation of the core, which produces the toroidal field from the dipole field, the cyclonic motions result in a complete self-regenerating magnetic dynamo. We conclude that any rotating, convecting, electrically conducting body of sufficient size will possess a magnetic field generated by this dynamo mechanism. The possibility of an abrupt reversal of the field is discussed.

512. (**1478**) PARKER, E. N.
   A Study of Cowling's Theorem.

Consideration is given to the generation of the Earth's magnetic dipole field by convective motions in the liquid electrically conducting core of the Earth. A three-dimensional magnetic field is expanded in a power series about the z axis where the first order terms represent a portion of the field with a neutral line coinciding with the z axis. The interaction of the magnetic field and a velocity field is analysed with the restriction that the velocity field vanishes at infinity. The analysis shows that all amplification of the field near a neutral point terminates after a finite time so that there is no possibility of building a stationary dynamo in the average with a single interaction of a magnetic and a velocity field. The conclusion is that if a self-sustaining dynamo is possible, it involves at least two stages of interactions with suitable feed-back coupling.

513. (**1479**) PARKER, E. N.
   A Theory of the Solar Magnetic Field, Earth's Magnetism and Magneto-Hydrodynamics.

The basic principles of operation of the terrestrial hydromagnetic dynamo are used to show that the solar convective zone generates travelling dynamo waves consisting of toroidal and poloidal magnetic fields. The waves migrate from the poles toward the equator near the top of the convective zone and in the opposite direction near the bottom. The thinness of the convective zone is responsible for a migratory dynamo in the sun rather than a stationary dynamo as in the earth. An investigation of the dynamics of hydromagnetic dynamos indicates that the poloidal field is strongest above the middle latitudes while the toroidal field is strongest below these latitudes. This result is in agreement with the observed non-uniform rotation and the appearance of sunspots in low latitudes.

514. (**1483**) PARKER, E. N. and KROOK, M.
Diffusion and Severing of Magnetic Lines of Force.
The general asymptotic form for the magnetic field in a diffusing flux tube is developed and applied to the problem of severing magnetic lines of force in a medium with finite electrical conductivity. Calculations of the details of the severing and reconnection of lines of force are given for the formation of an idealized free meridional magnetic ring in a hydromagnetic dynamo, for the merging of idealized neighbouring rings, and for the straightening of the lines in a twisted tube, in order to illustrate the general qualitative features of these processes as they would presumably occur in the core of the earth. The problem of two nearly intersecting slender flux tubes is considered in order to demonstrate how the lines of force of the lesser tube are diverted into the denser tube. (ASTIA)

515. (**1484**) PARKER, E. N. and TIDMAN, D. A.
Radio Emission from Plasma Shocks.
From recent calculations of the efficiency of r.f. emissions from longitudinal plasma oscillations, and from simple considerations of charge separation in collisionless plasma shocks, it is shown that one can predict a quantitative value for the energy of a type II solar radio burst in agreement with observation. Application of the same methods to the solar corona suggests that the radio spectrum of the quiet sun may be non-thermal below 20 Mc, and that the solar wind may generate at earth as much as a megawatt of power at 1 Mc.

516. (**1485**) PARTEL, G.
Qu'est-ce que la Magnétohydrodynamique?
Revue des applications de cette science à la propulsion spatiale, à la rentrée dans l'atmosphère, à la génération d'énergie électrique. Principales lois de la magnéto-hydrodynamique. 17 références bibliographiques. (SDIT)

517. (**1488**) PATRICK, R. M.
A Description of a Propulsive Device which Employs a Magnetic Field as the Driving Force.
A propulsion motor for space ships is described which produces thrust by using a magnetic field to expel a plasma. An electrically neutral plasma is produced as the accelerated mass. A comparison is made between this magnetic accelerator and other means of acceleration, in particular ion rockets. (TIL/MOS)

518. (**1489**) PATRICK, R. M.
High-Speed Shock Waves in a Magnetic Annular Shock Tube.
Experiments were carried out with two magnetic field configurations ahead of the shock front, the first with a magnetic field ahead of the shock front in the direction of motion of the shock. In the second configuration the magnetic field ahead of the shock had its principal component in the plane of the shock front and a small component in the direction of the shock motion. The continuum radiation emitted by the shock-heated plasma was measured with photomultipliers. Use of probes to measure the change in the local magnetic field in the shock front was investigated. With the second configuration, shock velocities in excess of 4×10^7 cm/sec were measured in hydrogen. For these high-speed shock waves, shock thicknesses, obtained from measured rise times of the emitted visible radiation, are thinner than the mean free path in the shock-heated plasma, an observation which agrees with a theoretical prediction.

519. (**1490**) PATRICK, R. M.
Magneto-Hydrodynamics of Compressible Fluids.
The equations governing non-viscous flows in magneto-hydrodynamics are discussed. A moving magnetic field experiment is analysed. The effect of the magnetic field on a shock wave is calculated. Flow properties at the nose and along the side of a blunt body are considered. (TIL/MOS)

520. (**1492**) PATRICK, R. M. and BROGAN, T. R.
One-Dimensional Flow of an Ionized Gas Through a Magnetic Field.
An ionized gas is composed of three species; electrons, ions, and neutral particles. To take complete account of all the phenomena occurring when the high velocity gas interacts with the magnetic field, the motion of all three species must be considered. When this is done, it is found that the electrical conductivity of the gas is a tensor dependent on both the magnitude and geometry of the magnetic field. However, when the collision frequency for the electrons is greater than their cyclotron frequency in a magnetic field, the gas may be considered a continuum with a scalar conductivity. When the gas state is adjusted to produce a scalar conductivity, all of the observed effects can be explained with a simple theory for two experimental geometries in which the gas current forms closed loops in the magnetic field. The interaction produces a flow completely analogous to pipe flow with friction and no heat transfer, where the wall friction force is replaced by the magnetic body force which chokes the flow and forces sonic speed at the exit of the field. Using the same experimental geometries, the gas state is then adjusted so that the electrical conductivity is a tensor. Outstanding among the observed effects are ion slip, where the ions and neutrals travel through the field at different velocities, and Hall currents, generated by the drift of the charged particles across magnetic field lines. The observed effects again agree with the predicted values. (ASTIA)

521. (**1498**) PENROSE, O.
Electrostatic Instabilities of a Uniform Non-Maxwellian Plasma.
A stability criterion is obtained starting from Vlasov's collision-free kinetic equations. Possible instabilities propagating parallel to an arbitrary unit vector e are related to a function $F(u) = \Sigma_j \omega_j{}^2 \int d^3v g_j(v) \delta(e \cdot v - u)$, where $g_j(v)$ is the normalized unperturbed distribution function, and $\omega_j \equiv (4\pi n_j e_j / m_j)^{\frac{1}{2}}$ the plasma frequency, for the jth type of particle. By using a method related to the Nyquist criterion, it is shown that plasma oscillations growing exponentially with time are possible if, and only if, $F(u)$ has a minimum at a value $u = \xi$ such that

$$\int_{-\infty}^{\infty} du(u - \xi)^{-2}[F(u) - F(\xi)] > 0.$$

A study of the initial value problem confirms that the plasma is normally stable if no exponentially growing modes exist; but there is an exceptional class of distribution functions (recognizable by means of an extension of the above criterion) for which linearized stability theory breaks down. The method is applied to several examples, of which the most important is a model of a current-carrying plasma with Maxwell distributions at different temperatures for electrons and ions. The meaning of the mathematical assumptions made is carefully discussed.

522. (**1499**) PESCHKA, W.
Contributions to the Vortex Laws in Magnetohydrodynamics.
(In German.) The vortex laws of Bjerkness and L. Crocco are generalized for magnetohydrodynamics. Further, two integrals of the magnetohydrodynamic equations are given for the case of an incompressible fluid with infinite conductivity. One corresponds to a solution of the Bernoulli equation of hydrodynamics and the

other to the Kármán vortex street. Neither solution, however, has the significance which it has in hydrodynamics.

523. (**1500**) PETSCHEK, H. E.
Aerodynamic Dissipation.
This report re-examines the derivation of the basic flow equations and discusses the dissipation in an ionized gas in the presence of a magnetic field.
(Cornell Aer. Lab.)

524. (**1506**) PEYRET, P.
Sur une Correspondance entre Certains Ecoulements de Magnétodynamique des Fluides et Ceux de la Dynamique des Gaz.
It is shown that certain magnetohydrodynamic problems can be reduced to those of the dynamics of fluid of fictitious thermodynamic properties appropriately chosen. (H. Temperley)

525. (**1507**) PFIRSCH, D. and BIERMANN, L.
Co-operative Phenomena and Diffusion of a Plasma in a Transverse Magnetic Field, II.
Using two examples of inhomogeneous plasmas the occurrence of microscopic instabilities is investigated. It is shown that an inhomogeneous one-component plasma with diffusion but without a magnetic field is stable in the limiting case of linearized theory and that in a similar plasma without diffusion, which is confined by a magnetic field, an instability of apparently fairly general character exists, but its range is not yet known.

526. (**1509**) PHILLIPS, N. J.
Ionization by Ion Impact in a Collapsing Current Sheet.
Russian results show that ionization by electron impact must be much slower than supposed in a previous theory, and that charge exchange is the dominant process in the compression of the gas in the collapsing pinch; this conclusion is reinforced by recent cross-section measurements by Fite (*Proceedings of the Uppsala Conference on Ionization Phenomena in Gases*, 1959).

527. (**1519**) PIDDINGTON, J. H.
The Transmission of Geomagnetic Disturbances Through the Atmosphere and Interplanetary.
The theory of the propagation of slowly varying electromagnetic disturbances through a partially ionized gas is developed and applied to the earth's atmosphere and interplanetary space. The medium must be regarded as two separate, co-existing gases, an electron-ion plasma and neutral atoms which move to some extent independently. Quantitative results are given for a model atmosphere out to several earth radii: (1) up to a few hundred kilometres the medium behaves for waves of all periods between 1 and 10^4 s, as a rigid conductor and as a dispersive medium; (2) above about 10^3 s, km the disturbances travel as hydromagnetic waves in the ion plasma alone. Losses are small in this region but transmission is likely to be complicated by anisotropic transmission of the O wave and by refraction and partial reflection; (3) the currents responsible for all observed geomagnetic disturbances must flow at levels below about 1000 km; (4) the problem of the penetration of solar gas into the earth's field is discussed; (5) some earlier theories of the main phase of an SC storm are discussed and an alternative suggested whereby some lines of force of the earth's field are carried away along the sun-earth line; (6) some properties of micropulsations are explained in terms of the transmission of hydromagnetic waves; (7) the "effective" conductivity (σs) of the atmosphere about several earth radii has its maximum at about 100 km, above which it rapidly falls to about 10^{-16} e.m.u. or less and does not rise again.

528. (**1521**) PIKELNER, S. B.
        Principes de Base de la Magnétoaérodynamique.
Exposé sommaire de la théorie. Influence du mouvement du milieu sur le champ
magnétique et l'action du champ magnétique sur le milieu. 13 références bibliographiques. (SDIT)

529. (**1522**) PIKELNER, S. B.
        *Structure d'une Onde de Choc Magnéto-hydrodynamique dans un Gaz Partielle-
        ment Ionisé.*
En russe. Elle est formée d'une discontinuité fine de caractère purement plas-
matique et d'une zone de transition. Pour cette dernière on résoud approximative-
ment les équations dans quelques cas particuliers. L'échange de charges n'apporte
pas de modification significative au caractère général du mouvement mais réduit
l'échelle. L'énergie dissipée ne dépend pas du degré d'ionisation tant qu'on peut
considérer l'onde comme stationnaire dans les limites de la zone de transition.
(C.N.R.S.)

530. (**1524**) PINTE, R. and SIMON, R.
        The Radial Oscillations and Stability of Cylindrical Plasma.
Considers an homogeneous cylindrical, completely ionized, plasma in equilibrium
under the action of its own gravity and in a longitudinal uniform magnetic field.
The vacuum surrounding the plasma is assumed to be pervaded by a longitudinal
uniform magnetic field and by a toroidal magnetic field caused by a sheet current
flowing on the surface of the plasma. Assuming the classical hypothesis of magneto-
hydrodynamics (scalar pressure, infinite electrical conductivity, adiabatic changes),
the dynamical stability of this equilibrium is discussed with respect to infinitely
small radial perturbations. Application to the pinch effect is obtained by neglecting
gravitation in the general results.

531. (**1526**) PLUMPTON, C. and FERRARO, V. C. A.
        On Toroidal Magnetic Fields in the Sun and Stars.
Torsional oscillations of a liquid sphere of infinite electrical conductivity in the
presence of a permanent axi-symmetric magnetic field are considered. It is shown
that axially symmetric oscillations can be excited in which the sphere oscillates in
shells generated by the rotation of the lines of force about the axis of symmetry.
The range of frequencies forms a continuous spectrum, but this degeneracy may be
due to the approximations made and may disappear when a rotating sphere is
considered. The bearing of this solution on problems of interest in solar magnetism
is also discussed.

532. (**1529**) POKALITOV, E. P.
        The Resonance of Charge Carriers Produced by an Ultrasonic Wave.
The interaction of charge carriers situated in a magnetic field with the electric
field produced by an ultrasonic wave is considered. The power absorbed in unit
volume is calculated for charges with scalar and tensor effective masses. The curve
for absorbed energy has peaks where the ultrasonic frequency is $n\omega_0$ (n being an
integer and ω_0 the cyclotron frequency of the carrier), provided the refraction
time $\tau \gg 1/\omega_0$. Because the ultrasonic wavelength is about 10^5 times smaller than
that of light at the same frequency, polarization effects should be absent in experiments on ultrasonic resonance; this prevents the use of cyclotron resonance in
semiconductors with a high concentration of free electrons.

533. (**1532**) POLOVIN, R. V. and TSINTSADZE, N. L.
        Theory of Longitudinal Oscillations in an Electron-Ion Beam.
Considers perturbations of the form $\exp [i(\omega t - \mu\phi - jz)]$ in cylindrical co-
ordinates. Uses results of an earlier paper in which $\mu = 0$ was assumed to obtain

the conditions of instability. These turn out to be identical with those of the double stream tube.

534. (**1534**) POPESCU, I.
Kinetics of Ions in Gases.
Describes an experimental retarding-field method from which it is possible to obtain the collision cross-section Q, drift velocity v_0, and energy distribution of ions at high values of E/p (E the electric field, p the gas pressure). On the assumption that charge transfer Hg^+ in Hg for $1000 < E/p < 33 \cdot 300$ V/cm/mm Hg, the motion of K^+ in Hg is discussed to illustrate how the method may be used when elastic collision predominates.

535. (**1538**) POST, R. F., ELLIS, R. E., FORD, F. C. and ROSENBLUTH, M. N.
Stable Confinement of High-Temperature Plasma.
An experiment is described in which it is claimed that a plasma of particle density 10^{13} to 10^{14} cm^{-3} is confined in a Mirror Machine for times up to 30 msec. The electron temperature is the order 10 to 25 keV, but measurements of ion temperature are inconclusive. These observations are contrary to the simple hydromagnetic theory which predicts rapid growth of "flute" instabilities. Measurements of the plasma expansion rate are consistent with classical diffusion theory, although any intense plasma oscillations would be expected to increase the diffusion considerably. A number of possible explanations are suggested, the most probable of which is associated with the effect of intersection of the field lines with the metallized lining of the discharge tube.

536. (**1540**) PRADHAN, T.
Plasma Oscillations in a Steady Magnetic Field: Circular Polarized Electromagnetic Modes.
Van Kampen's method of treating the singularity which occurs in the solution of Boltzmann's equation for plasma oscillations is applied to the corresponding problem in the presence of a uniform external magnetic field. The propagation of electromagnetic waves in the direction of the field is considered.

537. (**1541**) PRAKASH, S. and TANDON, J. N.
On the Reflection and Refraction of Magneto-Hydrodynamic Waves.
The laws of reflection and refraction of magnetohydrodynamic waves from the surface of discontinuity of two infinitely extended and infinitely conducting fluid media of different densities and having different homogeneous permanent magnetic fields have been derived. The laws are quite simple and depend on the orientations of the magnetic field of the respective media. It is also shown that reflection and refraction are possible only provided the incident wave is polarized perpendicular to the plane of incidence and the discontinuity of the magnetic field is perpendicular to the plane of incidence.

538. (**1543**) PREVOT, F., HUBERT, P. and GOURDON, C.
Sur la Possibilité de Formation d'un Plasma Thérmonucleaire par Injection d'Ions Accélérés dans une Configuration Magnétique à Miroirs.
On propose de former un plasma à très haute température par injection d'ions moléculaires rapides dans un champ magnétique de telle façon que les ions injectés à partir d'une source anulaire passent par l'axe de révolution du système a y sont dissociés. Les propriétés de ce mouvement laissent expérer des performances avantageuses de ce mode d'injection. Un exemple d'application numérique est donné.

539. (**1544**) Prokof'ev, V. K., Gurevich, D. B., Belusova, I. H. and Snigirev, Y. A.

The Time Required for Establishment of Thermodynamic Equilibrium in the Plasma of an Arc Discharge.

The authors measured the time required for establishment of thermodynamic equilibrium in a 5–15 A, 45 V d.c. arc, burning between carbon electrodes in air at atmospheric pressure, using short (10–25 μsec) pulses of 80–200 A across the arc gap. The time required for establishment of thermodynamic equilibrium was found to be 20–25 μsec.

540. (**1546**) Pupke, H. and Thom, H. G.

The Rotation of Plasmoids in a Magnetic Field.

Presents observations made and deductions drawn from experiments carried out (in connection with an investigation of the rotation of an electric arc in a transverse magnetic field) to determine whether plasmoids produced in a ring can also rotate in the presence of a magnetic field. (TIL/MOS)

541. (**1549**) Raizer, M. D. et Spigel, I. S.

Etude du Plasma à l'Aide des Ondes Radioélectriques Ultracourtes.

Conductibilité et constante diélectrique d'un gaz ionisé. Diverses méthodes d'étude du plasma. 55 références bibliographiques. (SDIT)

542. (**1550**) Ramamoorty, P.

Superposability of Two Axi-Symmetric Flows under Axi-Symmetric Magnetic Fields.

Two theorems are proved, namely (1) an axi-symmetric flow of an infinitely conducting fluid under axi-symmetric magnetic fields is always self-additive; (2) two axi-symmetric flows of an infinitely conducting fluid are superposable if the fluid velocity is parallel to the magnetic field in each of the two flows. The conclusion is also reached that an axi-symmetric self-additive system can never be a steady dynamo. (T. Toye)

543. (**1554**) Rawer, K. et Suchy, K.

La "Quatrième Condition de Réflexion" d'Ondes Electromagnétiques dans un Plasma.

Introduction d'un terme généralement négligé relatif à l'équation de Boltzmann modifiant l'expression de l'indice utilisé habituellement en théorie magnéto-ionique. (SDIT)

544. (**1559**) Reagan, D.

Transverse Compression Waves in a Stabilized Discharge.

An electric discharge which is compressed by its own magnetic field, and "stabilized" by means of an axial magnetic field, can have transverse wave motions which cause its periodic compression and expansion. This kind of motion can cause the heating of the ions in the discharge. The simplest of these wave modes are described and an estimate is given of the power available to the waves as a result of the interaction of the electrons in the discharge with an axial electric field. This interaction can cause the attenuation or spontaneous growth of the waves, depending upon the circumstances. It is likely that high current gas discharge experiments like these are examples of growing and decaying waves of this type.

545. (**1560**) Regirer, S. A.

[Stationary] Convective Motion of a Conducting Fluid between Parallel Vertical Plates in a Magnetic Field.

An exact solution of the magnetohydrodynamic equations is obtained for the case of a constant vertical temperature gradient. The critical value of Grasshof's number is determined for the case when the temperature of both plates is the same.

197

546. (**1561**) REGIRER, S. A.
Problème non Stationnaire de Magnétohydrodynamique pour le Demi-Espace.
Étude de l'écoulement unidimensionnel non stationnaire d'un fluide visqueux conducteur d'électricité dans un champ magnétique. 4 références bibliographiques.
(SDIT)

547. (**1562**) REID, W. H.
The Stability of Non-Dissipative Couette Flow in the Presence of an Axial Magnetic Field.
A calculation is made of the magnetic field strength H required to stabilize non-viscous flow between two rotating coaxial cylinders in the "small group" approximation. The work is based on an exact solution of the non-magnetic problem. H is found to be small for small, and also for large, angular velocity gradients; there is also a critical value for H above which the flow is stable for all angular velocity gradients.

548. (**1567**) RESLER, E. L. et SEARS, W. R.
L'influence d'un Champ Magnétique sur les Caractéristiques de l'Ecoulement d'un Gaz à travers une Canalisation.
Etablissement des équations pour l'écoulement "quasi unidimensionnel" d'un gaz conducteur électrique dans le cas d'un filet d'écoulement à section variable, sous l'influence d'un champ électrique et magnétique. Détermination de l'accélération de l'écoulement et de la variation du nombre de Mach. Possibilité d'accélération dans le cas d'une section constante du filet, dans certains domaines de vitesse. Utilisation d'un champ électromagnétique pour la création d'une "striction magnéto-aérodynamique." Accélération et décélération de l'écoulement, avec passage à travers le domaine des vitesses soniques. 3 références bibliographiques.
(SDIT)

549. (**1569**) RESLER, E. L., Jr., and SEARS, W. R.
Magneto-Aerodynamics.
The equations describing the flow of an electrically conducting fluid in the presence of electric and magnetic fields are written down with the aid of certain simplifications appropriate to aeronautical applications. In order to estimate the probable significance of magneto-aerodynamic effects, some data on conductivity of pure and "seeded" air are first examined. Dimensionless quantities representing the ratios of forces and of currents are then formed and their values studied for conditions of flight in the atmosphere. Some examples of magneto-hydrodynamic and magneto-gasdynamic effects in simple flows are given. These include two cases of Poiseuille flow of conducting liquids with applied magnetic fields and the case of quasi-one-dimensional gas flow with applied electrical and magnetic fields. In the last case, attractive possibilities are found for controlled acceleration or deceleration of gas at subsonic and supersonic speeds, even in constant-area channels. The behaviour of the flow is characteristically different in different regimes of Mach number and flow speed relative to certain "significant speeds" that are dependent on the ratio of electrical to magnetic field strengths. These are studied, and a chart is constructed to relate the length to the speed ratio of a maximum-acceleration constant-area channel. It is concluded that the advantages that may accrue from magneto-aerodynamic methods are sufficiently attractive to justify the considerable research and engineering development that will be required. Among the unsolved engineering problems are the reduction of surface resistance of electrodes in contact with a conducting gas, development of techniques for seeding, and provision of the required magnetic fields in flight.

550. (**1571**) Rhude, D. P.

Transmission of an Electromagnetic Wave Through a Hypersonic Shock Wave.
Hypersonic vehicles traversing the earth's atmosphere create a highly ionized shock region of heated and compressed air. The classical solution for electromagnetic ionospheric propagation may be best adapted to propagation through shock regions by introducing a complex dielectric constant. Shock region propagation may be considered the cumulative effect of cascaded homogeneous dielectric walls. The resultant equation may be solved by a digital computer if shock region temperature and density distribution are available. Calculations indicate that transmission is possible with less than 3 db loss if the incident frequency is greater than 20 per cent of the maximum plasma resonant frequency. (ASTIA)

551. (**1572**) Ribe, F. L.

Recent Experimental Results on Fast-Compression Plasma Heating and Rotating Plasmas.
Describes the results obtained at Los Alamos in connection with the Scylla and Ixion experiments. The first one gives estimates of the electron and ion temperature; the second one deals with the diamagnetism of the rotating plasma.

552. (**1579**) Rjazanov, E. V.

Quelques Solutions Précises des Equations de la Magnétogazdynamique en Présence des Forces de Gravitation Propre et d'un Gradient Nul de la Température.
En Russe. On donne quelques solutions précises décrivant le mouvement non stationnaire monodimensionnel d'un gaz parfait gravitant, pour le cas de la symétrie cylindrique quand on admet l'absence du gradient de t dans la région de l'écoulement.
(C.N.R.S.)

553. (**1581**) Roberts, P. H.

On The Equilibrium of Magnetic Stars.
A study is made of the mechanical equilibrium of bodies of incompressible fluid lying in a magnetic field. It is supposed that the system is symmetric about an axis. It is shown that, under certain simplifying assumptions, a series expansion can be derived for the equation of the free surface.

554. (**1584**) Roberts, P. H.

Propagation of Induced Fields through the Core.
A study is made of the hydromagnetic propagation of small magnetic disturbances from a source within a finitely conducting fluid to its boundary. The results are applied to the problem of the rate of growth of the magnetic field due to the centres of secular change.

555. (**1585**) Roberts, P. H.

On the Reflection and Refraction of Hydromagnetic Waves.
It is supposed that a plane harmonic hydromagnetic wave encounters the plane surface separating two fluids of infinite conductivity. The general laws of reflection and refraction are derived and are shown to depend on the orientation of the permanent uniform magnetic field which provides the exciting agency of the waves. In contrast to a similar problem solved by Ferraro (1954), the incident wave is supposed to have an arbitrary polarization. It is found that if this polarization has a component perpendicular to the interface, a disturbance is generated whose effect decays exponentially with distance from the interface. The skin depth of this disturbance is the same in both fluids and is infinite if the angle of incidence is zero. It is also found that, whatever the direction of incident polarization, the interface is undisturbed by the incoming wave. The reflection of a hydromagnetic wave from a free surface is also discussed in this paper.

556. (**1586**) ROBERTS, P. H.
Hydromagnetic Disturbances in a Fluid of Finite Conductivity, II.
In a previous paper the author studied the equation governing the propagation of Alfvén waves in an unbounded fluid of finite electrical conductivity. In this paper three-dimensional disturbances are investigated. It is shown that Green's functions may be derived, with the aid of which the course of an arbitrary disturbance may be followed. It is shown also that, along the direction of H_0, the disturbances are propagated in essentially the same manner as those discussed in Paper I. Walen's (1944) approximation is briefly examined and is exhibited as the first term of a series expansion of the exact solution.

557. (**1593**) ROSA, R. J.
Experimental Magnetohydrodynamic Power Generator.
Electric power is generated by drawing current from a plasma jet moving perpendicular to a 14,000 G magnetic field. A graph shows the voltage, power output, and upstream stagnation pressure as functions of the current drawn. Voltage and pressure vary linearly with current, in agreement with theory. The efficiency of this type of power generation is discussed briefly.

558. (**1596**) ROSE, P. H.
Physical Gas Dynamics Research at the Avco Research Laboratory.
Physical gas dynamic problems associated with the high temperatures involved in flight at hypersonic Mach numbers are being studied. The central concept of this study is that the important elements of the environment anticipated can be duplicated in shock tubes. For many phenomena, such as boundary layer problems (other than transition), the parameters important in classical, low-temperature aerodynamics, such as Mach and Reynolds Numbers, were shown to lose much of their importance in the high-temperature, dissociating-gas situation. Instead, the flow chemistry is shown to be a critical simulation parameter. The kinetics of the flow chemistry are simulated if the enthalpy and pressure of the gas are reproduced. The enthalpy and pressure attainable at the stagnation point of a blunt model in a shock tube are given and are shown to duplicate those encountered at the stagnation point in flight up to the satellite velocity. In addition, the condition in the hot gas behind both the moving shock wave and behind a shock wave reflected from the closed end of the tube are shown to be applicable to the study of many hypersonic flight phenomena. Several investigations, conducted in shock tubes, into critical gas dynamic problems associated with the high temperature are described. Heat-transfer measurements in the laminar, dissociated, boundary layer at the stagnation point are discussed. Measurements of the radiative emissivity and electrical conductivity of high-temperature air are described. Preliminary studies of magnetohydrodynamics are summarized.   (ASTIA)

559. (**1597**) ROSEN, P.
Variational Approach to Magneto-Fluid-Dynamics.
Author has previously shown [*J. Chem. Phys.* **21**, 1220, 1953] that the Rayleigh-Onsager principle of least dissipation of energy [*Phys. Rev.* **37**, 405, 1931] can be used to obtain a variational principle for the flow of a viscous incompressible fluid. Adding Joule losses to the viscous dissipation and suitably modifying the energy balance statement, he now arrives at a more general variational principle applying to the motion of a viscous adiabatic fluid with finite electrical conductivity. Displacement currents are omitted, as is consistent with the nonrelativistic character of the analysis.   (J. Rosen)

560. (**1598**) ROSEN, P.
Scattering of Electromagnetic Waves by Longitudinal Plasma Waves.
It is shown that Bragg reflection of electromagnetic waves from plasma oscillations is possible. The wave equation for the electromagnetic field passing through a

medium of plasma waves is derived, and it is found to be similar to that of Brillouin for a wave in a medium of variable dielectric constant.

561. (**1600**) ROSENBLUTH, M. N.
    Transport Properties of Ionized Gases in a Magnetic Field.
Etude du mouvement des particules et des collisions. Formules donnant le coefficient de diffusion et les conductibilités thermique et électrique. 2 références bibliographiques.   (SDIT)

561$_{bis}$. (**1604**)   ROSENBLUTH, M. N. and LONGMIRE, C. L.
    Stability of Plasmas Confined by Magnetic Fields.
The question of the stability of plasmas confined by magnetic fields is examined. Whereas previous studies of this problem have started from the magnetohydrodynamic equations, it has paid closer attention to the motions of individual particles. The results are similar to, but more general than, those which follow from the magnetohydrodynamic equations.

562. (**1605**) ROSENBLUTH, M. N. and KAUFMAN, A. N.
    Plasma Diffusion in a Magnetic Field.
The equations governing the diffusion of a fully ionized plasma across a magnetic field are derived. It is assumed that macroscopic quantities vary slowly across an ion radius of gyration, and that the interparticle collision frequency is much less than the gyration frequency. The relevant transport coefficients—electrical resistivity, thermal conductivity, and thermoelectric coefficient—are derived. Some similarity solutions of the equations are found.

563. (**1606**) ROSENBLUTH, M. N. and ROSTOKER, N.
    Theoretical Structure of Plasma Equations.
In high-temperature plasmas, collisions are very infrequent. Thus the charged particles travel on independent orbits determined by the electromagnetic field. At first sight this would seem completely different from a conventional fluid where particles are closely hemmed in by their neighbours. However, there can exist collective modes of motion in which the particles interact with each other by altering the fields. In this paper a new method is developed for the solution of the linearized transport equation. By facilitating direct use of the properties of particle orbits, a considerable simplification is achieved. In particular, a variational expression is derived for determining stability which is rigorous in the limit of small Larmor radius.

564. (**1608**) ROSNER, D. E. et CALCOTE, H. F.
    Generation of Supersonic Dissociated and Ionized Non-Equilibrium Streams
    (*Génération de courants supersoniques dissociés ionisés et en état de non-équilibre*).
Description d'une installation utilisant comme source d'énergie une décharge luminescente et permettant d'engendrer de tels courants. Etude de courants complètement détendus d'air, d'azote, d'argon et d'hélium aux nombres de Mach de 2 à 4. 10 références bibliographiques.   (SDIT)

565. (**1610**) ROSSOW, V. J.
    Boundary-Layer Stability Diagrams for Electrically Conducting Fluids in the Presence of a Magnetic Field.
Neutral stability curves pertaining to a two-dimensional infinitesimal sinusoidal disturbance are presented for the laminar flow of an incompressible, electrically conducting fluid over a semi-infinite flat plate in the presence of either a coplanar or transverse magnetic field. The magnetic field is found to be stabilizing in all of the cases studied except one.   (TIL/MOS)

566. (**1611**) Rossow, V. J.
On Flow of Electrically Conducting Fluids over a Flat Plate in the Presence of a Transverse Magnetic Field.
Several basic boundary-layer solutions for the velocity and temperature profiles are found for flow of electrically conducting fluid over a flat plate in the presence of a transverse magnetic field. It is concluded that the skin friction and the heat-transfer rate are reduced when the transverse magnetic field is fixed relative to the plate and increased when fixed relative to the fluid. The total drag is increased in all the cases studied.

567. (**1612**) Rossow, V. J.
Magnetohydrodynamic Analysis of Heat Transfer near a Stagnation Point.
The purposes of this note are to present the results of a heat-transfer analysis for the case in which changes in skin friction of a flat plate are brought about by a magnetic field perpendicular to it, and to compare the skin friction found with that obtained by a more approximate method in order to find the degree of approximation made by ignoring the secondary magnetic field which is induced by the motion of the fluid through the basic imposed magnetic field. (NASA)

568. (**1613**) Rossow, V. J.
L'influence de Forces Magnétiques sur les Couches Limites.
Etude de l'influence d'un champ magnétique normal à la couche limite d'un écoulement sur la répartition des vitesses et des températures dans cette dernière, dans le cas particulier d'une conductibilité électrique variable du fluide (air). Influence du champ magnétique sur les caracteristiques de frottement et de transmission de la chaleur dans le cas d'un champ magnétique fixe par rapport au fluide s'écoulant à une grande distance de la paroi. 5 références bibliographiques.
(SDIT)

569. (**1614**) Rossow, V. J.
On Series Expansions in Magnetic Reynolds Number.
The method of finding magnetohydrodynamic flow solutions by expansion of the flow parameters in a power series of the magnetic Reynolds Number $R_m = \sigma\mu Ul$ is discussed. The characteristics of the solutions so obtained are illustrated by several examples. The expansion in positive powers is a straightforward but tedious process. The expansion in negative powers is not so tedious but may not give realistic results for the terms of order higher than the first. (ASTIA)

570. (**1615**) Rossow, V. J.
On Rayleigh's Problem in Magnetohydrodynamics.
A comparison is made of three flow fields that may be described as Rayleigh's problem in magnetohydrodynamics and that differ only in the state of motion of the magnetic field. Deviations of approximate expressions for the velocity from the more exact relations are also presented when the ratio of the viscous and magnetic Reynolds Numbers is unity.

571. (**1619**) Rott, N.
A Simple Construction for the Determination of the Magnetohydrodynamic Wave Speed in a Compressible Conductor.
Etant donné un fluide compressible doué d'une conductivité électrique infinie, l'auteur indique une construction graphique qui permet d'obtenir, en chaque point dans chaque direction le carré des vitesses de propagation du son.
(H. Cabannes)

572. (**1620**) Rudakov, L. I. and Sagdeev, R. Z.
Oscillations of an Inhomogeneous Plasma in a Magnetic Field.
Small oscillations of a hot plasma confined by the pressure of a magnetic field are treated with aid of the kinetic equations in the "drift" approximation without the

collision integral. Two types of waves can exist for the wave vector lying in a plane perpendicular to the direction of the unperturbed magnetic field. One of these is a slow (drift) wave with a propagation velocity of the order of the mean electron (ion) drift velocity in the unperturbed state and the other is a magneto-acoustic wave. The first type of wave is characteristic only of an inhomogeneous plasma. For a certain interdependence between the zero magnetic field gradients, plasma density and plasma temperature the drift current in the unperturbed plasma may lead to amplification of such oscillations. The criteria for instability of this type are obtained.

573. (**1622**) RUDIN, M.
   Magnetic Channeling and the Nozzle.
It is demonstrated that one may numerically solve magnetic channeling problems, including boundary conditions, in a self-consistent manner. The only *necessary* assumptions are that a non-viscous, non-heat conducting, completely ionized gas is considered. In the method, one specifies the streamlines and computes the induced and applied magnetic field necessary to achieve this. This application to a magnetic nozzle is fully described.

574. (**1628**) SACERDOTI, G.
   Studio di un contenitore magnetico a forma di otto.
In questa nota viene studiato il moto di una particella carica in un campo magnetico di un solenoide a forma di otto. Consideriamo la intersezione della traettoria della particella con una sezione generica del solenoide. Questa intersezione ad ogni giro di rivoluzione della particella nel solenoide si sposta. Questi spostamenti possono essere descritti nel tempo come una somma di un moto uniforme piu un moto oscillatorio. Inoltre la traiettoria della particella subisce delle pendolazioni lungo l'azimut, aventi la durata di un giro di rivoluzione.

575. (**1629**) SACERDOTI, G.
   Studio del moto di una particella carica in un campo magnetico di un solenoide toroidale.
Oggetto di questo studio è la traiettoria di una particella carica che si muova nel campo magnetico di un solenoide toroidale. Vengono ricavate le formule che danno la velocità media della particella lungo l'asse del solenoide e il periodo di oscillazione della particella tra la massima e la minima distanza dall'asse del solenoide.

576. (**1630**) SACERDOTI, G.
   Studio del moto di una particella carica in un campo magnetico in presenza di un'onda elettromagnetica piána che si propaga nella direzióne del campo, nel caso non relativistico.
Si è studiato il moto di una particella carica elettricamente in un campo magnetico uniforme sotto l'azione di un'onda elettromagnetica piana polarizzata nel caso non relativistico. Si sono trovate delle formale approssimate del moto della particella; dalla loro discussione risulta che la particella è (se sono soddisfatte alcune relazioni tra la frequenza dell'onda incidente e la frequenza propria della particella nel campo magnetico) respinta dall'onda incidente indipendentemente dal segno della particella. Questo studio è di interesse nella fisica dei plasma dove si può pensare di usare un'onda elettromagnetica comestappos di un contenitore di plasmi. Si è forse ecceduto nell'esposizione del metodo matematico usato per la risoluzione del problema: abbiamo creduto opportuno fare ciò per, permettere a chi riprendesse a trattare questo argomento di avere uno schema utile per l'indagine teorica del problema. E' nostro parere che questo lavoro suggerisca anche idee e schemi per una ricerca sperimentale.

577. (**1633**) Sakkurai, T.
Two-Dimensional Hypersonic Flow of an Ideal Gas with Infinite Electric Conductivity Past a Two-Dimensional Magnetic Dipole.

Burgers and Tamaola have investigated the possibility of the existence of a so-called "frozen region", into which the flow surrounding a magnetic dipole may not penetrate. The fluid was supposed to be incompressible. In this note the author shows the possibility of the existence of such a region even in the hypersonic flow.

578. (**1636**) Sawyer, G. A., Scott, P. L. and Stratton, T. F.
Experimental Demonstration of Hydromagnetic Waves in an Ionized Gas.

A regular hydromagnetic oscillation was excited in a linear discharge tube with metal walls. An externally applied axial magnetic field and discharge currents less than 10^4 amperes were essential to the production of the oscillation. Complete spatial current distributions derived from measurements of the radial and time dependence of the three components of magnetic field showed a helical notch (screw thread) of reduced current density which rotated with uniform angular velocity. The pitch and apparent rotational frequency of the oscillation depended on the gas density, discharge current, and applied axial magnetic field; the right- or left-handedness and rotational sense depended on the relative orientation of the applied axial magnetic field and the self field of the discharge current. The helical regularity could be described as a superposition of hydromagnetic waves travelling in the axial and circumferential directions.

579. (**1651**) Schlüter, A.
On Magneto-Fluid-Dynamics.

The applicability of the usual magnetohydrodynamic equations is investigated, attention being focused on the range of strong magnetic fields and low density where the collision frequency is less than the gyro-frequency of the charged particles. By gradually increasing the complexity of the description of a plasma it is shown that the major modification of magnetohydrodynamic equations consists in splitting up the pressure into the pressures normal and parallel to the magnetic field while the main dissipative effect is due to gyro-relaxation which tends to equalize these pressures.

580. (**1666**) Schumann, W. O.
Sur les Ondes Hydromagnétiques dans les Plasmas.

Etude de la propagation des ondes électriques, compte tenu de la diffusion des électrons, dans un plasma soumis à un champ magnétique extérieur intense, dans le cas où la fréquence de giration du support est très supérieure au nombre de collisions du support par seconde. 9 références bibliographiques.   (SDIT)

581. (**1677**) Sears, W. R.
Magnetohydrodynamics in Aeronautics.

This discussion of the theory of magnetohydrodynamics covers such points as: the equations of motion in MHD, various dimensionless parameters, magneto-gas-dynamic channel flow, effects of varying magnetic Reynolds Number, small-perturbation plane incompressible flow, etc.   (Cornell Aer. Lab.)

582. (**1678**) Sears, W. R.
Magnetics May Aid Return of Satellites, Missiles and Rockets.

The new science of magneto-aero-dynamics may provide the means for the safe return of artificial satellites to the earth's surface, according to an advance summary of research results in this field presented by W. R. Sears in a lecture at the National Academy of Sciences.

583. (**1679**) Sears, W. R.
Some Solutions of the Macroscopic Equations of Magnetohydrodynamics.
A report is made on three different theoretical investigations concerning magneto-hydrodynamics of inviscid incompressible fluids. These three studies concern the following cases: (1) Thin airfoils and slender bodies in fluids of moderate conductivity; this pertains to flows having uniform, parallel magnetic and velocity fields in the undisturbed region. (2) An inviscid magnetic boundary layer; this is a non-linear treatment for fluids of large but finite conductivity and also involves the case of uniform, parallel fields in the free stream. (3) Some flows involving tensor conductivity; here some flows previously studied, namely steady flow past a corrugated wall and one-dimensional wave propagation (Alfvén waves) are generalized for a fluid in which the Hall effect is appreciable.

584. (**1680**) Sears, W. R. and Resler, E. L.
Theory of Thin Airfoils in Fluids of high Electrical Conductivity.
Steady plane flows of incompressible fluid past thin cylindrical bodies are treated with the undisturbed uniform magnetic field taken to be (1) parallel to, and (2) perpendicular to, the undisturbed uniform stream. Only flows with large (or infinite) conductivity are considered. The theory would apply to flows at high "magnetic Reynolds Numbers," e.g. to flows involving high gas temperatures or flows of liquid metals. The linearized equations are derived for flows with infinite conductivity. In case (1), the flow is shown to be irrotational (unless the stream velocity is equal to the Alfvén velocity) and current-free except for surface currents at the bodies. In case (2) the flow fluid is composed of a system of waves involving currents and vorticity. In case (1) flows with large finite conductivity are treated by a boundary-layer approximation, the surface currents being replaced by thin boundary layers of large current density. In case (2) flows with large finite conductivity cause damping of the wave system. Results are given for forces on sinusoidal walls and on airfoils. (A. Babister)

585. (**1681**) Sears, W. R.
Magnetohydrodynamic Effects in Aerodynamic Flows.
I. Reviewer feels that this is an excellent introduction to the theory of magneto-hydrodynamics, with particular reference to the effects of interest to aeronautical engineers. A brief survey of possible practical applications, and a good bibliography are included. (D. Holder)
II. Rappel des phénomènes nouveaux qui interviennent dans l'aéromagnétodynamique; équations du mouvement, écoulement dans les canaux, influence du nombre de Reynolds magnétique, théorie des petites perturbations, applications à l'aéronautique. 52 références bibliographiques. (SDIT)

586. (**1688**) Sen, H. K.
Structure of a Magnetohydrodynamic Shock Wave in a Plasma of Infinite Conductivity.
The structure of a magnetohydrodynamic perpendicular shock wave (magnetic field perpendicular to the direction of propagation) in a plasma of infinite conductivity has been analysed. For the non-magnetic case, the width of the shock front is found to be larger than in a non-ionized gas. Further, the width of the shock (in terms of mean free path within the shock) as a function of the shock strength as determined from the Stokes-Navier equations (which applies to weak shocks) is found to join smoothly at $M \simeq 1 \cdot 3$ with the same function as derived from the Mott-Smith analysis (which applies to strong shocks). The magnetic field tends to make the shock front narrower for shocks of moderate strength. It does not have appreciable effect for strong shocks. Application of the above results to solar radio noise and current theories of the origin of cosmic rays is indicated.

587. (**1699**) SENIOR, T. B. A.
Diffraction by an Imperfectly Conducting Wedge.
Author considers the problem of an electromagnetic wave incident upon a wedge whose conductivity is large but not infinite. Previous solutions of this problem proved to be unsatisfactory. The basis of the author's method is one developed by A. S. Peters for the exact solution of a mixed boundary-value problem in hydrodynamics involving the equation $\Delta^2\phi - k^2\phi = 0$. By means of the Laplace transform, the electromagnetic wave boundary-value problem is transformed into one involving a difference equation for the determination of an analytic function whose real part represents the velocity potential. Although the method used is essentially that of Wiener-Hopf, it is of wider scope since it is not necessarily restricted to cases involving discontinuities in parallel planes. Reviewer believes that the method presented here increases significantly the number of problems in electromagnetic wave theory that can be solved analytically. (E. Scott)

588. (**1701**) SEYMOUR, P. W.
Drift of a Charged Particle in a Magnetic Field of Constant Gradient.
An exact solution is obtained for the drift velocity. The method easily yields as approximations of Alfvén's results (1940 and 1950) and the case of circular orbit, and includes the case of zero mean field, for which perturbation methods are inappropriate.

589. (**1704**) SHAPHRANOV, V. D.
On the Stability of a Cylindrical Gaseous Conductor in a Magnetic Field.
Hydrodynamical conditions are obtained for the stability of an ideal cylindrical gaseous conductor in an external magnetic field.

590. (**1706**) SHAPHRANOV, V. D.
On Magnetohydrodynamical Equilibrium Configurations. Appendix: Criteria for the Stability of a Perfectly Conducting Cylinder with a Surface Current.
Investigation of the equilibrium conditions for bounded systems of a conducting gas in a magnetic field. The equilibrium conditions for a gravitating ring with current embedded in a gaseous atmosphere, and for a ring in an external magnetic field are considered. A theorem is formulated showing the analogy between the magnetohydrodynamical equilibrium systems and the hydrodynamical vortices. The problem of the equilibrium conditions for magnetohydrodynamical configurations is reduced to the theory of stationary flow of an incompressible fluid by this theorem. General equilibrium conditions for an axially symmetric system are considered. (Aero/Space)

591. (**1707**) SHAPHRANOV, V. D.
Propagation of an Electromagnetic Field in a Medium with Spatial Dispersion.
General formulas are obtained for the propagation of an electromagnetic field in a semi-infinite, homogeneous, anisotropic medium with spatial dispersion. The propagation of a transverse wave along a magnetic field in a plasma is investigated, taking account of the thermal motion of the electrons. Strong absorption of the field is found in the region for which Cerekov radiation is possible in the plasma.

592. (**1708**) SHANKARANARAYANA, R. B.
A Note on Rotating Configuration Associated with Toroidal Magnetic Field.
The equilibrium form of an incompressible fluid mass rotating about an axis in presence of a toroidal magnetic field, whose axis coincides with the axis of rotation, is discussed and the conditions that the equilibrium configuration may be a sphere, a prolate spheroid or an oblate spheroid are derived.

593. (**1710**) SHARIKADZE, D. V.

Mouvements Automodèles et l'Explosion Ponctuelle dans la Magnétogazo-dynamique dans le Cas de Conductibilité Infinie du Gaz.

(En russe.) Etude analytique dans l'hypothèse que l'*i* du champ magnétique puisse etre représentée comme une fonction de l'entropie. (C.N.R.S.)

594. (**1713**) SHERCLIFF, J. A.

The Flow of Conducting Fluids in Circular Pipes Under Transverse Magnetic Fields.

The flow rate of liquid metals is commonly measured by electromagnetic flow-meters. In these the fluid moves through a region of transverse magnetic field, inducing a potential difference between two electrodes on the walls of the pipe. The ratio signal-to-flow rate is dependent on the velocity profile, and this is affected by electromagnetic forces. In this paper the ultimate steady velocity profile and its associated pressure gradient and induced potential are calculated for the case of laminar flow in a circular pipe whose walls are conducting but without contract resistance. Laminar flow is encouraged by a transverse field. When the fluid conductivity and field strength are sufficiently high, boundary layers occur with a thickness inversely proportional to normal field intensity. The induced potential difference is then 0·926 of the value corresponding to the case of uniform velocity if the walls are non-conducting. The distance the fluid must travel after entering the transverse field before the steady state is next estimated by a Rayleigh approxi-mation. The inlet velocity is taken to be uniform and effects which occur at the edge of the field are neglected. The process falls into two stages, first a boundary-layer growth and then an adjustment of the velocity away from the walls, occupying a much greater length of pipe. The entry length is shorter than it is in the case of flow in a rectangular pipe, but is still too long for appreciable distortion of the velocity profile to occur within practical flowmeters except at flow rates. The pressure drop associated with the adjustment of the velocity profile is found to be independent of field strength, if this is high, and about one-eighth of the drop which occurs in the non-conducting case. Experiments are described in which steady-state pressure gradients and potential differences were measured in mercury flowing along Perspex pipes of 0·5 and 0·25 in. bore in transverse fields up to 14,500 gauss. The results confirmed the steady-state theory within the limitations of experimental accuracy and the assumption in the theory of high conductivity and an intense field. The experiments also covered the entry region in many cases, and showed that theoretical entry lengths were correct in order of magnitude but over-estimated. However, the exact entry condition was uncertain, and steady readings were difficult to obtain in the entry region.

595. (**1714**) SHERCLIFF, J. A.

Relation between the Velocity Profile and the Sensitivity of Electromagnetic Flowmeters.

In a transverse field flowmeter of circular section with non-conducting walls, the sensitivity is known to be independent of velocity profile provided this is axially symmetric. This paper develops a general solution for the case of non-symmetric profiles, and shows that the flowmeter sensitivity may then vary very greatly and even become negative, if the profile is sufficiently distorted, e.g. by upstream effects.

596. (**1715**) SHERCLIFF, J. A.

Some Engineering Applications of Magneto-Hydrodynamics.

The sensitivity of an electromagnetic flowmeter depends on the form of the velocity profile, which is affected by upstream conditions and, when the fluid is a highly conducting liquid metal, by magneto-hydrodynamic forces. The steady state of the velocity profile and the distance necessary for it to be reached are predicted and compared with experiment. Other results concern the settling of the motion in a flowmeter downstream of an obstruction.

597. (**1718**) SHERCLIFF, J. A.
Experiments on the Dependence of Sensitivity on Velocity Profile in Electromagnetic Flowmeters.

Mercury was passed along a non-conducting circular tube bearing flowmeter-type electrodes situated in a transverse magnetic field downstream of a small offset orifice. When the flow was concentrated near the electrodes the ratio of induced potential difference to the product of magnetic field and flow rate was found to reach more than twice the value appropriate to axially symmetric velocity profiles. When the flow was concentrated at the side of the tube this ratio could fall to zero and even change sign. Further downstream a steady state was reached, sometimes in an oscillatory manner.

598. (**1720**) SHERCLIFF, J. A.
Electromagnetic Flowmeter without External Magnet.

Further characteristics of Kolin's proposed flowmeter, in which the field is excited by an axial current in the fluid, are pointed out. These include improved insensitivity to the form of velocity profile if the walls are conducting, and the advantage that ferromagnetic walls present no difficulty.

599. (**1721**) SHERCLIFF, J. A.
Magnetogasdynamics and its Possible Aeronautical Applications.

At hypersonic speeds, ionization, like dissociation, produces real gas effects but also makes the air electrically conducting so that the flow may be affected by electromagnetic body forces. At the same time any imposed magnetic field will be affected by currents in the air. The dimensionless groups governing these two and other effects are discussed. Electromagnetic interaction also affects the energy and entropy equations. Possible applications include the increase of drag without surface heating, electrical energy generation by the flow, and electrically driven high-energy ground-test equipment.

600. (**1723**) SHIROKOV, M. F.
Interaction Between Gravitational-Capillary and Magnetohydrodynamic Waves.

Demonstration of the uniqueness theorem for the solutions of the hydrodynamic equations for an incompressible strongly conducting ideal liquid. A procedure to determine the Walen solution for gravitational-capillary and magnetohydrodynamic waves is shown. Relations for the stability conditions and the penetration depth are derived for potential and vortex harmonic waves. It is shown that the strongest effect on the concentration of the potential magnetohydrodynamic waves in the surface layer is that due to the capillary forces, and that the current density for the potential surface waves is exactly zero.   (Aero/Space)

601. (**1725**) SHMOYS, J. and MISHKIN, E.
Hydromagnetic Waveguide with Finite Conductivity and Arbitrary Cross Section.

Low pressure magnetohydrodynamic waveguides of arbitrary cross-section, having a diaxial magnetic field, exhibit both TE and TM modes. The longitudinal electric field vanishes when the conductivity of the plasma is infinite, converting the TM modes into principal ones. The propagation constants for both modes are derived from the solutions of the eigenvalue problems. Linearized magnetohydrodynamic equations are used.

602. (**1726**) SHPIGEL, I. S.
Plasma Acceleration.

We consider acceleration of plasma in vacuum in an axially symmetric, inhomogeneous pulsed magnetic field. The density of the plasma bunches is approximately 10^{12} particles per cm^3. The maximum energies for various atomic ions are as follows: nitrogen and oxygen, approximately 190 eV; helium, approximately 280 eV; hydrogen, approximately 120 eV.

603. (**1728**) SIEGEL, R.

Effect of a Magnetic Field on Forced Convection Heat Transfer in a Parallel Plate Channel.

The steady flow of a conducting liquid, between two parallel plates, under the influence of a transverse magnetic field has been studied by Hartmann and Lazarus [see T. G. Cowling, "Magneto-fluid-dynamics," *Interscience*, 1957, p. 13]. Their solution is used in the present paper to determine the temperature distribution in the liquid, which depends partly on the heat transfer across the plates and partly on Joule heating. Relatively simple expressions are found for the constant temperature gradient along the direction of flow and for the wall temperature in terms of the mean temperature of the fluid. (K. Stewartson)

604. (**1731**) SILIN, V. P.

The Oscillations of a Degenerate Electron Fluid.

The oscillations of an electron fluid are treated on the basis of the Landau theory of the Fermi fluid. The oscillations reduce to longitudinal plasma waves, transverse electromagnetic waves, zeroth sound, and spin waves.

605. (**1733**) SIMON, A.

Ignition of a Thermonuclear Plasma by High-Energy Injection.

Some prototypes of thermonuclear machines use ions accelerated to high energies and then injected into a magnetic container ("mirror geometry"). The terminal ion density is reduced by charge exchange with residual neutral molecules, converting the fast ion into a fast neutral which escapes the magnetic container and leaves only a slow ion behind. Author shows that for sufficiently large input currents a condition designated as "burnout" can be achieved in which neutrals entering the magnetic containment region are ionized and removed through the leakage of the container more rapidly than they can enter. Approximate equations for these conditions are numerically integrated and it is found that the density of the neutral gas background may be reduced by orders of magnitude. (W. Elsasser)

606. (**1738**) SIMON, A. and HARRIS, G. E.

Kinetic Equation for Plasma and Radiation.

The starting point is the Liouville equation for the density in phase space of a system of charged particles and a denumerably infinite set of field oscillators. By integrating out the co-ordinates of all but a finite number of particles and oscillators one obtains a chain of equations relating the reduced distribution functions. A complete solution to the chain is obtained by a generalization of the expansion method of Rosenbluth and Rostoker. In lowest order, a coupled set of self-consistent field equations in the one-particle and one-oscillator distribution is obtained. These are partially decoupled to give the usual Vlasov equations and a companion equation for the oscillator distribution. In first order one obtains a similar set of equations for the two-particle and the particle-oscillator correlation functions. An entirely similar pair of equations then relates the first-order distribution functions themselves. It appears that the general solution is obtained by the steady unfolding of higher correlation functions in terms of higher and higher self-consistent field equations. The first order equations can be regarded as a "Fokker-Plank" equation for particles and a "Fokker-Plank" equation for radiation.

607. (**1740**) SIMON, R.

On the Reflection and Refraction of Hydromagnetic Waves at the Boundary of Two Compressible Gaseous Media.

The reflection and refraction of a hydromagnetic plane wave at a plane boundary between two semi-infinite homogeneous media of infinite electrical conductivity are discussed when a uniform magnetic field is present. It is shown that, owing to the compressibility of the two media, one must expect any incident plane wave to give rise to three types of reflected waves and three types of refracted waves; these six waves can be either real or imaginary, depending on circumstances. In the particular case when the prevailing magnetic field is perpendicular to the plane boundary, a detailed analysis of the laws of reflection and refraction is given.

608. (**1747**) Sisco, W. and Fiskin, J. M.
Shock Ionization Changes EM Propagation Characteristics.
Whenever a space craft leaves or enters a planet's atmosphere, the propagation characteristics of its electronic equipment change sharply for the simple reason that the craft creates enough of a disturbance in the molecules surrounding it to charge their dielectric constants and conductivities. Fortunately, these effects of "shock ionization" can be fairly well estimated in advance.

609. (**1749**) Skabelund, D. E.
Hydromagnetic Waves of Finite Amplitude in a Homogeneous Magnetic Field.
An investigation was made of the most general conditions under which there exist wave solutions of finite amplitude to the hydromagnetic equations for an ideal, incompressible, perfectly conducting, and unbounded fluid in a homogeneous magnetic field, subject to the condition that there be no interaction between waves travelling in opposite directions. It is found that P and Q, the field variables appearing in the symmetrized hydromagnetic equations, must satisfy the relation $(P)Q = (Q \cdot \nabla)P = \nabla \psi$. After proving that wave solutions exist only when $\nabla \psi$ vanishes, the solutions are obtained in explicit form; they are of two types: (1) P and Q are parallel plane waves. (2) P and Q are parallel and plane polarized. The entire problem is shown to be equivalent to finding all superpositions of Alfvén waves.

610. (**1750**) Skuridin, G. A. and Staniukovich, K. M.
An Approximate Solution of a Problem Concerning the Motion of a Conducting Plasma.
One-dimensional motion of an imperfectly conducting gas in a transverse magnetic field is considered. The energy equation is apparently disregarded, and the remaining equation describing the motion is approximately solved by assuming that the magnetic field has the form

$$(\partial/\partial x)A(x, t) \exp [i\omega f(x, t)]$$

where $A^{-1}\partial^2 A/\partial x^2 \ll \omega^2(\partial f/\partial x)^2 = \text{const } k$, and k is the magnetic viscosity.
(O. Penrose)

611. (**1751**) Skuridin, G. A. and Staniukovich, K. M.
Motion of a Conducting Plasma Under the Action of a Piston.
The results obtained in the preceding abstract are specialized to a case where a uniformly accelerated piston, initially at rest, moves into the gas. The part of the motion which precedes the formation of a strong shock is ignored.

612. (**1754**) Slepian, J.
Hydromagnetic Equations for Two Isotopes in a Completely Ionized Gas.
The hydromagnetic equation for a completely ionized gas of high density with a single isotope is given, and from it the two hydromagnetic equations with two isotopes is derived. The difference between the accelerations of the isotopes at any internal point is then equal to $S \, M/M$ times.

613. (**1756**) SMIRNOV, A. G.
        Free Thermal Convection of Mercury in a Closed Circular Tube in a Transverse Magnetic Field.
An experimental study is made of the effect of a homogeneous magnetic field (from 70 to 7000 gauss) on the free convective motion of mercury in a closed circular glass tube inclined at 10° with the vertical under certain thermal conditions. Two cases are studied: (A) the direction of the magnetic field is perpendicular to the plane of separation of the rising and descending currents in the tube, and (B) the direction of the magnetic field is parallel to this plane.   (Appl. Mech. Rev.)

614. (**1757**) SMIRNOV, A. G.
        Theory of Certain Magnetohydrodynamic Phenomena occurring in the free Laminar Thermal Convection of an Electrically Conducting Fluid in a Round Vertical Pipe Located in a Weak Magnetic Field.
Considers the way the magnetic action does not essentially distort the hydrodynamic currents, so that it is possible to refer to magnetic corrections.

615. (**1766**) SOROKIN, V. S. and SUSHKIN, I. V.
        Stability of Equilibrium of a Conducting Liquid Heated from Below in a Magnetic Field.
The influence of a uniform magnetic field on the stability of equilibrium of a conducting liquid heated from below in a cavity of arbitrary form is investigated in a general form. The time variation of the perturbations appearing in the liquid is always monotonic. The critical value of the Rayleigh number, C_0^2, above which equilibrium is unstable increases monotonically with the Hartmann number M, so that the inequality $dC_0(M)/dM < C_0(M)$ is observed. For small values of M the critical Rayleigh number is proportional to M^2, and the proportionality coefficient can be exactly evaluated. The asymptotic behaviour of the function $C_0(M)$ for $M \to \infty$ depends on the shape of the cavity and the direction of the field.

616. (**1772**) SPITZER, L., Jr.
        The Stellarator Concept.
All the work dealing with the attainment of economic nuclear fusion and actively under way since about 1950 has recently been declassified. Project Matterhorn, located in Princeton, has been concerned with a discharge in a torus. High-temperature plasma is confined by means of a magnetic field. In order to avoid certain types of instability, the longitudinal lines of force produced by an external coil are spirally twisted in a prescribed way. The resulting device, known as the stellarator, had originally a figure-8 form, but later it proved possible to return to a single torus on producing an equivalent twist by means of auxiliary coils. After initial breakdown, complete ionization of the gas and heating is produced by a longitudinal electric current. Since this was found to have certain drawbacks, other methods of heating such as resonance absorption of microwaves are under active investigation. The paper under review, written by the director of the project, expounds the basic principles of the magnetic confinement and heating to high temperatures of an ionized gas in a machine of this type. It forms the introduction to a quite lengthy series of papers contained in *Physics of Fluids*, **1**, Nos. 4 and 5, 1958, in which a number of collaborators discuss a variety of theoretical and practical problems of the stellarator. This includes geometry of magnetic fields, problems of the stability of magnetically confined ionized gases, problems of heating by various methods, and parasitic phenomena and their prevention.
                                                                            (W. Elsasser)

617. (**1777**) SPORN, P. and KANTROWITZ, A.
        Magnetohydrodynamics—Future Power Process?
Article discusses briefly various methods for direct conversion of thermal energy to electrical energy for power applications. The developments in thermoelectric

generation, thermionic generation and magnetohydrodynamic generation are briefly compared with power production by means of fission processes and steam turbo-generators. The magnetohydrodynamic generator system is explored non-technically in terms of anticipated economic advantage and feasibility. Major problem areas in the path of rapid technical exploitation are outlined. The article suggests that there will exist in the future a concerted effort by the utility companies to exploit the magnetohydrodynamic generation system. (R. Drake)

618. (**1778**) Stambler, I.
    La Magnétohydrodynamique.
Aperçu des recherches actuelles, effectuées en particulier par la firme Giannini Plasmadyne, concernant les applications des plasmas à la propulsion et l'utilisation des phénomènes magnétohydrodynamiques pour la rentrée dans l'atmosphère.
    (SDIT)

619. (**1779**) Stanjukovich, K. P.
    Ondes Magnétohydrodynamiques, Cylindriques et Planes.
Etude théorique des ondes cylindriques formées dans un milieu conducteur sous l'action du champ magnétique. Dans le present article on se limite au cas de la conductibilité infinie et de l'isentropicité du mouvement avec condition de la perpendicularité du champ magnétique à la direction de la *v*. (C.N.R.S.)

620. (**1781**) Stanjukovitch, K. P.
    Quelques Mouvements Stationnaires Relativistes d'un Gaz dans un Milieu Conducteur.
Etude des mouvements quasi-unidimensionnels en présence d'un champ magné-tique perpendiculaire à la vitesse. Cas des mouvements à symétrie cylindrique. 1 référence bibliographique.
    (SDIT)

621. (**1784**) Starr, W. L.
    A Propulsion Device Using an Exploding-Wire Plasma Accelerator.
A device that accelerates a plasma derived from an exploding wire to velocities of 8×10^6 cm/sec has been developed. A description of the experimental apparatus used and the results attained is given in this report. The impulse produced is about 10^3 dyne sec and, for a firing rate of 1 sec^{-1}, a thrust of 50 dynes/cm^2 is presently attainable. A brief analysis of the accelerating forces and their dependence on circuit parameters is also presented.
    (Lockheed)

622. (**1785**) Starr, W. L.
    Impulse from an Exploding-Wire Plasma Accelerator.
Specific impulses considerably in excess of those possible with current chemical systems have been obtained with a plasma accelerator operating in a vacuum and using the vapour from an electrically exploded fine-wire as the propellant.
    (Lockheed)

623. (**1791**) Steketee, J. A.
    The Oscillating Plate in Magnetohydrodynamics.
Paper considers harmonic oscillations of a flat plate parallel to itself when it is immersed in a slightly viscous conducting field in presence of a normal magnetic field. Both a magnetic and a viscous boundary layer are seen to arise whose thickness is inversely proportional to the inverse square roots of the respective Reynolds Numbers.
    (L. Trilling)

624. (**1792**) Steketee, J. A.
    An Introduction to the Equations of Magnetogasdynamics.
The purpose of this review is to facilitate the study of magnetohydrodynamics and magnetogasdynamics for aerodynamic scientists. The review is divided into two parts. In part A a short discussion of Maxwell's equations in isotropic media at rest is given while the modifications are indicated which have to be made if the

media are in motion. In part B the equations of Maxwell and the hydrodynamic equations are combined to obtain the usual equations of magnetohydrodynamics. No special solutions of the equations are discussed; on the contrary the discussion finishes where the ordinary research report begins.

625. (**1794**) STEPANOV, K. N.
   Low-Frequency Oscillations of a Plasma in a Magnetic Field.
The low frequency electron-ion longitudinal oscillations in a plasma confined by a magnetic field are considered.

626. (**1795**) STEPANOV, K. N.
   Penetration of an Electromagnetic Field into a Plasma.
The depth of penetration of an electromagnetic field into a semi-infinite plasma in a magnetic field perpendicular to the plasma boundary is calculated.

627. (**1798**) STEPANOV, V. G., ZAKHARENKO, V. F. and BEZEL, V. S.
   On a Rotating Plasma.
(In Russian.) Description of experiments with a plasma and a rotating magnetic field (3000 rpm). A mercury arc provides the plasma and a small vane indicates the rotation of the fluid. Authors note that large centrifugal accelerations are possible and that mechanical strength is not the limit.   (R. Betchov)

628. (**1804**) STIX, T. H.
   Generation and Thermalization of Plasma Waves.
The generation of hydromagnetic and ion cyclotron waves by an induction coil is considered. Rapid thermalization of transverse plasma waves occurs when appreciable numbers of ions stream through the periodic perturbation with velocities such that in their own rest frames these ions "feel" the perturbation at their own cyclotron frequency. This effect, termed cyclotron damping, makes an efficient plasma heating scheme for thermonuclear reactors possible. (Appl. Mech. Rev.)

629. (**1805**) STIX, T. H.
   Absorption of Plasma Waves.
The propagation of waves through a plasma, wherein the density and/or magnetic field strength are slowly varying functions of position is discussed. If the local propagation constant, k_x, is a slowly varying function of x, the adiabatic approximation will be valid. However, k_x^2 may pass through zero as a function of x. Using the WKB linear turning point connection formulas, examination shows that an incoming plasma wave is totally reflected in the region where $k_x^2 \approx 0$. A similar analysis for the case where kx is a singular function of x shows that absorption of an incoming wave occurs in the vicinity of the singularity. Such singular behaviour in k_x^2 can occur for propagation along the magnetic field when the wave frequency is equal to the local ion electron cyclotron frequency. For propagation transverse to the magnetic field, an apparent singularity occurs at a frequency somewhat below the ion cyclotron frequency, and at the two hybrid frequencies of Auer, Hurwitz and Miller. A detailed examination, including higher order effects in electron mass $\div$ ion mass, finite electron and ion temperatures, and ion-ion and ion-electron collision shows that the absorption will take place at the apparent singularity, only if the physical damping processes are strong enough to swamp the reactive effects of the higher order corrections. Otherwise the higher order reactive effects introduce a new propagation mode into the dispersion equation with a root which is in the vicinity of the apparent singularity instead of absorption. It is, however, conjectured that some of the original mode energy may be reflected into the new mode. As the new mode recedes from the region of the apparent singularity, its wavelength can become comparable to the particle Larmor radius. Energy in this mode may then be absorbed by phase-mixing processes which are of high order in the quantity Larmor radius $\div$ wavelength. Wave reflections

from the apparent singularities will then heat ions in the case of the transverse ion cyclotron mode, and electrons in the case of the upper hybrid frequency.

630. (**1806**) STIX, T. H.
Oscillations of a Cylindrical Plasma.
The natural modes of oscillation of a cylindrical plasma of finite density at zero pressure in a longitudinal magnetic field are examined. When one considers frequencies well below the electron plasma and electron cyclotron frequencies, there appear in two limiting cases hydromagnetic waves, and waves whose natural frequencies are close to the ion cyclotron frequency. This cyclotron frequency resonance occurs when the wavelength of the oscillation in the Z direction is short compared to the wavelength for light in vacuum corresponding to the root square sum of the ion plasma frequency and the ion cyclotron frequency.

631. (**1807**) STIX, T. H. and PALLADINO, R. W.
Experiments on Ion Cyclotron Resonance.
The theory indicates the possibility of heating a plasma by feeding radio-frequency radiation (about 10 Mc). The article describes a small stellarator and the technique used to feed the energy, excite a helium plasma at the cyclotron frequency of the doubly charged ions, and measure the adsorbed power. Experiments at the milliwatt level support the theory and indicate efficiency of at least 60 per cent.

(R. Betchov)

632. (**1808**) STIX, T. H. and PALLADINO, R. W.
Observation of Ion Cyclotron Waves.
The existence of ion cyclotron waves had been inferred from theoretical calculations and indirectly from experimental observation. In this paper direct experimental observations are repeated of phenomena appropriate to these waves in hot plasma. An induction coil energized at 11·5 Mc with approximately 200,000 W of r.f. power surrounds a deuterium plasma confined in a 16-kilograms magnetic field. A single-turn r.f. magnetic probe located in the plasma about 50 cm down the axis from the centre of the induction coil is used to detect the propagated wave. The probe is movable. Radial motion of the probe shows the expected penetration of the transverse r.f. field into the centre of the plasma. Axial motion of the probe shows a 300-cm damping length and an oscillation wavelength 64 per cent longer than the calculated value. The probe signals disappear when the ion cyclotron frequency is less than the induction coil frequency, which is a result predicted from the ion cyclotron wave dispersion relation.

633. (**1810**) STONE, I.
La Giannini Plasmadyne Corp. Etudie les Applications des Jets de Plasma.
Aperçu des recherches effectuées par cette firme sur les applications des plasmas à l'aérodynamique et à la propulsion, la magnétohydrodynamique, les matériaux pour températures extrêmes, etc. (SDIT)

634. (**1811**) STUART, J. T.
On the Stability of Viscous Flow Between Parallel Planes in the Presence of a Co-Planar Magnetic Field.
Linearized equations are derived which govern the stability of a viscous, electrically conducting fluid in motion between two parallel planes in the presence of a co-planar magnetic field. With one suitable approximation, which restricts the valid range of Reynolds number of the theory, the problem of stability is reduced to the solution of a fourth-order ordinary differential equation. (TIL/MOS)

635. (**1813**) STURROCK, P. A.
Excitation of Plasma Oscillations
The theory of Bohm and Gross and the experiments of Looney and Brown upon the excitation of plasma oscillations by two stream mechanisms, which appear

superficially to be in disagreement, are shown to be compatible with each other and with selected experiments.

636. (**1818**) SUTTON, G. W.
   Electrical and Pressure Losses in a Magnetohydrodynamic Channel due to End Current Loops.

USAF-supported investigation of the problem of end losses in magnetohydrodynamic flow for incompressible inviscid flow in a rectangular channel. Termination of the magnetic field at the ends of the electrodes leads to electrical losses which increase with decreasing aspect ratio of the electrode section of the channel. The losses are also increased with increasing values of the generator coefficient. These electrical losses can be corrected by extensions of the magnetic field beyond the electrode region, but these corrections adversely affect the net pressure change through the device. (Aero/Space)

637. (**1820**) SUTTON, G. W.
   Design Considerations of a Steady DC Magnetohydrodynamic Electrical Power Generator.

USAF-supported evaluation of the design requirements of a steady, dc magnetohydrodynamic electrical power generator. Expressions are derived for the generator power, size, efficiency, and magnet power. Losses due to heat transfer and electrical effects are calculated. Considerations of the Hall effect indicate that there is a relation between the pressure and magnetic field which yields the minimum length generator. (Aero/Space)

638. (**1824**) SYKES, J.
   The Equilibrium of a Self-Gravitating Rotating Incompressible Fluid Spheroid with a Magnetic Field.

It is shown that there exists a solution of the equations of hydromagnetic equilibrium such that the field vanishes; identically outside an oblate spheroid of small eccentricity, containing conducting fluid in non-rigid rotation.

639. (**1825**) SYROVATSKII, S. I.
   Sur la stabilité des ondes de choc en magnétohydrodynamique.

Étude de l'interaction des ondes de choc dans un champ magnétique avec les ondes magnétohydrodynamiques de faible amplitude. 6 références bibliographiques. (SDIT)

640. (**1827**) SYROVATSKII, S. J.
   Magnetic Hydrodynamics.

The fundamental results obtained, which disclose the characteristic features of the cycle of phenomena for plasma moving in a magnetic field, are discussed, and explained. With few exceptions, applications of these results are not considered. A detailed bibliography refers to various phases of the subject field.

(TIL/MOS)

641. (**1833**) TALWAR, S. P. and ABBI, S. S.
   On the Change in Shape of a Gravitating Fluid Sphere in a Uniform External Electric Field.

The stability of a conducting, gravitating, incompressible fluid sphere in a uniform external electric field is discussed by two different methods—the "energy method" and the "equilibrium method." The results obtained by both methods show that the stable configuration is a prolate of ellipticity,

$$\epsilon/R = \frac{5E^2R^2}{2GM^2}.$$

642. (**1835**) Tandon, J. N.
A Note on the Oscillations of an Infinite Cylinder Subject to Radial Magnetic Field.

The oscillation of a cylindrical fluid in the presence of a permanent magnetic field has been considered. The magnetic field has been assumed due to infinite axial line magnetic pole.

643. (**1836**) Tandon, J. N. and Talwar, S. P.
Radial Pulsation of an Infinite Cylinder in the Presence of Magnetic Field.

The general equation governing the radial pulsations of an infinite cylinder having volume currents has been derived and the integral formulae for the frequency of pulsations are deduced for two models of current density, viz., (i) circular currents and (ii) line currents. It is found that the cylinder remains dynamically stable for the two models of current system.

644. (**1837**) Taniuti, T.
Sur la Propagation des Ondes Hydromagnétiques dans un Fluide Compressible Ionisé.

Etude mathématique, basée sur la méthode des caractéristiques, de la propagation d'ondes due au mouvement combiné de l'écoulement hydrodynamique et du champ magnétique. 8 références bibliographiques.   (SDIT)

645. (**1840**) Tao, L. N.
Magnetohydrodynamic Effects on the Formation of Couette Flow.

This paper is concerned with the problem of the formation of Couette flow, i.e. the problem of how the velocity profile varies with the time tending asymptotically to that of the steady flow of an electrically conducting viscous fluid in the presence of a magnetic field. The governing equations and boundary conditions are established and discussed. The cases of both vanishing and non-vanishing mean induced electric field strengths are solved in terms of complimentary error functions as well as some elementary functions. It is shown that the solutions are reducible to that of the steady case as the time approaches infinity, and to that of the non-magnetic field as the Hartmann number becomes zero. Some numerical calculations are given. The results indicate that in the presence of a magnetic field the flow rate is reduced depending on the magnitude of the Hartmann number, and that the magnetic field "assists" the flow to reach its steady condition.

646. (**1844**) Tayler, R. J.
Hydromagnetic Instabilities of a Cylindrical Gas Discharge, Pt. 1.

Hydromagnetic instabilities of a simple model of a cylindrical gas discharge have been studied by Kruskal and Schwarzchild. In this report, their methods are extended by the introduction of several additional factors, and the consideration of more general disturbances of the equilibrium position. Methods of stabilizing the discharge have been considered, but in all the models some instabilities remain. Indication is given of problems involved in a more realistic study of the discharge.

(TIL/MOS)

Tayler, R. J.
Pt. 2. Influence of Viscosity.

In a previous report (TP/R2374) hydromagnetic instabilities of an inviscid perfectly conducting plasma were considered. The results obtained were a generalization of those previously found by Kruskal and Schwarzschild, and in common with these they predicted that disturbances of the shortest wavelength were intrinsically the most unstable. This cannot be true in the presence of viscosity because of the large viscous stresses which would be called into play, and this report demonstrates the existence of a mode of maximum instability, and obtains a first approximation to the value of the corresponding wave number. (TIL/MOS)

TAYLER, R. J.
Pt. 4. Stable Configurations Under the Joint Influence of a Trapped Magnetic Field and Conducting Walls.

It is shown that there exist stable configurations of a cylindrical gas discharge, in which there is a trapped axial field, if the discharge is in a conducting tube. The particular stable configuration obtained is one in which the axial field is concentrated inside the plasma and the current is carried on the plasma surface. No such stability exists when the current is uniformly distributed throughout the plasma and the magnetic field in the vacuum exceeds that in the plasma. It seems likely that there are more general stable configurations in which the current is mainly carried near the plasma surface and the trapped magnetic field has its maximum value near the plasma centre.   (TIL/MOS)

Pt. 3 deals with the influence of steady axial magnetic fields, and Pt. 5 deals with the influence of alternating magnetic fields.

647. (**1846**) TAYLER, R. J.
A Note on Hydromagnetic Stability Problems.

It is shown that care must be taken in the application of the principle of interchange of stabilities, particularly to problems in which the wave number–growth rate relation contains transcendental functions. Particular application is made to recently studied problems of hydromagnetic stability.

648. (**1859**) THOMPSON, W. B.
The Physical Basis of Magnetohydrodynamics.

We have seen that the most interesting magnetohydrodynamic phenomena occur in plasmas and that, on the laboratory scale, the mean free part is often long. However, we have shown how strictly two-dimensional linearized magnetohydrodynamics can be obtained from the motion of non-colliding particles. The derivation is not complete, since it is not capable of producing local hydrodynamic equations for non-symmetric flow, or even in the symmetric case for non-adiabatic flow.

649. (**1867**) THOMSON, G.
The Containment of Plasma by the Pinch Discharge.

When a strong current is flowing axially in a plasma, with cylindrical geometry, the charged particles of the plasma will be prevented from striking the cylindrical wall both by the self-magnetic field of the current and, in the case of the positive ions, by the electric field of the current and by the electric field due to the negative charge in the region of the current. Calculations are made of these effects, which are relevant to the loss of heat by conduction from a thermonuclear device of the ZETA type. It is shown that in order to reduce the loss of heat by conduction to a value less than the energy generated in the discharge by a thermonuclear reaction in deuterium, it is necessary either to have a magnetic field corresponding to a current of the order of a thousand million amps, or to have a substantial electric field, giving a radial potential difference between the axis and wall of the order of 250–500 kV, together with currents of a few million amps. Reasons are given for supposing that such an electric field would in fact be set up as a concomitant of the current and the reaction.

650. (**1874**) TIDMAN, D. A.
Structure of a Shock Wave in Full Ionized Hydrogen.

The Fokker-Plank equations are used to examine the structure of a shock wave in fully ionized hydrogen. This is done by assuming a bimodal Maxwellian distribution for the protons in the interior of the shock wave and noting that the electrons

217

are in thermal equilibrium with themselves but not necessarily with the protons. The method is essentially an extension of that used by Mott-Smith in his analysis of the Boltzmann equation for a shock wave in a gas of neutral atoms.

651. (**1877**) Tolansky, S.
Dynamique du Plasma et Magnétohydrodynamique.
Compte rendu du congrès tenu aux Etats-Unis en juin 1958 traitant en particulier de l'erreur possible dans l'évaluation de la température réelle atteinte par la pile ZETA.   (SDIT)

652. (**1904**) Udy, L. L.
Propagation Characteristics of Detonation Generated Plasmas.
Electrical conduction measurements were made in the highly ionized plasma region produced by detonating high explosives. The plasma was determined to originate directly from reaction of the high explosive rather than from thermal ionization associated with the accompanying shock wave. The mechanism of conduction was considered, and it was shown that electron flow through the plasma accounted for practically all of the current. With this in mind, it was concluded that the current flow through the plasma region was of the same nature as current flow in a metal. Conduction measurements in atmospheres of chlorine, oxygen, nitrogen, helium, and air showed that the rate of decay of the plasma was dependent upon the gaseous medium and can be explained on the basis of negative ion formation. The plasma exhibited pulsations and it was concluded that an adhesive attraction exists in the plasma through a quasi-lattice structure. Electron densities of 10^{16} electrons/cm^3 were calculated from conduction measurements of the plasma after it had spread from the 1-in. diameter charge to a 2-in. diameter constraining tube.
                                                                        (Appl. Mech. Rev.)

653. (**1905**) Vali, V. and Gauger, J.
Plasma Acceleration by Means of a Rotating Magnetic Field.
Development of a technique for accelerating hydrogen plasmas to velocities of the order of 1 per cent of the velocity of light. At this velocity, the kinetic energy per particle of a deuterium plasma is approximately 10^5 eV. The system would utilize an electrodeless discharge so that no high atomic number contaminants are introduced, other than those boiled off the gas container walls. The apparatus would consist of a cylindrical glass tube with four radio-frequency oscillator coils placed around it to produce a rotating magnetic field.   (Aero/Space)

654. (**1906**) Vandakurov, Y. N.
Possible Equilibrium Configurations for a Thin Circular Plasma Conductor in a Magnetic Field.
Configurations with surface currents (both components) and a volume current are considered.

655. (**1907**) Vandakurov, Y. N. and Perel, V. I.
The Motion of Positive Ions in a Natural Gas Under the Effect of Electric and Magnetic Fields.
The velocity distribution function is obtained for the case in which the mean energy of the ions is much larger than the mean energy of the neutral atoms. It is assumed that the main interaction mechanism between the ions and the atoms is resonance charge exchange.

656. (**1910**) Van de Hulst, H. C.
The Interstellar Plasma.
Observations on the distribution of matter and velocity in the galaxy are described. The possibility of synchrotron radiation being the main source of light and radio

waves is considered, particularly with regard to the crab nebula. The presence of magnetic field in interstellar space is considered in the light of current theories of force-free fields.

657. (**1911**) VAN DE HULST, H. C.
Density and Velocity Distribution of the Interstellar Gas.
This paper reviews knowledge about the interstellar gas derived forming a basis of an irreducible representation of T_d, of the irreducible fourth-order tensors of angular momentum components involved in this series development.

(J. Hagwood)

658. (**1917**) VEDENOV, A. A.
Certain Solutions of the Equations of Plasma Hydrodynamics.
Considers exact solutions of the hydrodynamic equations of cold plasma in the presence of an external magnetic field, and also in its absence. For simplicity the ions are regarded as being at rest. (TIL/MOS)

659. (**1919**) VEDENOV, A. A. and LARKIN, A. I.
Equation of State of a Plasma.
The free energy F of a completely ionized gas is given in terms of an expansion in the density n: $F = F_{\text{ideal}} + An^{3/2} + Bn^2 \ln n + Cn^2$. The term $An^{3/2}$ is identical with the familar Debye-Hürcel term. Expressions for B and C have been obtained. A diagram technique has been used to carry out the calculations.

660. (**1920**) VEKSLER, V. I. and KOVRIZHNYKH, L. M.
Cyclic Acceleration of Particles in High-Frequency Fields.
The feasibility of using high-frequency fields for controlling the motion of particles in cyclic accelerators is indicated.

661. (**1921**) VELIKHOV, E. P.
Stabilité de l'Ecoulement d'un Liquid Infiniment Conducteur entre des Cylindres Tournant dans un Champ Magnétique.
(En russe.) Condition suffisante de stabilité dans des champs axial et torique. Valeurs critiques des champs magnétiques stabilisateurs et interprétation physique des résultats. (C.N.R.S.)

662. (**1922**) VELIKHOV, E. P.
Stability of an Ideally Conducting Liquid Flowing Between Cylinders Rotating in a Magnetic Field.
Sufficient conditions for the stability of an ideal liquid flowing in axial and toroidal magnetic fields are derived. Critical values of the magnetic fields which stabilize the flow are obtained and a physical interpretation of the results is presented.

663. (**1923**) VELIKHOV, E. P.
Stability of a Plane Poiseuille Flow of an Ideally Conducting Fluid in a Longitudinal Magnetic Field.
Author investigates stability of the laminar flow of an incompressible ideally conducting fluid in a longitudinal magnetic field with respect to infinitesimally small disturbances. The well-known method of Heisenberg and Lin is used. The motion of the fluid is described by the Navier-Stokes equation (with the electromagnetic force added) and the set of Maxwell's equations. The character of the flow is determined by three parameters: hydrodynamic Reynolds number, magnetic Reynolds number, and Alfvén number. At the critical values of these parameters the flow becomes unstable. Velocity, pressure, and magnetic field are

represented as sums of large stationary values and small disturbing increments. Velocity is assumed to be parallel to x-axis and all quantities depend only on z-co-ordinate. Since the most critical are two-dimensional disturbances, only these are considered, leading to a sixth-order differential equation for the z-component of the disturbance of the magnetic field. The z-component of the velocity is connected with the z-component of the magnetic field, hence the boundary conditions are superimposed upon the velocity. The problem reduces to determination of eigenvalues of frequency of the disturbances. The sufficient condition for the stability of flow is that the Alfvén number must be positive. After lengthy calculations author obtains asymptotic expression for the linearly independent solutions of the equation. The next problems discussed are: stability of plane flow for the infinite Reynolds number and Poiseuille flow by numerical method. The obtained conditions refer to Alfvén number (as above) and to characteristic induction of magnetic field.

664. (**1924**) VERESS, G.
> *Design and Operation of Electromagnetic Pumps, Parts I, II.*

(In Hungarian.) Author reviews the governing equations in their elementary forms both for the electromagnetic body forces and for hydraulics in pipes. In treating the design problem of pumps for liquid metals he uses the analogy with electrical engineering (both d.c. motor and induction motor analogies).

(L. Kovasznay)

665. (**1928**) VOLKOV, T. F.
> *Ion Oscillations in a Plasma.*

The effect of high-frequency electromagnetic field on ion oscillations is considered. It is shown that the frequencies of the quasi-acoustic longitudinal plasma oscillations are functions of the field amplitude. Possible instability mechanisms are discussed.

666. (**1933**) WANIEK, R. W.
> *Problems of Magnetic Propulsion of Plasma.*

In the case where a plasma structure can be made to have ideal or nearly ideal diamagnetic properties a magnetic field will act on the gaseous ionized boundary like a piston and will impart to the configuration net momentum. This paper will deal with theoretical problems and experimental results obtained during the course of a study aimed at accelerating ionized gases by means of strong transient magnetic fields. Recently developed strong magnetic field techniques are discussed in view of their possible application to high field plasma thrustors. Special air-core magnet configurations are shown and their characteristics as intermittent plasma propulsors are outlined.

667. (**1938**) WATSON, K. M.
> *Use of the Boltzmann Equation for the Study of Ionized Gas of Low Density.*

The Boltzmann equation is studied for the case of a low-density ionized gas in an externally applied electromagnetic field. Particle-particle collisions are neglected, but long-range collective interactions are included. In Part I the static-problem is treated in detail. For this case the Boltzmann equation is solved using individual-particle-orbits, an approach which emphasizes the physical basis of the solution.

668. (**1950**) WEIBEL, E. S.
> *Oscillations of a Non-Uniform Plasma.*

The oscillations of a plasma which is confined by an r.f. field are investigated. The confining potential is approximated as $\psi(x) = \frac{1}{2}m\omega_0^2 x^2$. Longitudinal plasma oscillations in the x direction are determined from the self-consistent Boltzmann transport equation without the collision term (Vlasov equation). This equation is linearized about equilibrium velocity distribution $f_0 = \exp\left[-\left(\psi + \tfrac{1}{2}mv^2\right)/kT\right]$. By expanding the electric field in Hermite polynomials, it is possible to reduce exactly the resulting integro-differential equation to an infinite system of linear equations for the expansion coefficients. The resonant frequencies are the roots of the determinant of the system. The frequency spectrum so obtained is quite unlike those obtained from Sturm-Liouville problems. This spectrum contains the integral multiples of ω_0 as limit points. As $e^2 n/m\omega_0^2 \to 0$, the resonant frequencies coalesce into these limits points, each of these frequencies $\mu\omega_0$ ($\mu =$ integer) being infinitely degenerate. Since all frequencies are real, the oscillations are not damped. The resonant frequencies are determined approximately as functions of $e^2 n/m\omega_0^2$ as are the roots of principal sub-determinants of finite order N. This procedure converges rapidly with increasing N.

669. (**1955**) Weibel, E. S.
   On the Confinement of a Plasma by Magnetostatic Fields.
The plasma is treated as an assembly of classical particles having masses m_+ and m_- and charges $\pm e$. It is shown that if such a plasma is in thermodynamic equilibrium it is unaffected by a magneto-static field. In particular, it cannot be confined by a magnetostatic field and at the same time be in equilibrium. In absence of collisions there exist stationary solutions for the magnetic field and the particle distribution in phase space such that the gas is confined. The solutions are self-consistent, meaning that the particle motions generate the field, which in turn maintains the particle distribution. However, this distribution may not be Maxwellian. As an example the linear pinch is treated. The fields, the particle number densities, and the current density are calculated for one particular case. The confinement of a completely ionized gas by a magnetic field is investigated using a simplified model for the gas. It is shown that there exist, in the absence of collisions, stationary solutions for the magnetic field and the particle distribution in phase space such that the gas is confined. The linear pinch is treated as an example. The solutions are self consistent, meaning that the particle motions generate the field which in turn maintains the particle distribution stationary. However, the velocity distribution may not be Gaussian. A Gaussian distribution automatically leads to a uniform density everywhere, even if the magnetic field is maintained by external sources and even in the absence of collisions. A gas in thermodynamic equilibrium cannot be confined by a static magnetic field. Two results are given. First proves that a plasma under thermodynamic equilibrium is not affected by magnetostatic fields. Second gives one stationary solution for the linear pinch for the collision-free case which is non-Maxwellian.

670. (**1958**) Wentzel, D. G.
   Motion of Charged Particles in a Force-Free Magnetic Field.
In a force-free magnetic field with axial symmetry and $I =$ constant, charged particles are constrained to move around a line of force, and in the guiding-centre approximation no particles can escape from a region with one value of I into another; in particular, cosmic rays cannot escape a stellar or nebular system involving such a field. This result is independent of the energy of the particle and of the complexity of the field.

671. (**1959**) Westfold, K. C.
   Magnetohydrodynamic Shock Waves in the Solar Corona, with Application to Bursts of Radio-Frequency Radiation.
Starting from a set of transport equations previously investigated for an ionized gas, it is shown that in quasi-static electromagnetic fields the coronal medium satisfies an adiabatic equation of state and that the magnetic field lines are effectively "frozen" into the medium.

672. (**1961**) WETSTONE, D. M., EHRLICH, M. P. and FINKELSTEIN, D.
Experiments on Plasmoid Motion Along Magnetic Fields.
Time-integrated photographs are presented of collimated plasmoid motion parallel to magnetic fields, into and around magnetic flux diverters, into and out of magnetic mirrors, and along curved fields. Field strengths up to 3 weber/m² were employed. The material projected along the field lines was substantially copper plasma, created by short vacuum spark bursts (plasmoids), and injected into a vacuum chamber. Flux diverters and non-uniform solenoids expanded or compressed the plasmoid, which followed the field lines. In the case of curved fields, at least parts of the plasmoid appeared to be guided by the field lines, the guidance improving with decrease in plasmoid density. In general the behaviour was more complicated than with straight geometries because of the presence of internal polarization fields. Photomultiplier studies were employed with some geometries to estimate centre of mass and expansion velocities which, in later experiments, reached 5·5 and 1·9 cm/sec. The latter figure gives an upper bound to ion temperature of 120 eV for copper. This ion energy is considerably higher than those normally encountered in spark channels and is a substantial fraction (0·12) of the axial energy. A mechanism is described for achieving such a thermal energy through the interaction of strong shock waves with the initial discharge channel, thermalizing a large fraction of the axial energy. The upper bound for ion Larmor radius was that of the plasmoid. In order to extend the well-known treatment of the mirror reflection phenomenon to such a dynamical plasma, a theoretical total reflection coefficient is derived for a plasmoid entering a magnetic mirror. The experimental equipment is described, and a machine-computational method is outlined for mapping the flux distribution and density in a wide variety of solenoid geometries and combinations.

673. (**1969**) WHITHAM, G. B.
Converging Cylindrical Shocks in Magnetohydrodynamics.
The approximate method of R. F. Chisnell (unpublished) for treating converging cylindrical shocks in ordinary gas dynamics is applied to the corresponding problem in magnetohydrodynamics. The Lundquist (*Arkiv för Physik* **5,** No. 15, 1952) equations of magnetohydrodynamics are used together with shock and other relations given by K. O. Friedrichs (Nonlinear wave motion in magnetohydrodynamics, Los Alamos report, 1955).   (ASTIA)

674. (**1970**) WHITHAM, G. B.
Some Comments on Wave Propagation and Shock Wave Structure with Application to Magnetohydrodynamics.
The author considers an equation like

$$(1) \qquad \prod_{r=1}^{n} \left(\frac{\partial}{\partial t} + a_r \frac{\partial}{\partial x} \right) \phi + \lambda \prod_{r=1}^{m} \left(\frac{\partial}{\partial t} + a_r \frac{\partial}{\partial x} \right) \phi = 0$$

(where $m < n$), which is of order n and has characteristic speeds of propagation $a_1 \ldots a_n$. He shows that, in fact, the system is unstable unless both $m = n - 1$ and the inequality $c_1 > a_1 > c_2 > a_2 > \ldots > a_n - 1 > c_n$ holds, but that solutions of (1) do asymptote in this case to solution of (2) as $\lambda \to \infty$. The ideas are particularly valuable after extension to non-linear problems; a special case noticed before [Whitham, *Proc. Roy. Soc.*, London Ser. A **219** (1955), 281–316; MR 17, 912] is concerned with roll-waves (the unstable case) and flood waves (the stable case), and the author generalizes his previous diagnosis of the structure of roll-waves to a wide class of unstable, non-linear problems. Both the linear and non-linear theories are illustrated by reference to one-dimensional longitudinal wave propagation in a transverse magnetic field.   (M. Lighthill)

675. (**1975**) WILCOX, J. M., BOLEY, F. I. and DE SILVA, A. W.
> *Experimental Study of Alfvén-Wave Properties.*

Alfvén hydromagnetic waves are propagated through a cylindrical plasma. The wave velocity, attenuation, impedance, and energy transfer are studied. The theoretical equations predict correctly the functional dependence of the velocity and attenuation, and from these quantities accurate measurements of plasma density and temperature can be obtained. A qualitative agreement between theory and experiment is obtained for the hydromagnetic coaxial waveguide impedance, and the energy transferred from an oscillating circuit to the hydromagnetic wave is measured to be 43 ± 10 per cent.

676. (**1976**) WILCOX, J. M. and BOLEY, F. I.
> *Comments on Experimental Demonstration of Hydromagnetic Waves in an Ionized Gas.*

Sawyer, Scott and Stratton (Abstr. 3655 of 1959) reported the observation of hydromagnetic waves in a discharge plasma. It is pointed out here that under these experimental conditions hydromagnetic waves would theoretically be strongly damped.

677. (**1982**) WILLIAMS, J. C.
> *The Decaying Plasma as a Method of Heating a Supersonic Gas Stream.*

Paper investigates dissociative recombination as a mechanism of heat addition in supersonic flow. Specifically, the decay of a slightly ionized nitrogen gas in one-dimensional flow is analysed. One-dimensional conservation equations are presented. An approximate solution is given by assuming that the species continuity equations are uncoupled from the other conservation equations. This mathematical simplification makes the solution more convenient, but the results nearly physically meaningless. An interesting result is that a very long decay time is indicated. Discussion of the general characteristics of supersonic heat addition is naive and at times incorrect. The entropy, being a state point function, is not dependent upon the mechanism of heat addition. The conclusion that the most efficient method of heating is to add heat at a constant low supersonic Mach number implies either a two-dimensional channel (not discussed or analysed) or very small heat addition.

(R. Gross)

678. (**1983**) WILLIAMS, W. E.
> *Exact Solutions of the Magnetohydrodynamic Equations.*

Exact one-dimensional solutions of the magnetohydrodynamic equations of an incompressible fluid are considered. It is shown that one class of plane wave solution of the linearized equations is also a possible class of solution of the general equations including the effect of displacement current. A similar result is also established for the solution for a horizontally stratified fluid. For the particular case when the viscosity is equal to the magnetic diffusivity an exact solution is obtained for the magnetohydrodynamic Rayleigh problem for a semi-infinite plate. It is shown that this solution may be employed directly to give the solution for liquids of small, but not necessarily equal, viscosity and magnetic diffusivity.

679. (**1984**) WILLIAMS, W. E.
> *Reflection and Refraction of Hydromagnetic Waves of the Boundary of Two Compressible Media.*

The reflection and refraction of a hydromagnetic plate wave at a plane boundary between two semi-infinite homogeneous media of infinite electrical conductivity are discussed when a uniform magnetic field perpendicular to the plane of separation is present. It is shown that, if the incident wave is not an Alfvén one, there will be at most two reflected and two refracted plane waves and that, for the case of an incident Alfvén wave, there will be only one reflected and one refracted wave.

It is also shown that a general solution of the hydromagnetic equations may be obtained in terms of two independent scalar fields.

680. (1985) WILLIAMS, W. E.
Propagation of Small Amplitude Magnetohydrodynamic Waves.
The solution of the linearized magnetohydrodynamic equations of a viscous fluid is generated in terms of one-component electric and velocity vector potentials. Applications of the approach to plane wave propagation and to a particular eigenvalue problem are considered.

681. (1986) WILSON, T. A.
Remarks on Rocket and Aerodynamic Applications of Magnetohydrodynamic Channel Flow.
Equations of magnetohydrodynamic channel flow are developed and the results are applied to rocket propulsion with unlimited energy supply. Two rocket configurations are described in which the energy is limited to the energy supplied by the fuel of the rocket. Rocket payload energy is increased for a given rocket fuel energy by redistributing this energy; magnetohydrodynamics is a feasible way to accomplish the redistribution. Descriptions are presented of a magnetohydrodynamic generator, two magnetohydrodynamic devices of aerodynamic interest, a hypersonic wind tunnel, and a diffuser. (ASTIA)

682. (1992) WRIGHT, J. P.
Diffusion of Charged Particles Across a Magnetic Field Due to Neutral Particles.
A calculation of the diffusion of charged particles across a magnetic field arising from the presence of neutral particles is compared with the diffusion arising from charged particles. The ratio of the flux of charged particles, arising from the presence of neutral particles, and the flux arising from charged particles is found to be of the order 10^2 to 10^5. The actual value of the ratio depends on the types of particles, the temperature, the number densities, and the density gradients.

683. (1993) WU, C. S. and HAYES, W. D.
Axisymmetric Stagnant Flow of a Viscous and Electrically Conducting Fluid Near the Blunt Nose of a Spinning Body with Presence of Magnetic Field. Part I: Exact Solution of Incompressible and Constant-Properties Model.
This is the first part of a series of studies of the stagnation point flow of a viscous and conducting fluid near the blunt nose of a moving and spinning body in the presence of magnetic field. The body under consideration is axisymmetric and the fluid is assumed to be incompressible and has constant physical properties. Exact similar solution is verified in existence. The final differential systems contain one principal system and two subordinate systems. Only general discussions are given in this report.

684. (1994) WU, C. S.
Axisymmetric Stagnant Flow of a Viscous and Electrically Conducting Fluid Near the Blunt Nose of a Spinning Body with Presence of Magnetic Field. Part II: Consideration of Realistic Conditions—Compressible Viscous Layer and Small Magnetic Reynolds Number.
This is the second part of the present study of the axisymmetric stagnation point flow of a viscous and conducting fluid near a spinning body. A more realistic physical model is adopted in the present case. The compressibility and variable physical properties are taken into consideration. In the viscous layer, boundary-layer approximation is employed. Again, since magnetic Reynolds number is postulated to be small, mathematical simplification of the induction equations is obtained.

685. (**1995**) Wuerker, R. F., Shelton, H. and Langmuir, R. V.
Electrodynamic Containment of Charged Particles.
Electrically charged iron and aluminium particles having diameters of a few microns have been contained in a confined region of space by means of alternating and static electric fields. The theory is essentially that of alternating gradient focusing; here the motion is governed by Mathieu's equation. Under certain circumstances, when many particles are confined, the three-dimensional focusing force and the Coulomb repulsion results in a "crystalline" array which can be melted and re-formed.

686. (**1996**) Wyld, H. W., Jr.
Dynamic Stability of a Self-Pinched Discharge.
Study of the stability of a rapidly contracting self-pinched discharge using three different models for the plasma dynamics: the free particle model, the snow-plough model, and the shock wave model. For each model the growth in time of a small perturbation on a time-dependent unperturbed solution of the equations of motion is obtained. It is shown that the free particle model and the shock wave model predict instabilities, and that an initially small perturbation becomes large in times comparable to the pinch time. The snow-plough model predicts stability for the initial stages of the pinch, although instabilities probably develop later on.

(Aero/Space)

687. (**1998**) Yankov, V. V.
Behaviour of a Conducting Gaseous Sphere in a Quasi-Stationary Electro-Magnetic Field.
The stability of a homogeneous plasma sphere of infinite conductivity in an external quasi-stationary electromagnetic field is investigated by perturbation-theory methods.

688. (**1999**) Yavorskaya, I. M.
The Oscillations of an Infinite Gas Cylinder with its own Gravitation in Magnetic Field.
The unidimensional unsettled motions of a gas are examined which can be associated with the problems of the motion of cosmic masses taking place under the action of magnetic fields. (TIL/MOS)

689. (**2003**) Yih, C. S.
Ring Vortices Generated Electromagnetically.
If an electric current of uniform density j_0 is passed axially through a stationary fluid between concentric cylinders of radii r_1 and r_2 ($> r_1$), the fluid is stable to axisymmetric disturbances only if damping provided by viscosity and electrical resistivity is sufficiently large. It is shown that the fluid may also be stabilized by passing a line current J along the axis, sufficient condition for stability being $J \leqslant -\pi j_0(r_2{}^2 - r_1{}^2)$ or $\geqslant \pi j_0 r_1{}^2$. The values of J needed to stabilize the fluid for non-zero viscosity and finite conductivity are calculated for the case $r_2 - r_1 \ll r_1$. In the latter case, the ring vortices which exist under conditions of neutral stability are exactly the same as those for flow between rotating cylinders if J and j_0 have the same sign and if J is not very small compared with $\pi j_0 r^2$. (Appl. Mech. Rev.)

690. (**2004**) Yih, C. S.
Effects of Gravitational or Electromagnetic Fields on Fluid Motion.
For the case of an inviscid, incompressible fluid, having negligible magnetic viscosity, the author shows that the effects of gravity or an electromagnetic field are to stiffen the fluid along isopyenic surfaces or lines, or along lines of force, respectively.

691. (**2005**) YIH, C. S.
Inhibition of Hydrodynamic Instability by an Electric Current.
Paper presents analytical treatment of hydrodynamic instability in vertical cylinder of viscous fluid heated from below with temperature decreasing linearly with height. Objective is to show great difference in effectiveness of circular magnetic fields on inhibiting different modes of instability. Results indicate that longitudinal electric currents have strong inhibiting effects on unsymmetrical modes of convection, but no effect on axisymmetrical modes. Author points out interesting situations at Rayleigh number 452·1 (critical for axisymmetric convection). For electric currents greater than critical value required to inhibit unsymmetric convection, only axisymmetric convection can occur, whereas for currents less than critical the first mode of unsymmetric convection prevails.

692. (**2008**) YOSINOBU, H. and KAKUTANI, T.
Two-Dimensional Stokes Flow of an Electrically Conducting Fluid in a Uniform Magnetic Field.
Analysis of a two-dimensional flow of a viscous, incompressible and electrically conducting fluid past a cylinder in a uniform magnetic field, using Stokes approximation. Detailed calculation is carried out for the flow past a circular cylinder in two cases: (1) in a parallel magnetic field and (2) in a transverse magnetic field. The expansion formulas for the drag per unit span of the cylinder are obtained in terms of the Hartmann Number in each case. (E. Wattendorf)

693. (**2011**) ZABABAKHIN, E. I. and NECHAEV, M. N.
Electromagnetic-Field Shock Waves and Their Cumulation.
We consider electromagnetic waves with narrow transition regions between the initial and final states, and in particular a converging cylindrical wave. It is found that as such a wave converges its amplitude increases without bound. A qualitatively new phenomenon, cumulation, is found. This is the occurrence of infinitely strong fields at finite distances from the axis, on the front of the wave reflected from the cylindrical axis. This property is not peculiar to electromagnetic phenomena, but is related to the cylindrical geometry. Acoustical waves have the same property, but for them this solution is valid only for weak waves, whereas this restriction does not apply to electromagnetic field waves.

694. (**2012**) ZABUSKY, N. J.
Hydromagnetic Stability of a Streaming Cylindrical Incompressible Plasma.
A dispersion relation is derived and analysed for the case where the equilibrium velocity of an incompressible, non-resistive, cylindrical plasma has a spiral motion along magnetic field lines. The symmetric hydromagnetic equations are used to derive the plasma hydromagnetic pressure. The dispersion relation is found by mapping plasma and outer-region hydromagnetic pressures across a sharp-moving interface. The zeros of the dispersion relation are obtained by a sequence of mappings between three complex planes. The presence of flow introduces overstable modes. For $m = 0$ the time-divergences are removed by flow. For $m = 1$ the divergences are enhanced by flow such that the growth rates and oscillation frequencies increase linearly with the flow velocity. The smaller is the wavelength of the disturbance in the z direction, the larger are the overstable eigenvalues.

695. (**2013**) ZAGORODNOV, O. G., FAINBERG, YA. B. and EGOROV, A. M.
Reflection of Electromagnetic Waves from a Plasma Moving in Slow-Wave Guides.
Electromagnetic wave reflections from a moving plasma were investigated experimentally. It was found that when the wave was greatly slowed down [(1/200)–(1/375)c] the double Doppler effect observed in reflection increased the frequency by 11–20 per cent. The measurements were carried out at 24·75 Mc/s.

The slow-wave structure was a helix. The possibility is indicated of using this effect to amplify microwaves and to multiply their frequencies, to improve the dynamic stability of the plasma, and to perform measurements in plasma.

696. (**2018**) ZEL'DOVICH, Y. B. and RAIZER, Y. P.
Physical Phenomena that Occur when Bodies Compressed by Strong Shock Waves Expand in Vacuo.
The glow of an initially solid opaque body, that appears after its compression by strong shock waves, with subsequent expansion into a vacuum, is studied. Condensation of the vapour of the substance and recombination of ions and electrons under these conditions are also considered.

697. (**2023**) ZHARINOV, A.
Study of the Transverse Motion of Ions in a Discharge in a Strong Longitudinal Magnetic Field.
Analysis showing that the establishment of the overall nature of the transverse motion of ions is made possible by a plane rotating probe. The ion energy acquired in the radial electric fields of a discharge is evaluated. (IAS)

698. (**2025**) ZHIGOULEV, V. N.
On a Class of Motion in Magnetohydromechanics.
Motion is considered in a medium with vanishing viscosity and thermal conductivity, and infinite electrical conductivity, under the restriction that neither the magnetic field vector H nor the velocity v should vary along lines of force. The following results are obtained (1) if the flow is isentropic and the quantity $|H|\rho$ is constant (ρ is the density), then the circulation $\oint v \cdot dc$ taken around a container moving with the fluid is constant in time; (2) an analogue to Bernoulli's equation is proved if the motion is steady; (3) if the motion is unsteady but irrotational, then $\partial\phi/\partial t + v^2/2 + \int(dp/\rho) + H^2/4\pi\rho = \omega_1(t)$, where ϕ is the velocity potential, and ω_1 a function of time. (H. Herenbery)

699. (**2029**) ZHIGOULEV, V. N.
Sur le Phenomène de "Striction" Magnétique du Courant de Milieu Electro-conducteur.
(En Russe.) Etude de l'écoulement autour d'un corps, ayant un champ magnétique propre, d'un courant de gaz conducteur. On donne la démonstration, pose le problème et le résout dans le cas plan, dans le cas ou il existe le phénomène de "striction" du milieu conducteur pour de grands nombres magnétiques de Reynolds. Example: écoulement d'un courant de gaz hypersonique autour d'un corps à courant électrique linéaire. (C.N.R.S.)

700. (**2030**) ZIEMER, R. W.
Experimental Investigation in Magneto-Aerodynamics.
A 3-in. diameter electromagnetic shock tube is studied as a means of producing the hyper-velocity and ionized air flow required for magneto-aerodynamic experimental research. The simple construction and operation of the shock tube is described, and an evaluation is made of its performance. It is shown that although usable test times are only about 20 microseconds, velocities up to 12,000 metres per second, and stagnation temperatures up to 25,000 K are readily produced, well into the range suitable for magneto-aerodynamic studies. The electromagnetic shock tube is used to study magneto-aerodynamic interaction in the ionized flow about a blunt body. The test body is a hemispherical cylinder containing a coaxial pulsed magnet coil in the nose, which produces field strengths at the stagnation point of up to 40 kilogauss. Quantitative measurements are made of the change in the bow shock standoff distance upon application of the

magnetic field. The magnetic field displaces the bow shock upstream and the standoff distance increases by a factor of 7·5 for the condition $(\sigma_3 B_0^2 r_3 / \rho_2 u_2) = 69$. The experimental results are compared with theory, and good agreement is obtained within the range of experimental conditions.

701. (**2038**) ZYRYANOV, P. S. and TALUTS, G. G.
   Electroacoustic Phenomena in a Degenerate Electron-Ion Plasma.
Electrical phenomena occurring in an electron-ion plasma in which acoustic waves are propagated are considered. The space attenuation coefficient (absorption coefficient) of the waves is computed.

(The Abstracts, the sources of which are not indicated, have been compiled by the authors or by the editors, or have been presented in the specialized reviews, as *Technical Abstracts Bulletin, Physical Abstracts, Mathematical Reviews, Applied Mechanics Review*, etc.)

LIST OF THE ENTRIES INCLUDED IN BIBLIOGRAPHY NO. 1

1	150	311	394	539	672	844	980	1098	1206	1322
6	151	312	395	540	689	848	982	1099	1208	1324
8	155	313	397	541	691	858	983	1100	1209	1329
9	156	314	400	545	692	859	984	1101	1212	1330
11	164	315	406	548	693	861	985	1102	1223	1331
12	165	316	407	562	700	865	986	1103	1226	1332
13	168	317	408	564	702	866	987	1108	1231	1333
15	169	318	409	566	704	869	989	1112	1233	1334
18	180	319	414	567	705	870	991	1115	1234	1338
19	182	320	415	572	707	877	992	1123	1235	1339
21	184	321	416	573	708	878	997	1124	1236	1340
23	186	325	417	578	709	880	999	1129	1237	1341
24	191	326	422	580	714	881	1001	1130	1238	1349
41	192	328	427	581	715	883	1007	1132	1239	1355
43	195	329	432	586	718	887	1009	1139	1241	1356
48	200	330	434	587	726	891	1010	1140	1245	1357
52	203	331	437	588	731	894	1011	1143	1246	1358
54	205	332	444	589	733	905	1018	1150	1247	1363
58	207	335	445	590	734	907	1019	1151	1248	1366
60	209	336	449	591	744	910	1022	1152	1250	1370
62	212	340	451	592	745	915	1024	1153	1257	1374
63	232	342	453	594	746	916	1027	1154	1260	1379
64	234	348	455	595	754	917	1028	1155	1261	1381
65	235	350	459	596	757	920	1029	1159	1264	1382
66	236	354	469	602	758	930	1036	1160	1266	1386
67	237	368	470	606	764	933	1040	1161	1267	1387
70	239	369	475	613	766	936	1042	1171	1269	1388
71	240	370	476	625	767	938	1047	1176	1272	1389
89	241	371	477	627	768	940	1048	1177	1273	1391
90	242	372	482	629	769	944	1049	1178	1274	1392
91	245	374	485	630	773	948	1050	1180	1277	1393
94	254	376	486	631	781	951	1052	1181	1279	1394
98	259	377	487	632	787	954	1057	1182	1281	1395
102	266	378	488	634	788	956	1059	1183	1283	1396
104	270	379	489	644	794	957	1064	1184	1285	1399
109	271	380	490	647	795	958	1065	1185	1301	1400
122	276	381	491	649	800	959	1066	1186	1302	1404
123	277	382	492	650	821	961	1074	1187	1303	1405
124	278	383	493	657	822	963	1075	1189	1304	1406
125	279	384	498	658	824	965	1076	1190	1305	1408
131	281	385	499	662	828	966	1079	1191	1310	1409
136	289	386	510	663	831	969	1081	1193	1312	1410
137	292	387	512	665	833	970	1082	1194	1313	1411
138	297	389	514	666	836	973	1083	1196	1315	1412
139	301	390	529	667	837	974	1086	1198	1316	1413
141	302	391	530	669	838	975	1088	1199	1317	1414
149	306	393	532	671	840	979	1096	1202	1318	1415

1417	1458	1492	1565	1600	1663	1720	1780	1844	1901	1959
1419	1459	1499	1566	1601	1675	1721	1781	1846	1903	1961
1421	1460	1500	1567	1604	1676	1722	1784	1848	1905	1965
1426	1467	1501	1538	1605	1677	1723	1786	1849	1908	1969
1427	1470	1503	1574	1606	1679	1728	1788	1850	1917	1990
1428	1471	1510	1575	1608	1680	1733	1792	1851	1933	1994
1431	1472	1511	1576	1610	1681	1740	1800	1855	1938	1996
1435	1473	1512	1579	1611	1704	1747	1804	1858	1940	1999
1446	1474	1516	1518	1612	1705	1748	1806	1859	1944	2001
1447	1475	1521	1582	1613	1706	1749	1810	1861	1945	2006
1449	1476	1522	1583	1619	1712	1754	1811	1866	1946	2012
1450	1477	1526	1585	1636	1713	1756	1824	1867	1947	2017
1451	1478	1528	1586	1636	1714	1759	1827	1874	1949	2020
1452	1479	1540	1590	1640	1715	1760	1828	1877	1952	2023
1453	1483	1541	1591	1649	1716	1765	1832	1884	1953	2030
1454	1485	1542	1595	1650	1717	1773	1837	1891	1954	2031
1455	1486	1546	1596	1651	1718	1775	1839	1896	1955	2033
1456	1488	1548	1597	1653	1719	1778	1843	1898	1958	2034
1457	1490	1554	1599	1657						

INDEX TO AUTHORS

231

233

237

SUBJECTS INDEX

I. MAGNETOHYDRODYNAMICS

I. 1. Fundamentals, Reviews

I. 2. General

I. 3. Ideal Fluid

I. 4. **Real Fluid**

9	376	499	836	951	1189	1338	1391	1460	1714
21	377	566	837	1096	1191	1340	1392	1527	1718
25	378	573	838	1098	1193	1341	1409	1610	1719
109	379	708	840	1108	1198	1370	1410	1611	1728
139	380	709	859	1129	1226	1374	1411	1612	1811
164	383	731	920	1183	1252	1384	1428	1613	1923
238	414	733	936	1185	1285	1386	1452	1712	2017
359	493	770	938	1186	1322	1388	1456	1713	2024
372									

II. **MAGNETO-GAS-DYNAMICS**

II. 1. **Fundamentals, Reviews** (*see also* I, 1)

205	700	981	1457	1501	1568	1569	1590	1685	1859
645									

II. 2. **General**

16	236	415	630	958	1119	1315	1451	1579	1778
22	237	418	650	959	1120	1330	1454	1590	1780
41	242	432	671	963	1143	1333	1453	1596	1781
89	245	445	703	970	1150	1338	1457	1597	1791
91	254	449	726	974	1151	1340	1459	1611	1792
122	266	455	746	975	1154	1348	1460	1649	1801
123	297	476	758	979	1155	1354	1462	1651	1802
124	313	477	766	980	1159	1375	1478	1676	1803
125	320	479	767	1101	1178	1376	1485	1677	1827
137	328	483	768	1007	1180	1377	1490	1679	1828
141	335	534	759	1019	1220	1379	1503	1681	1867
150	336	545	773	1036	1227	1386	1506	1721	1908
151	340	567	785	1047	1244	1387	1510	1747	1909
156	348	586	788	1049	1247	1388	1516	1750	1917
168	368	589	821	1050	1249	1392	1521	1754	1921
207	385	592	828	1065	1250	1394	1539	1755	1922
209	389	595	881	1076	1278	1395	1541	1760	1983
232	400	602	883	1117	1279	1404	1566	1770	2019
234	408	627	842	1118	1310	1448	1568	1773	2032
235	414	629	948						

II. 3. **Ideal Fluid**

6	241	328	485	649	744	930	999	1101	1208
41	242	329	498	662	746	957	1024	1143	1209
90	245	332	508	663	795	961	1040	1158	1223
123	266	340	520	667	822	965	1042	1159	1236
124	274	342	532	669	844	973	1050	1162	1239
125	276	357	541	695	848	974	1065	1177	1245
150	278	390	545	696	870	985	1074	1196	1247
173	279	391	572	702	880	987	1075	1199	1267
209	302	409	606	726	907	989	1076	1201	1277
237	319	455	613	732	910	997	1081	1202	1301

IV. 2. **Shock Waves**

41	540	775	927	1065	1199	1303	1489	1640	1826
126	541	776	934	1085	1221	1304	1491	1673	1850
178	565	795	953	1084	1223	1360	1505	1683	1874
319	606	835	964	1088	1245	1363	1522	1688	1901
337	618	844	971	1107	1267	1382	1533	1705	1959
339	699	850	985	1128	1277	1419	1591	1747	1962
459	701	862	1023	1150	1290	1449	1595	1765	1969
510	702	870	1040	1177	1301	1450	1626	1782	1970
516	729	907	1041	1196	1302	1484	1631	1825	2011
539	747	926	1048						

V. **PLASMA PHYSICS**

V. 1. **Fundamentals, Reviews**

280	413	420	478	741	1152	1291

V. 2. **General**

7	154	293	581	799	1016	1216	1462	1726	1877
28	165	317	597	801	1017	1217	1477	1727	1882
31	166	318	600	816	1024	1218	1496	1733	1885
32	169	320	601	817	1027	1233	1507	1739	1893
34	170	325	628	820	1031	1234	1510	1742	1896
36	171	326	644	824	1043	1235	1540	1744	1900
37	180	334	652	831	1046	1241	1546	1748	1904
38	182	350	657	834	1047	1265	1550	1750	1905
42	183	362	665	833	1049	1266	1552	1751	1906
43	190	364	666	858	1052	1281	1554	1770	1917
44	191	380	678	880	1059	1282	1555	1773	1919
46	195	400	679	898	1069	1283	1572	1784	1933
50	192	434	682	908	1071	1292	1599	1785	1935
68	200	437	687	910	1086	1297	1601	1786	1937
75	214	444	689	920	1087	1305	1604	1788	1944
82	216	451	704	923	1088	1306	1605	1798	1946
85	203	458	707	933	1091	1328	1606	1804	1947
86	209	472	710	940	1093	1366	1607	1806	1949
89	223	473	713	942	1099	1342	1623	1809	1952
104	227	475	714	943	1101	1350	1634	1810	1954
105	228	506	715	954	1102	1352	1635	1817	1955
108	249	512	721	956	1103	1359	1642	1848	1961
116	259	514	735	982	1114	1366	1649	1850	1972
117	271	532	750	984	1115	1405	1650	1854	1973
122	274	542	752	986	1138	1407	1654	1855	1978
123	275	543	759	991	1152	1408	1655	1856	1982
127	276	548	770	1003	1160	1426	1656	1857	1988
132	277	562	773	1007	1187	1427	1657	1860	1990
134	281	565	781	1009	1194	1431	1658	1861	1996
144	289	578	787	1010	1211	1435	1663	1864	2012
152	292	579	796	1013	1212	1437	1664	1871	2038
153									

VI. 1. **Astrophysical and Geophysical Applications** (*continued*)

639	887	905	1164	1299	1475	1526	1632	1859	1913
720	893	906	1168	1309	1477	1563	1639	1908	1931
848	891	979	1171	1471	1479	1568	1653	1909	1932
855	896	1008	1180	1472	1515	1581	1700	1910	1959
877	897	1102	1187	1473	1518	1590	1822	1911	1963
878	902	1124	1269	1474	1519	1591	1830	1912	1965
881									

VI. 2. **Aero-Astronautical Applications**

1	347	649	864	980	1132	1330	1411	1611	1802
67	348	653	866	983	1133	1331	1412	1612	1803
156	349	663	867	984	1142	1332	1422	1613	1810
184	362	692	869	997	1180	1334	1456	1633	1819
186	416	711	882	998	1187	1337	1460	1647	1820
230	434	712	886	999	1227	1340	1488	1677	1832
232	437	714	897	1027	1244	1350	1493	1678	1873
242	446	715	907	1028	1247	1382	1501	1680	1905
259	531	753	910	1029	1248	1386	1519	1711	1933
224	561	754	920	1030	1274	1387	1550	1715	1963
325	562	757	959	1049	1275	1388	1565	1721	1965
329	564	760	960	1082	1312	1391	1568	1776	1986
330	569	778	961	1095	1313	1392	1590	1777	1990
332	575	779	962	1100	1317	1405	1591	1784	2002
334	583	788	978	1101	1318	1409	1608	1785	2006
335	603	790	979	1102	1329	1410	1610	1801	2033
336	644	848							

VI. 3. **Laboratory Applications**

98	202	350	609	907	1048	1209	1356	1593	1720
105	206	384	644	910	1049	1210	1358	1596	1772
110	215	387	691	920	1054	1233	1370	1619	1905
113	232	388	692	929	1056	1234	1374	1636	1933
119	233	413	714	965	1057	1235	1412	1674	1949
125	263	434	715	979	1073	1240	1419	1675	1952
139	274	437	756	982	1143	1257	1427	1712	1954
155	276	450	788	984	1150	1305	1442	1713	1961
156	278	451	831	985	1172	1317	1452	1714	1964
158	284	474	838	986	1173	1318	1501	1715	1990
193	301	507	858	987	1187	1330	1508	1716	2030
197	307	578	872	990	1196	1346	1550	1718	2031
198	310	570	873	1000	1208	1355	1591	1719	2032
203	348	572							

VI. 4. **Thermonuclear Applications**

59	156	429	715	1049	1161	1308	1587	1736	1899
65	180	656	717	1050	1167	1525	1590	1753	1949
83	218	664	781	1057	1214	1543	1592	1810	1952
88	260	687	828	1136	1268	1568	1733	1863	1954
115	336	714	980	1137					